Pictured Key
Nature Series

# How To K

# THE BEETLES

Pictured-Keys for identifying many of the
beetles which are most frequently seen, with
aids for their study and with other helpful
features.

H. E. JAQUES
*Professor of Biology*
*Iowa Wesleyan College*

**wcb**

WM. C. BROWN COMPANY PUBLISHERS
Dubuque, Iowa

Library of Congress Catalog Card Number: 52-4037

ISBN 0–697–04831–4 (Cloth)
ISBN 0–697–04830–6 (Paper)
Thirteenth Printing, 1971

## THE PICTURED-KEY NATURE SERIES

### How To Know The—

Printed in United States of America

# CONTENTS

# INTRODUCTION

 **B**EETLES are usually covered with a heavy coat of horn-like material and have wingcovers of the same horny chitin. It is these sheath-like wings (elytra) from which the name Coleoptera has been derived for this largest order of insects.

Well over 250,000 species have been caught and described and, of course, this number will be greatly enlarged through further collecting and study. Specimens of beetles are easily found, mounted and cared for. Their many shapes and sizes lend interest and their widely varying and sometimes brilliant colors make them attractive. It is not at all surprising that many insect collectors specialize on the beetles or some group of them.

Many beetles are of little consequence to man; others cause untold loss. Their study may be either an avocational pleasure or an economic necessity.

Several hundred of the species of beetles the beginner is most likely to find are pictured, keyed and briefly described and many more are described in association with a similar species, making in all about 1500 species of which some 900 are pictured. Large as these numbers appear they are very small as compared with the total known species, yet it is hoped beginning Coleopterists may find in this book some of the help they have been sorely needing.

It should be noted that in an effort to make the keys more easily handled by beginners they have been made artificial instead of natural in places, and that group names have been at times used rather loosely.

Leng's catalog has been followed for arrangement and terminology and the Leng catalog numbers given in each case.

Many of the illustrations are originals, drawn by our artists from the specimens. Numerous other illustrations have been reproduced by permission and the source of such pictures are credited in each case. We are very grateful to all who have helped us in this and in many other ways.

Mt. Pleasant, Iowa
February, 1951

# ABOUT BEETLES

 HERE is much that could be said concerning beetles all of which should be helpful to the one who wishes to study these interesting insects. Since most of the readers will already have a copy of "How to Know the Insects" we are referring to the carefully written explanations in its earlier pages where many of the basic matters which every biologist needs to know are discussed.

Begin at page 1 of "HOW TO KNOW THE INSECTS" to learn about scientific names, the importance of insects, their structure and development and many other matters. How to catch, kill and mount beetles and many places to look for them are all given in helpful detail.

Beetles vary rather widely in size, a few tiny ones being only 1/100 of an inch long, while at the other extreme are some clumsy giants measuring 6 or more inches. When we pause to realize that it would take some forty million of these midgets to weigh as much as one of the giants we get a better appreciation of the wide range in size.

Figure 1
Every fifth living thing is a beetle.

Lincoln attributed the great numbers of common people to God's love. It is apparent that Nature has likewise favored the beetles. Line up all the plants and all the animals of the world by species; every fifth one would be a beetle. If we were to put it on an individual basis the percentage might be even larger. The beetles have surely taken seriously the injunction "Be fruitful and multiply and replenish the earth."

All insects have a hard outer covering (exoskeleton) of chitin to which their muscles and working parts are attached. The beetles not doing things by halves, have in most species developed exceptionally sturdy skeletons. This is what protects them so well in

1

life and makes a collection of them so easily cared for, if a few precautions are taken. Skin beetles, cockroaches and mice find insect collections most toothsome as beginning collectors sometimes learn from sad experience. Aside from a few easily prevented hazards, a collection of beetles may retain its beauty and interest long beyond the life of the collector.

Since your collection may last so long, and be viewed and used by so many we wish to re-emphasize what you have already read in "How to Know the Insects."

Use only good insect pins of proper size; get small neat labels and complete them accurately and with your best skill. Mount your specimens with great care keeping them and the labels at uniform height. Unless the species or record cannot be duplicated, do not retain broken, discolored or sloppily mounted specimens. Prospective employers could often tell more accurately about the character of a person by looking at his insect collection, than by studying the testimonials furnished by his well-wishing friends.

The classification of the beetles is based almost wholly on their external characters. To be able to handle the keys quickly and ac-

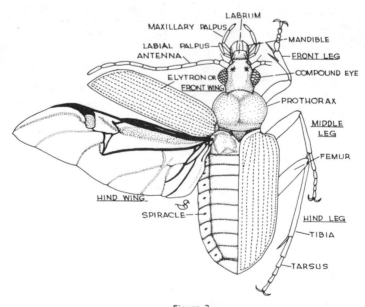

Figure 2
Dorsal view of a typical beetle naming some parts with which every student should be familiar.

curately a knowledge of the external anatomy of the beetles is desirable. Simple diagramatic sketches are here given. Figs. 2, 3, and 4. It will be well for the beginner to study them carefully and to refer to them again and again. Many parts are explained and pictured in the glossary and often within the keys at the place the term is used. When viewed from above, beetles show three usually definitely separated sections; *head, thorax* and *abdomen.* All insects possess these three parts but in the beetle as examined dorsally, what passes for the "thorax" is really only the *pronotum* covering the *prothorax.* The *elytra,* which are horny first wings, when at rest in most species cover the remainder of the thorax and the entire abdomen and this part is

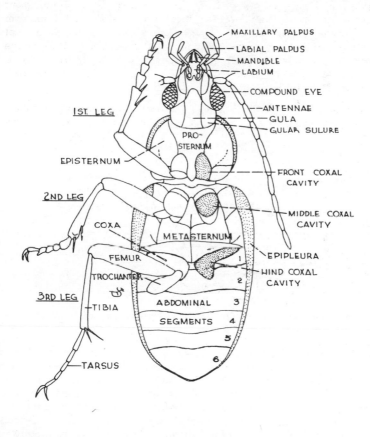

Figure 3
Ventral view of a typical beetle (Carabidae) with the more important parts named.

3

spoken of as the "abdomen" though not technically being so. It will be observed that the elytra are hinged to the fore part of the second section of the thorax (mesothorax) and are held out and back at an angle when the beetle is in flight. The elytra provide ideal protection for the beetle when it is not flying, but are doubtless pretty much of a hindrance when their owner takes to the air.

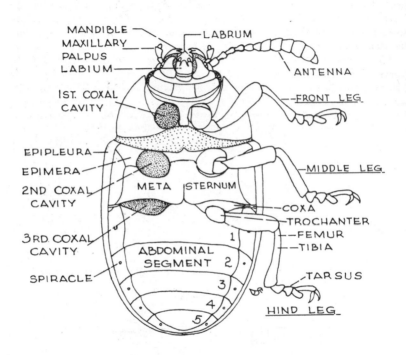

Figure 4
Ventral view of a typical beetle (Chrysomelidae) showing the more important parts.

A membranous second pair of wings when not in use are folded under the elytra and over the true abdomen. These wings arise from the third part of the thorax (metathorax) in which are borne the muscles to operate these important flight structures. These second wings, it is then seen, must be sufficiently sturdy and effective to overcome the resistance of the clumsily erected elytra and be solely responsible for the beetle's flight. Most all other insects have two pairs of flight-functioning wings; the Diptera and occasional species in other orders possess but one pair of wings. In some beetles (e.g. Staphylinidae) the elytra are greatly reduced in length but still function to cover the true wings which are ingeniously folded and put away beneath these reduced wing covers. Some of these beetles are often the best flyers of the order. Occasional species possess no membranous wings and are flightless. In some of these the elytra are fused at the suture and can not be separated or raised appreciably.

The thorax also supports the three pair of legs. These are better understood when studied from the ventral side. The reason for the three segments of the thorax is at once apparent as each supports a pair of legs. The legs are numbered from head to rear and designated "left" or "right." They are also known by the section of the thorax supporting them; thus the 2nd legs become the "meso-legs" or "mesothoracic legs" etc.

Here again we, who sometimes think of other animal structures in terms of our own bodies, must revise our thinking. The insect leg has no bone through its center, but instead is covered with a stiff case which functions in forming joints and providing points of attachment for the muscles. These muscles work from the inside of the skeleton instead of from the outside as with the vertebrates.

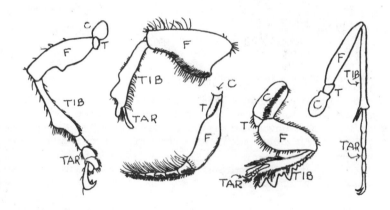

Figure 5

Some typical beetle legs. C, coxa; T, trochanter; F, femur; TIB, tibia; TAR, tarsus.

Legs are attached by a ball and socket joint but the entire end of the leg (the coxa) is the "ball" which rotates in a socket within the wall of the body. This socket is known as the coxal cavity. The legs of all beetles are alike in possessing in order from the attached end to the apical end, a coxa, a trochanter, a femur (usually the largest and heaviest segment of the leg), a tibia, usually long and slim and a tarsus or foot made of from three to five segments in linear succession (occasionally fewer, or wholly wanting). The last tarsal segment usually bears two claws. (These claws are not considered when counting tarsal segments). The legs of beetles are much modified to equip the bearer for successfully getting around in its environment and for digging or other activities. Leg characters are used much in making identifications. Fig. 5.

Now let us consider the heavily armored head (Fig. 6). This important part varies greatly in relative size, shape and position. Beetles

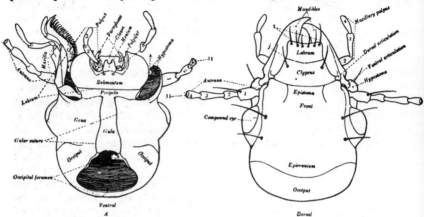

Figure 6
Head of a ground beetle, **Pterostichus.** A, ventral view; B, dorsal view.
(After Hopkins, U.S.D.A.)

chew their food by means of a pair of usually heavy jaws (mandibles) and are aided by some accessory parts. These mouth parts may be directed forward or downward according to the habits of the species. The great family Curculionidae and a few associated families num-

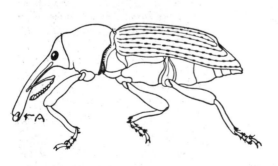

Figure 7
A typical curculionid, **Pissodes fraseri.** A, mouth parts.
(After Hopkins, U.S.D.A.)

bering in all close to 50,000 known species have the working mouth parts placed near the tip of a more or less elongated snout (Fig. 7). It seems on first consideration a rather awkward arrangement. The curculionids employ this long slim snout to eat out a narrow deep hole to the heart of the young fruit of many plants. An egg is then pushed into this hole which is shortly over-

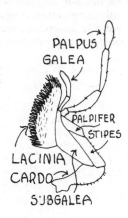

Figure 8
A typical maxilla with parts named.

grown leaving the hatching grub to feed within the nut or other fruit. Their immense numbers indicate that the scheme has been a successful one.

The mouthparts of insects meet in a vertical plane instead of a horizontal plane as do ours. That changes the whole process of operation. As already indicated the mandibles do the heavy work. They are supplemented by a pair of *maxilla* operating just below the *mandibles;* each member of the pair bears a toothed *lacinia* and a finger-like *galea;* to the outside of these parts is a *maxillary palpus* consisting of a few jointed segments. It helps to support bits of food and likely functions most largely in a sensory way such as taste and smell. Still lower is a single *labium* or lower lip with two united *mentums* and on either side a *labial palpus* with structure and function much the same as the *maxillary* palpi. These palpi are often spoken of as "palps."

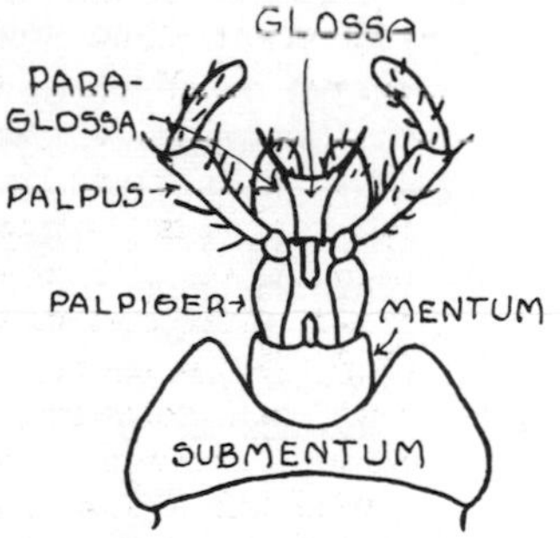

A broad plate-like structure is spread above all these mouth parts and functions with the labium to keep the food in line with the mouth. It is called the upper lip or *labrum.* At its base is a narrow supporting strip the *clypeus.*

The beetle head bears a pair of compound eyes. A compound eye is made up of many eye units, each possessing a more or less six-sided lense. These eyes may be wholly divided as in the Gyrinidae where one pair is ventrally situated for peering into the water while the other pair provides normal aerial vision. The compound eyes of some beetles are deeply notched where they partly (or completely) surround the antennae.

Figure 9
A typical labium with parts named.

7

Figure 10
A beetle head showing
labrum and clypeus.

Many insects possess three *ocelli* in addition to the compound eyes. A few beetles have ocelli but their presence is rare in the Coleoptera. A few species of beetles are wholly without eyes.

The antennae are highly important structures. They may be small or obscurely placed but just one pair is always present (unless broken away as often occurs in carelessly handled collections). They are highly variable and much depended upon in determination work. The antennal segments for a very large percentage of all the beetles number 11, but among the remaining species some have as few as 2 segments. The top number known seems to be 27.

For the beetles, their antennae serve many functions. The tactile sense is keenest there. The end organs of hearing and smell are also often located on the antennae. Living or dead, it is unfortunate for a beetle to lose its antennae.

The different forms of antennae have been given many names. We are picturing the more important ones. (Fig. 12)

The abdomen is covered with normally 9 or 10 telescoping chitinous rings. They are numbered from the thorax to the rear. Only five to eight of these segments are usually visable the others being drawn within the tip of the body. *Spiracles*, fairly large breathing pores where the tracheae open to the exterior, are often apparent. They usually occur on the membrane connecting the upper and lower sclerites.

The abdomen bears no appendages. The reproductive organs *(genitalia)*, quite prominent in many insects, are usually hidden within the abdomen of beetles. In some species where the genitalia offer the most reliable characters for acurate species determination these parts may be squeezed out of the abdomen or withdrawn by use of a hooked needle.

Figure 11
The lenses in the compound eyes of insects are six-sided.

Many beetles with square cut elytra *(truncate)* have the upper surface of the last one or two segments of the abdomen exposed. This is then known as the *pygidium* and if the preceeding segment is also visible it is known as the *propygidium*.

The keys which follow are largely self explanatory. If the reader has familiarized him-

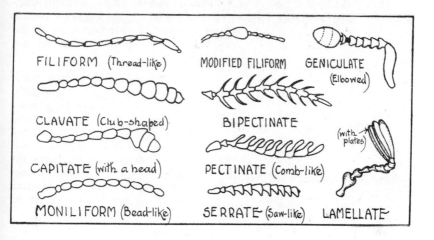

FILIFORM (Thread-like)   MODIFIED FILIFORM   GENICULATE (Elbowed)

CLAVATE (Club-shaped)   BIPECTINATE

CAPITATE (with a head)   PECTINATE (Comb-like)   (with plates)

MONILIFORM (Bead-like)   SERRATE (Saw-like)   LAMELLATE

Figure 12
Some typical beetle antennae.

self with the parts pictured and described here; he should find no unusual difficulty in determining the specimens in his collection.

It should be *loudly* re-emphasized however that while it has been
attempted to select for inclusion in this book the species most frequently collected, only about one out of twenty of the beetles known
for our country could be included. The chances are that your specimen is in the book but it is altogether possible that it is not. You
will then need to refer to more complete literature. You could even
have a species "new to science"; one which has never before been
taken and described. Don't be too quick to think your specimens are
new to science, but if you are a persistent collector you'll likely get
a few new ones. You'll need to refer them to a specialist in the
family to determine that. The coleopterists in our large museums will
often determine the hard ones.

And further: — keys are never infallible — they are only aids for
easy identification and should be considered in their entirety. Do not
descend on some random section of a key and expect to get reliable
results. One can often save a lot of time by beginning well over
in a key but he should be sure his specimen belongs within the part
he is considering. A small red beetle with black spots on its back
can be run up and down the Coccinellid keys for hours without results if the beetle happens to be a Chrysomellid.

9

# PICTURED-KEYS TO THE FAMILIES, GENERA AND SPECIES OF SOME COMMON BEETLES

1a Mouth parts reduced, front of head usually prolonged into a slender snout (beak). Gular sutures on under side of head fused into one, or lacking. Tarsi 5 segmented, the 4th often very small. Prosternal sutures lacking. (Snout Beetles, Weevils, Engraver Beetles, etc.)

Fig. 13. Sub-order RHYNCHOPHORA.....................page 307

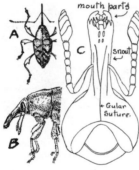

Figure 13

Fig. 13. A, dorsal view of a snout beetle; B, side view; C, ventral view of head and snout showing gular sutures, mouth parts and antennae.

This is a large group of characteristically shaped beetles. The snout is sometimes short but usually of medium length and at other times surprisingly long. The larvae, usually spoken of as weevils, often live within nuts, other fruits and stems where they may cause much damage.

1b Head not prolonged into a narrow cylindrical snout (beak). The two gular sutures distinct at both ends and not united. Prosternal sutures distinct. Fig. 14. COLEOPTERA GENUINA..............2

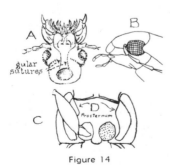

Figure 14

Fig. 14. A, ventral view of head showing the two distinct gular sutures, mouth parts, etc.; B, side view of head; C, ventral view of prothorax showing prosternal suture (D).

This great group of beetles includes a very large percentage of all the species in the order. They are highly diversified in shape, size, color, habits and habitat.

2a Hind tarsi with the same number of segments as the fore tarsi. (See fig. 15)..............................................................3

2b Hind tarsi with only four segments. Fore tarsi with five segments. HETEROMERA .......................................page 138

3a All tarsi with five segments. (If the fourth segment is obscure as in fig. 16a, take 3b.) Fig. 15......................5

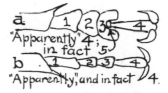

Figure 15

3b All tarsi with less than 5 segments...........................4

4a All tarsi with apparently four segments. (In many cases a very small obscure segment makes actually 5.) Fig. 16. TETRAMERA......page 174

Figure 16

4b All tarsi with apparently three segments. Fig. 17. TRIMERA.....page 89

Figure 17

5a Outer lobe of galea of maxilla (B) palpiform; first ventral segment of abdomen completely divided by hind coxal cavities (C); Fig. 18, Antennae* almost always filiform (A). Sub-order ADEPHAGA.....6

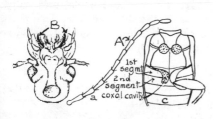

Figure 18

Seven families, 4 of which are aquatic fall in this suborder. They have well developed mouth parts and live an active predacious or carnivorous life. The ventral abdominal segments count one more along the sides than at the middle, a character which makes identification of the group more positive.

*If the antennae are filiform the first ventral segment should always be examined.

11

**5b** Outer lobe of galea of maxilla not palpiform; first abdominal segment not completely divided by hind coxal cavities. Antennae* of
various shapes, usually not filiform. (See fig. 12). Sub-order POLY-
PHAGA (in part) Fig. 19.................................page 64

Figure 19

This is a much larger sub-order and contains
many highly variable families. Everything that
does not fall within the Adephaga and Rhynchophora belongs to the Polyphaga, but part of the
groups of that great sub-order have already been
taken out by 2b and 3b, above.

## Sub-order ADEPHAGA

**6a** Eyes divided, one pair on the upper surface and one on the lower
surface of the head (B); antennae very short and irregular (auri-
culate). (See fig. 12). Legs for swimming (C). (Whirligig Beetles)
Fig. 20. Family 7. GYRINIDAE........ .................page 63

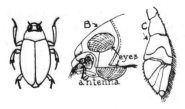

Figure 20

These small to medium sized
beetles have world-wide distribution.
Their surface is smooth and hard;
black is the usual color. The short,
thick, odd-shaped antennae have
eleven segments.

**6b** Eyes not divided; antennae filiform (thread-
like) or nearly so. Fig. 21...............7

Figure 21

*If the antennae are filiform the first ventral abdominal segment should always be examined.

7a Aquatic beetles; hind legs with fringes of long hair (a), and a long spur (b). (The Predacious Diving Beetles) Fig. 22. Family 6. DYTISCIDAE.............................................page 57

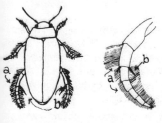

These beetles vary widely in size and coloring. Blackish or dull green is a common color but markings of white or subdued yellows are frequent. Some species display rather brilliant colors. The mandibles are hollow for sucking the juices of their prey. The 11-segmented antennae are filiform.

Figure 22

The Dytiscids are excellent swimmers. In contrast with other water beetles both members of a pair of legs move together instead of alternately. The adults bury themselves in mud at the bottom or sides of the water-courses to spend the winter. The front tarsi of many of the males bear suction cups to better enable them to cling to the female in mating.

7b Hind legs without fringes of long hair........................8

8a Small oval water beetles; antennae with 10 segments, entirely smooth; hind coxae forming large plates covering the base of the abdomen (a). (Crawling Water Beetles) Fig. 23. Family 5. HALIPLIDAE .....................................................page 55

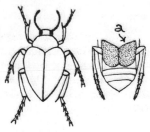

These rather small oval beetles are often marked with spots and frequently display some yellow colors. The legs seem poorly equipped for swimming but are useful in climbing through aquatic vegetation. Some species crawl out on the shore at night.

Figure 23

8b Terrestrial; antennae with at least the apical 6 segments pubescent; hind coxa normal. Fig. 24...................9

Figure 24

**9a** Head including the eyes almost always wider than the thorax (a); inner lobe of maxilla with movable hook at its end; clypeus extending laterally beyond the base of the antennae, (b). Antennae arising above the base of the mandible. (Tiger Beetles) Fig. 25. Family 1. CICINDELIDAE................................page 15

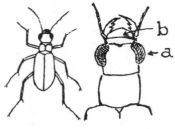

Both the markings and habits could suggest the name tiger beetles. Many brilliant metallic and iridescent colors with white or ivory markings are common. They are mostly of medium size and have long slender legs.

Figure 25

The long, sharply-pointed, overlapping mandibles are characteristic. The filliform antennae bear 11 segments. Many species are strong flyers, but the members of the genus *Omus* do not possess membranous wings and are flightless. The larvae await at burrows to grasp passing prey. A peculiar hooked-hump located about midway of the dorsal abdomen, enables the larva to hold itself within its burrow while subduing a struggling insect.

**9b** Head almost always narrower than the thorax; inner lobe of maxilla without a movable hook at its end. (See figs. 26 and 27). Clypeus not extending beyond the base of the antennae. Antenna arising between the eye and the base of the mandible................10

**10a** Beetles of round convex form; not over 8 mm. in length. Scutellum concealed. Prosternum scoop-shaped, entirely covering the metasternum. Fig. 26. Family 4. OMOPHRONIDAE.........page 53

The members of this little family are small to medium sized. Blackish greens, browns and subdued yellows often with a bronzed sheen are frequent colors. Some species are marked with spots or with rather intricate patterns.

Figure 26

**10b** Usually elongated in form. Small to large in size; form highly variable; often black but sometimes with brilliant metallic colors. Fast running. (Ground Beetles.) Fig. 27. Family 2.
CARABIDAE............................................ page 24

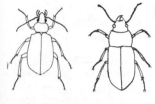

Figure 27

The members of this large family vary widely in size, shape and color, yet one soon learns to recognize the family so well that he knows a new one at sight. The legs are usually long and slender and the antennae 11 segmented. They are found in all continents, and are usually helpful.

# Family 1   CICINDELIDAE
## Tiger Beetles

Medium sized, often brilliant colored, swift moving land beetles. Both larvae and adults feed on insects which they pounce upon to catch. The larvae await their prey at the doorway of the tunnels in which they live. Members of the family are distributed all over the world but are at their best in the tropics. About 2,000 species are known.

They are favorites with collectors. When flushed they fly some distance and alight facing their pursuer. Some species are very difficult to catch.

**1a** Third coxae touching each other (a); eyes large, prominent. Fig. 28...........................5

Figure 28

**1b** Third coxae separated (b); eyes small. Fig. 29...................................2

Figure 29

15

**2a One inch or more in length. Sides of elytra widely inflexed. Fig. 30.**

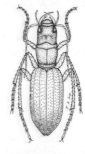

Figure 30

**1. Amblycheila cylindriformis Say**

LENGTH: 30-38 mm. RANGE: Kan., Colo., Ariz., Okla., N. M., Tex.

Brown or blackish with pale brown elytra; head large, eyes small; elytra with three ridges; legs long and heavy; tarsi short; wingless.

They are nocturnal in habit and live in holes in clay banks. When moving the body is raised high and the antennae kept in continuous motion.

Another species, A.* baroni Riv. (2) is known from Arizona. It is considerably smaller than cylindriformis.

**2b Less than one inch in length. Sides of elytra narrowly inflexed. Flightless beetles with elytra fused at the suture. Usually black. Genus Omus ................................................... 3**

**3a Elytra with distinct pits (fovea). Usually more than 2/3 inch in length. Fig. 31.**

Figure 31

**4. Omus dejeani Reiche**

LENGTH: 15-21 mm. RANGE: B. C., Wash., Ore., Mont.

Black. Elytra with conspicuous pits; side margins of thorax apparent at front only; labrum with two notches; head and thorax much wrinkled.

The members of this genus hide by day and hunt at night. Trapping by placing finely chopped meat under a board is said to yield good results.

**3b Elytra without distinct pits. Usually less than 2/3 inch long..... 4**

*This "A" refers to **Amblychella**. It is often customary to thus abbreviate the generic name when it appears a second or more times in close association with the place where it is spelled out in full.

16

**4a Thorax with deep wrinkles; shining.  Fig. 32.**

**12 *Omus californicus* Esch.**

LENGTH: 14-17 mm.   RANGE: Northern Cal. near coast.

Black, shining; thorax deeply wrinkled all over; elytra moderately coarsely punctured; head wrinkled all over; elytra widest at middle; antennae slender.

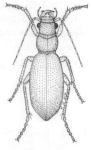

The sexes of the genus may be thus distinguished. Males: Three tarsal joints of front legs dilated and spongy pubescent beneath, last ventral segment deeply notched at middle.

Females: Front tarsi simple; last ventral segment without notch, oval at tip.

O. *edwardsii* Cr. (17) is similar in size but with shallower wrinkles on the thorax.  It has been found in Eldorado, Placer and Sierra Counties in California.

Figure 32

O. *lecontei* Horn (21), measuring 15-16 mm., is slender with its greatest width in front of the middle.  The labrum is truncate while in O. *intermedius* Leng (19) (17 mm.), it is bisinuate.

**4b Thorax entirely smooth without any wrinkles; elytra usually smooth and dull.  Fig. 33.**

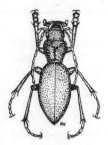

**34 *Omus laevis* Horn**

LENGTH: 13-16 mm.   RANGE: Calif.

Dull black; antennae stout; sides of thorax somewhat sinuate, elytra widest at middle.

This species once quite rare was later reported to be rather abundant.

Figure 33

17

5a Body, heavy, cylindrical; third segment of maxillary palpi longer than the fourth. (See fig. 35a). Fig. 34.

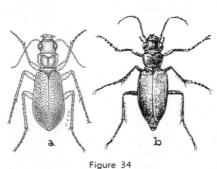

Figure 34

(a) 38 *Megacephala virginica* L. LENGTH: 20-24 mm. RANGE: Pa. to Fla. and west to Neb. and Tex.

Dark golden green, last ventral segments and antennae rusty brown, lateral margins of thorax and elytra metallic green, middle black; no lunule (moon-shaped mark) on elytra.

(b) 37 *M. carolina* L.

LENGTH: 20 mm. RANGE: entirely across southern U. S.

Light golden green, elytra purplish at middle with a lunule at the apex.

These two are the only species of this genus in our region. They hide by day and are active at night often attracted by lights.

5b Elytra usually somewhat flattened; third segment of maxillary palpi shorter than the fourth. Fig. 35b. Genus *Cicindela*............6

Among the members of this genus are some of our most beautiful beetles. They are often brilliantly colored and live such an active life that it offers rare sport to catch them.

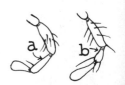

Figure 35

6a Humeral angles distinct; with flying wings.....................7

**6b Humeral angles rounded; small flightless species. Fig. 36.**

**91** *Cicindela celeripes* **Lec.**

Figure 36

LENGTH: 6-8½ mm.  RANGE: Ill., Ia., S. Dak., Neb., Kans., Ark.

Brown-bronze, head and thorax greenish; undersides and legs green; tibia and palpi pale; eyes very large, labrum with one tooth; elytra with scattering short hairs and coarse green punctures, the markings arranged as shown in the picture are rather indistinct and often wanting in part.

This is one of our smallest tiger beetles.  They cannot fly but run "like a deer" as the species name indicates.  It seems to prefer prairie hillsides.

*Prothyma leptalis* Bates, found in Mexico, is only 6 mm. in length. This genus as well as several other genera of tiger beetles have no representatives within our region.

**7a Thorax cylindrical with no margin.............................8**

**7b Thorax with narrow margin, abdomen not hairy, elytra much flattened.  Fig. 37.**

**93** *Cicindela unipunctata* **Fab.**

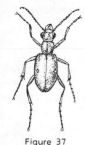

Figure 37

LENGTH: 16-18 mm.  RANGE: N. Y. and N. J. west to Ia. and Mo. and south to Ga. and N. C.

Dull brown, dark blue beneath; the flattened elytra, rough and with green pits and punctures.  A small triangular white spot near the margin of each elytron is its only mark.  (After Leng)

This species lives along shaded woods paths and hides instead of flying when disturbed.

**8a Pubescence beneath either erect or absent; outer margin of elytra of female not angulate........................................9**

**8b Pubescence on under parts prostrate; outer margin of female angulated near apex (a); elytra distinctly bronzed. Fig. 38.**

Figure 38

108 *Cicindela cuprascens* Lec.

LENGTH: 12-14 mm.  RANGE: Eastern half of U. S.

Coppery or greenish bronzed above with complete markings of ivory as pictured.  Thorax squarish flattened.  Thinly clothed below with decumbent white hair.

They frequent sandbars along water courses but are usually comparatively rare.  Two varieties *macra* and *puritana* have been named.

**9a. Thorax narrowed behind; markings almost always reduced to dots or spots.....................................................10**

**9b Thorax not noticably narrowed behind; markings largely connected and entering the interior of wing cover.......................11**

**10a (a, b, c) Bright green or bluish-purple above with 2 to 8 white dots, rarely none.  Not hairy beneath.  Elytra punctate.  Fig. 39.**

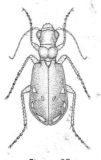

Figure 39

69 *Cicindela sexguttata* Fab.

LENGTH: 10-14 mm.  RANGE: much of the U. S. east of the Rockies.

Bright green above, often with a bluish or purplish reflection.  Each elytron may have from one to five white dots or sometimes has no markings at all.

Several varieties have been named, *violacea* Fab. (69b) having a rich violet color and is usually without dots though not always so.

This highly attractive species is fairly common along sun-lit paths where green vegetation grows.

**10b Black, dark bronze or green-bronze above with rather indistinct markings. Fig. 40.**

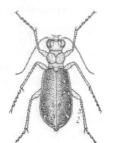

Figure 40

**74 Cicindela punctulata Oliv.**

LENGTH: 10-13 mm. RANGE: much of the U. S. and Can. except the extreme west and north.

Form slender, legs long; black dark bronze or greenish-bronze above; greenish-blue beneath. The markings of bands or small dots are usually indistinct and sometimes wanting.

It is a very common species, seems to like dusty paths, often flies to light and in summer may frequently be seen on city streets.

**10c Elytra practically without punctures. Color variable leading to several varieties; var. lecontei here pictured. coppery-bronze or greenish-bronze. Fig. 41.**

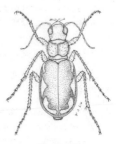

Figure 41

**68 Cicindela scutellaris Say**

LENGTH: 11-13 mm. RANGE: East of the Rockies.

Head and thorax green or sometimes blue; elytra coppery or greenish with marginal dots distinct or connected or unmarked. Some varieties are—

Var. unicolor Dej. (68e)—Unmarked green or blue.

Var. modesta Dej. (68g)—Black with apical lunule and one or two marginal dots.

Var. nigrior Schaupp (68f) — Wholly black.

Var. rugifrons Dej. (68c)—Green or blue with apical lunule and one or two marginal dots.

21

**11a Coppery-red (sometimes brown or green shaded above) large. Fig. 42.**

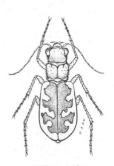

Figure 42

**39** *Cicindela formosa* **Say**
LENGTH: 16-18 mm. RANGE: East of the Rockies to the Missouri river.

Red cupreous; under parts metallic blue or green, thorax broader than long, much hair on head, sides of thorax, the abdomen, trochanters and femora; labrum with three teeth.

This species is found near sand dunes and blow-outs.

Var. *generosa* Dej. (39b) Dull red, green-bronze or brown-bronze above, green beneath; markings variable but when complete, as pictured. It ranges from Colo. and Manitoba east to the coast.

Var. *manitoba* Leng (39a) (c) has heavy white markings.

**11b Brown-bronze above; smaller. Fig. 43. 50** *Cicindela repanda* **Dej.**

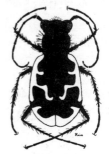

Figure 43

LENGTH: 12-13 mm. RANGE: U. S. and Canada east of the Rockies.

Brown-bronze usually with a strong greenish or coppery reflection above, underparts green; labrum short, one toothed. Underparts rather thinly clothed with long white hairs. This is a very common and widely distributed species. It is easily confused with *Cicindela duodecimguttata* Dej. (49) which is similar in color and range. It is more flattened than *repanda* and usually has incomplete markings.

## OTHER TIGER BEETLES

Only a comparatively few species of any family, large or small, can be included in a book of this size but since the Tiger Beetles are such strong favorites with collectors we are reproducing from Charles W. Leng's "Revision of the Cicindelidae," some drawings of the left wing cover of a number of species. These figures are all drawn to the same scale and are but slightly larger than natural size. In variable forms the most completely marked pattern is shown.

Leng's catalog numbers are used to identify the figures. The scientific names follow. All belong to the genus *Cicindela*. The chief color of the elytra is given. Fig. 44.

41 *C. limbata* Say (green)
42 *C. purpurea* Oliv. (cupreous)

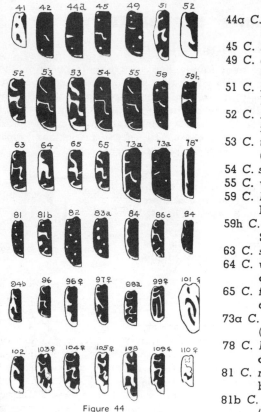

44a C. *limbalis transversa* Leng (cupreous)

45 C. *limbalis* Klug. (cupreous)

49 C. *duodecimguttata* D e j. (brown-bronze)

51 C. *hirticollis* S a y (bronze-brown)

52 C. *latesignata* Lec. (brownish-black)

53 C. *tranquebarica* Hbst. (black)

54 C. *sierra* Leng (bright green)

55 C. *vibex* Horn (bright green)

59 C. *longilabris* Say (black, brown or green)

59h C. *longilabris perviridis* Schp. (bright green)

63 C. *senilis* Horn (dull black)

64 C. *willistoni* Lec. (brown or green bronze)

65 C. *fulgida* Say (red-cupreous or green)

73a C. *obsoleta vulturina* Lec. (black or green)

78 C. *lemniscata* Lea. (cupreous)

81 C. *rufiventris* Dej. (dark brown)

81b C. *rufiventris hentzi* Dej. (black)

Figure 44

82 C. *sedecimpunctata* Klug (black)

83a C. *flavopunctata rectilatera* Chd. (dark brown)

84 C. *marginipennis* Dej. (olive or brown)

86 C. *carthagena haemorrhagica* Lec. (greenish black)

94 C. *pusilla* Say (dull black)

94b C. *pusilla cinctipennis* Lec. (brown, green, blue or black)

96 C. *circumpicta* Laf. (green, blue, brown or black)

97 C. *californica* Men. (dark bronze)

98a C. *trifasciata tortuosa* Lec. (brown)

99 C. *gabbi* Horn (olive bronze)

101 C. *dorsalis* Say (bronze)

102 C. *pamphila* Lec. (dull olive)

103 C. *hamata* Aud. and Br. (brown or green bronze)

104 C. *marginata* Fab. (brown or green bronze)

105 C. *blanda* Dej. (green bronze)

108 C. *cuprascens* Lec. (cupreous or greenish bronze)

109 C. *sperata* Lec. (brown to bright green)

110 C. *lepida* Dej. (green or bronze)

## Family 2  CARABIDAE
## The Ground Beetles

The members of this great family live very largely on or in the ground and feed on other insects which they catch, usually being active at night. They vary widely in size and form. For the most part they are dull colored though some are brilliantly metallic. They are found in all lands, more than 20,000 species being known. Many tropical species live in trees. The larvae are usually active predacious forms, able and ready to fight it out with the prey they encounter.

1a Middle coxal cavities entirely enclosed by the sterna alone, the epimeron not touching the coxa on its outer side; one or more bristly hairs above each eye. Fig. 45. Sub-family HARPALINAE ............. 10

This is the major group of ground beetles, representing around 85% of the entire family.

Figure 45

1b The epimeron aiding the sterna to enclose the middle coxal cavities. Fig. 46. Sub-family CARABINAE ............................ 2

This much-smaller sub-family includes some of the largest and most attractively marked-and-colored members of the family.

Figure 46

A large percentage of the beetles taken from under stones, logs and debris, especially in the spring, belong to this family. A good share of the beetles flying to lights are often carabids. A few species have a partial diet of seeds and fruit but their food habits on the whole make them friends of the gardner.

2a Front coxal cavities open behind. Fig. 47a ............. 3

2b Front coxal cavities closed behind. Fig. 47b ............. 7

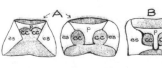

Figure 47

3a Hind coxae not separated; labrum not forked .................... 4

**3b** Hind coxae separated; labrum deeply forked, antennae with 4 basal joints glabrous, thorax nearly as wide as elytra, the sides elevated. Fig. 48. (a) 125 *Scaphinotus elevatus* (Fab.)

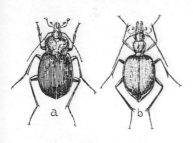

Figure 48

LENGTH: 18-20 mm. RANGE: middle and eastern U. S., not common.

Violaceous or cupreous. Antennae long and slender. Thorax with hind angles prolonged over the elytra, margins of both thorax and elytra reflexed. This species which runs to several varieties is one of a group of snail eating beetles which usually live in moist woods and are found under logs. (After Leng)

(b) **130 S. germari Chaud.**

LENGTH: 19-22 mm. RANGE: from Ind. eastward.

Blackish beneath; violet with iridescence above. Disk of thorax nearly smooth with punctures at the sides. (After Leng)

Other species are *Brennus interruptus* (Men.) (146) 16-18 mm. long. Black shining with a purplish metallic sheen; found in Cal.

*Sphaeroderus nitidicollis* Chev. (164), 20-22 mm. in length, bronzy black with iridescent sheen is found in Canada and our northeastern states and *Scaphinotus fissicolis* (Lec.) (135) with a length of 10-13 mm., deep violaceous ranges in East and South. This latter species has but 2 basal antennal joints glabrous.

**4a** Third segment of antennae compressed. Genus *Calosoma*......5

**4b** Third segment of antennae cylindrical. Fig. 49.

Figure 49

**173 Carabus vinctus Web.**

LENGTH: 25-30 mm. RANGE: U. S., not abundant.

Dull black, bronzed, thorax tinged with greenish at borders, without punctures though finely rugose; elytral striae with irregular granulate punctures.

*C. sylvosus* Say (170) 27-30 mm. East and South. Black, margins of thorax and elytra blue; 3 rows of pits on each elytron.

**5a** Elytra without rows of metallic spots..........................6

**5b Elytra black, each with three rows of golden spots.  Fig. 50**

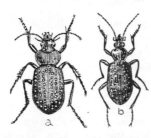

Figure 50

(a) 204 *Calosoma calida* Fab.
LENGTH: 20-25 mm.  RANGE: U. S.

Heavy.  Black above and below; elytra with three rows of reddish or coppery pits. Elytral striae deep with broad intervals.

(b) 183 *C. frigidum* Kby.
LENGTH: 22-24 mm.  RANGE: east half of the U. S. and Canada.

More slender than *calida* elytra with green punctures and greenish margin, ranges through our northeast.

The members of this genus are highly useful in killing caterpillars and grubs, often climbing trees to find them.

**6a Elytra metallic green with red margins.  Fig. 51.**

180 *Calosoma scrutator* Fab.
LENGTH: 27-32 mm.  RANGE: U. S.

Metallic and highly iridescent throughout.  Disk of thorax blue or dark purple, the margins golden or red; legs blue; abdomen green and red.  Male distinguished by a dense brush of hairs on inner surface of curved middle tibiae.

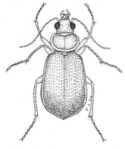

Figure 51

*C. willcoxi* Lec. (181) is very much like *scrutator* but only 17 to 20 mm. long.

*C. sycophanta* L. (182) with a length of 25-30 mm. is an European species which has been introduced in our East to destroy the Gipsy Moth.  Its thorax is blue and the elytra brighter green than in *scrutator*, the elytral margins are also green.

**6b Elytra black with blue border.  Fig. 52.**

176 *Calosoma externum* Say
LENGTH: 28-32 mm.  RANGE: east of Mo. river

Black, somewhat dull; thorax and elytra with blue side margins.  Elytra parallel for ¾ of length, striae distinctly punctured.  (After Leng)

*C. lecontei* Csiki (195) is a plain shining black species about the size and shape of *scrutator*.  It ranges through Texas but we have a number of Iowa records for it, where it occasionally flies to lights.

*C. carbonatum* Lec. (196) is plain dull black.  It belongs to the whole Southwest.

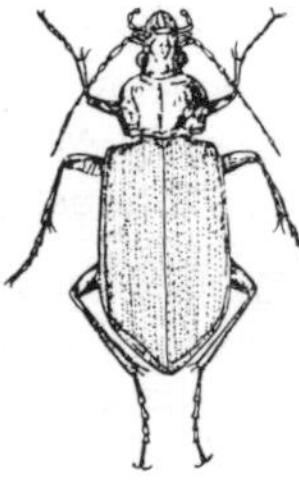

Figure 52

**7a** Base of antennae covered by a frontal plate; body pedunculate (thorax and elytra joined by stem like part); scutellum not visible. Tribe SCARITINI . . . . . . . . . . . . . . . . . . . . . . . . . . . . . . . . . . . . . . . . . . . . . . .8

**7b** Base of antennae not covered; base of elytra joining closely with thorax; scutellum visible. Fig. 53.

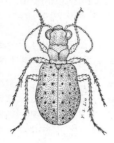

Figure 53

**233 *Elaphrus ruscarius* Say**
LENGTH: 8-10 mm. RANGE: northern half of U. S. and parts of Canada.

Dull drab with metallic sheen above; metallic green beneath; large impressed pits on elytra dull purplish, legs reddish brown.

The members of this genus of which there are several similar species may be found running on mud or sand flats on sunny days. They are sometimes mistaken for Tiger Beetles which they somewhat resemble in shape and habits. The head including the eyes is wider than the thorax. (See 9a-9b, p. 14)

**8a** 15 or more mm. in length; basal joint of antenna long; one bristle-bearing puncture above the eye and one at hind angle of thorax . . .9

**8b** Less than 10 mm. long; basal joint of antennae short; two bristle-bearing punctures above each eye and two at hind angles of thorax. Fig. 54.

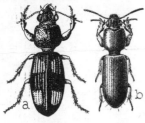

Figure 54

**(a) 375 *Clivinia bipustulata* (Fab.)**

LENGTH: 6-8 mm. RANGE: Eastern half of the U. S.

Black, with two more-or-less-obscure reddish spots near base of elytra and another pair near apex; elytral striae deeply punctate; legs and antennae reddish brown. Often taken abundantly at lights.

**(b) 359 *C. impressifrons* Lec.**

LENGTH: 6-6.5 mm. RANGE: Eastern half of the U. S.

A similarly shaped uniformly reddish-brown beetle, sometimes eats sprouting grains of corn and thus becomes a "black sheep" in a, for-the-most-part, helpful family.

**9a Large broad beetles with hind angles of thorax distinct. Fig. 55.**
**309 *Pasimachus punctulatus* Hald.**

LENGTH: 27-30 mm. RANGE: Central and Southern States.

Black with blue margins; elytra usually with pairs of punctures; mandibles deeply and coarsely striate. (After LeConte)

*P. sublaevis* Bov. (302), 21-28 mm., ranging east of the Mississippi, is colored like *punctulatus* but differs in having the elytra striate, and the tips of the elytra rounded instead of angulate.

These beetles are found under stones etc. in open woods, pastures and along cultivated fields where they feed on caterpillars and other larvae.

Figure 55

**9b Medium sized narrow beetles, without angles at back of thorax. Fig. 56.**
**317 *Scarites substriatus* Hald.**

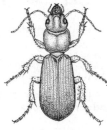

LENGTH: 25-30 mm. RANGE: Central and Eastern U. S. Abundant.

Black, shining. Elytra with striae but without punctures.

*S. subteraneous* Fab. (316), with a length of 15-20 mm. is common. Its marked difference from the preceding species is its smaller size.

These beetles are found under stones etc. near cultivated fields and are highly beneficial in killing other insects.

Figure 56

**10a Head with two punctures above the eye, with a single heavy bristle in each. Fig. 57a.............................................11**

**10b Head with but one bristle-bearing puncture above the eye. Fig. 57b.........54**

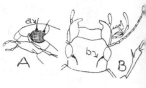

Figure 57

**11a Mandibles with a bristle-bearing puncture (a) in the groove on the outer side. Fig. 58.....12**

Figure 58

11b Mandibles without a bristle-bearing puncture (see a, fig. 58) in the groove on outer side...................................18

12a (a, b, c) Last joint of palpi awl-shaped; mesosternal epimera wide; length less than 8 mm.........................................13

12b Last joint of palpi elongate, obtuse at tip or subcylindrical; mesosternal epimera narrow. Fig. 59.

Figure 59

901 *Patrobus longicornus* (Say)

LENGTH: 12-14 mm.  RANGE: NE U. S. and SE Can.

Black above; under parts piceous; antennae reddish brown; legs paler. Thorax slightly broader than long, a median impressed line and a front transverse impression deep, punctured. Striae of elytra deep and punctured. (After Wickham)

The above genus includes a number of species, most of which range north of the United States . *Trechus chalybeus* Dej. (910), 5 mm. long, black with a bluish sheen and antennae and legs reddish-brown, ranges widely, especially in colder areas. It has several named varieties.

12c Last joint of palpi slender, without eyes.  Fig. 60.

Figure 60

921 *Pseudoanophthalmus tenuis* (Horn)

LENGTH: 4.5-6 mm.  RANGE: E. U. S.

Shining. Pale brownish-yellow. This beetle is one of several species of eyeless ground beetles found in the remote parts of caves. Eight species are known from Ky., Ind. and Va.

13a Front tibia not obliquely truncate at apical end; sutural striae of elytra not recurving at tip of elytra.  Genus *BEMBIDION*......15

13b Front tibia obliquely truncate at apex; sutural striae recurving at tip of elytra.  Very small beetles............................14

**14a Thorax with broad translucent margins. Fig. 61.**

**898 *Tachymenis flavicauda* (Say)**

Figure 61

LENGTH: 1.5-1.8 mm. RANGE: U. S. and Can.

Dark piceous to black with 1/3 of elytra yellowish at tips. Antennae and legs reddish yellow. Frequently found under bark of trees. (After Blatchley)

*Tachyta nana* (Gyll.) (890) differs from the above in being larger (2.2-3 mm.), jet black throughout, and in having a narrow opaque margin on the thorax. It is common and apparently widely distributed.

**14b Margins of thorax narrow and not translucent; recurved arm of sutural stria at tip of elytra, short. Fig. 62.**

**805 *Tachyura incurva* (Say)**

Figure 62

LENGTH: 1.7-2.5 mm. RANGE: U. S. and Can. Common.

Shining. Dark reddish brown to nearly black. Antennae brownish except basal joints which with legs are dull yellow. Indistinct stripe on elytra pale yellow. Found in open woods and in ants' nests.

*Tachys scitulus* Lec. (851) found in rubbish near water and on mud flats is from 2.5 to 3 mm. long, dull reddish yellow, the head darker. The elytra have an indistinct darker crossband behind their middle. It is widely distributed.

**15a Dorsal punctures (2) on the third striae of elytra**..............**16**

**15b Dorsal punctures (2 or more) on the third interval of elytra. Fig. 63.**

**408 *Bembidion inaequale* Say**

Figure 63

LENGTH: 4.5-5.5 mm. RANGE: E. U. S.

Bronzed, shining; antennae piceous, with pale red basal joints; legs greenish; tibia and base of femora dull yellow; third and sixth intervals irregular. (After Blatchley)

The genus *Bembidion* includes almost 400 species in our region, many of which are attractively marked.

**16a Thorax not appreciably narrower at base than at apex**........**17**

**16b Base of thorax narrower than its apex, very small. Common.**
**Fig. 64.**          **723 Bembidion versicolor (Lec.)**

Figure 64

LENGTH: 2.5-3.2 mm.  RANGE: E. U. S. and Can.

Convex.  Head and thorax bronzed greenish-black; elytra dull yellow marked in black or near black as shown.  Striae deep and punctate at basal half of elytra.

B. fraternum Lec. (731), is another somewhat similar small species (4-4.5 mm).  Its elytra are greenish bronze with 2 transverse pale stripes.

**17a Brownish or black, marked with dull yellow as pictured.  Fig. 65.**

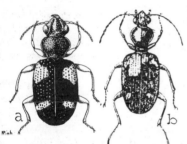

Figure 65

**(a) 737 Bembidion quadrimaculatum (L.)**
LENGTH: 2.7-3.7 mm.  RANGE: U. S.

Head and thorax shining dark bronzed; legs and basal part of antennae dull yellow.

**(b) 744 Bembidion pedicellatum Lec.**
LENGTH: 3-3.7 mm.  RANGE: E. half of U. S.

It is closely similar in color and markings to quadrimaculatum.  The elytral spots are smaller and less distinct.

**17b Elytra dull yellow with black markings as pictured.  Fig. 66.**

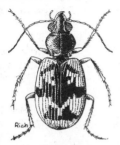

Figure 66

**651 Bembidion patruele Dej.**
LENGTH: 3.5-4.7 mm.  RANGE: N.E. U. S.

Head and thorax dark bronzed elytra dull yellow with black markings; legs reddish brown.  Often taken at lights.  Common.

B. variegatum Say, (660), is quite similar except that the elytra are black with a few dull yellow markings.

B. americanum Dej. (432), 5-6 mm. long and colored a uniform blackish bronze in a very common species of wide distribution.

**18a** Margin of elytra interrupted at posterior third
(a) with a distinct internal fold.  Fig. 67..19

**18b** Margin of elytra without an internal fold;
not interrupted........................32

**19a** Head not constricted behind the eyes....20

Figure 67

**19b** Head constricted behind the eyes then enlarged into a roll around
the neck.  Reddish-brown marked with black.  Fig. 68.

**399 *Panagaeus fasciatus* Say**

LENGTH: 7-9 mm.  RANGE: east of the Rockies.  Scarce.

Head and thorax elytra reddish brown, the elytra
marked with black as pictured; legs piceous; thorax
with coarse deep punctures; elytra with deep striae
and punctures.  (After Wickham)

*P. crucigerus* Say. (398) with a length of 10-12 mm.
and much the same range as *fasciatus* is black with
two large red spots on each elytron.

Figure 68

These very interestingly marked beetles differ so much in appearance from the average run of ground beetles that beginners often try
to locate them in some other family.  We had a student some years
ago who could bring them in on short order.  He found them under
lumps of coal along the railroad tracks.

**20a** Next to the last segment of labial palpi with
but two bristles.  Fig. 69a................21

**20b** Next to the last segment of labial palpi with
more than two bristles.  Fig. 69b.........29

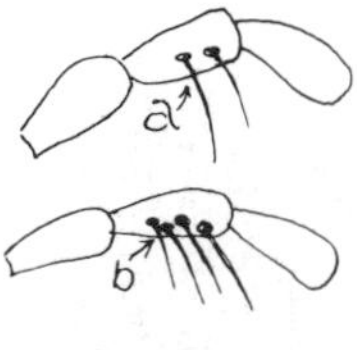

Figure 69

**21a** Front tarsi of male normally dilated; tooth of submentum usually
emarginate  .................................................22

**21b Front tarsi of male obliquely dilated (a); tooth of submentum usually entire, pointed; dorsal punctures one. Fig. 70.**

1209c *Loxandrus lucidulus minor* (Chd.)

LENGTH: 9-10 mm. RANGE: N. and S. Central States.

Black, iridescent, shining; antennae, tibiae and tarsi dark reddish-brown. Elytral striae shallow, very finely punctured. Often abundant. (After Blatchley)

Similar in color but smaller (5.5-7 mm.), *Loxandrus agilis* (Dej.) (1223), lives in the Eastern States south to Florida. It is found under bark of oak logs and stumps.

Figure 70

Still another species, *L. rectus* (Say) (1217), shining black with reddish-brown legs, antennae and palpi, and having a length of 11-13 mm., differs from *minor* in having its thorax one-half wider than long.

**22a With two or more dorsal punctures on each elytron. Fig. 71a............24**

**22b With but one or not any dorsal punctures. Fig. 71b.................23**

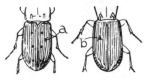

Figure 71

**23a With no dorsal punctures; head very large. Fig. 72.**

933 *Cylindrocharis rostrata* (Newn.)

LENGTH: 14-16 mm. RANGE: N. C. to Ga.

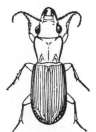

Black, thorax quadrate with broad, basal impressions. *Pterostichus adoxus* (Say) (1006), with a length of 13-15 mm. and ranging through much of Eastern U. S. and Can., is like *rostrata* in having no dorsal puncture; the head is smaller and the thorax much narrowed behind. (After Wickham)

All of the species falling under 21a (to 29a) were once put in the genus *Pterostichus*. That genus has since been split up and several new genera formed. In older books the student will find all of these species listed as *Pterostichus*. Csiki '30 proposed putting all these in the one genus, but that now creates so many problems that some systematists prefer the arrangement used here.

Figure 72

33

**23b** One dorsal puncture on each elytron, placed on the third interval behind the middle; but one basal impression on thorax. Fig. 73.

1024 *Gastrellarius honestus* (Say)

LENGTH: 8 mm.  RANGE: N.E. U. S.

Figure 73

Black; antennae and legs reddish-brown; basal impressions of thorax narrow and deep, the space between them with a few coarse punctures. Elytra quite convex, the striae deep and without punctures. (After Wickham)

*Ferestria obsoleta* (Say) (1080) is about 2 mm. longer than *G. honestus* and of similar color and range. The hind angles of the thorax are rounded instead of being rectangular as in *honestus*.

**24a** Usually 10 or more mm. in length, last segment of palpi cylindrical with truncate tip..........................................**25**

**24b** Not over 8.5 mm.; last segment of palpi elongate oval, scarcely truncate. Fig. 74.

1181 *Pseudargutor erythropus* (Dej.)

LENGTH: 8-8.5 mm.  RANGE: Central and Eastern U. S. and Can.

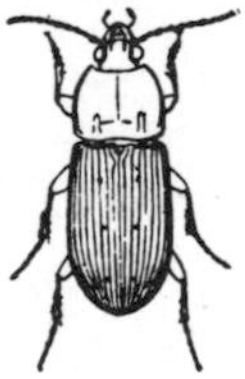

Convex, black, much shining; antennae and legs reddish-brown. Elytral striae without punctures. It lives near water and is often very abundant. (After Wickham)

*Micromaseus femoralis* (Kby.) (1183) is a similar species. It is black but not so shining. Its length is 7.5 mm. and is common in its range throughout our Middle and Western States.

Figure 74

**25a** Side pieces of metathorax less than twice as long as their width at base. Fig. 75a .........................**26**

**25b** Side pieces of metathorax long, narrowed from base to apex, their length being more than twice the width at base.  Fig. 75b..................**27**

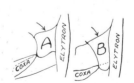

Figure 75

**26a Thorax narrower at base than apex; hind angles of thorax carinate.**
**Fig. 76.**                    (a) 1190 *Bothriopterus oblongonotatus* (Say)

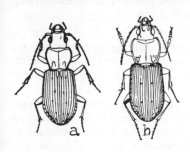

Figure 76

LENGTH: 11 mm. RANGE: Can. and Northern U. S.

Black, sides of prothorax broadly depressed, hind angles obtuse, dorsal punctures five or six. (After Wickham)

(b) 1093 *Euferonia coracina* (Newn.)

LENGTH: 15-18 mm. RANGE: E. U. S. and Can. Often abundant.

Black, shining, basal impressions of thorax deep. Striae of elytra deep but without punctures. (After Wickham)

Another very common black species is *Euferonia stygica* (Say), (1089), measuring 14-16 mm. The basal impressions have a tooth-like projection which distinguishes it from *coracina*.

Still another closely similar to the two above species, *E. relicta* (Newn.) (1085), differs in that the hind angles of the thorax are not carinate and that the elytral striae are deeper with their intervals being narrower and more convex. It measures 16-17 mm. and ranges from Indiana east and north.

**26b Thorax broader at base than apex; dorsal punctures two. Fig. 77.**
                    1103 *Abacidus sculptus* (Lec.)

Figure 77

LENGTH: 13-15 mm. RANGE: South and West.

Black. Thorax about as wide as elytra with deeply impressed mid-line; dorsal punctures on the third striae. (After Wickham)

*A. permundus* (Say), (1105). Length 12-14 mm. is a similar species differing in that it has three dorsal punctures. It is black or purplish and often displays an iridescent sheen. It is frequently common in the North Central States.

**27a Basal joints of antennae smooth without a ridge. Color black or purplish** ..................................................................28

35

**27b Three basal joints of antennae bearing a ridge, upper parts green or bluish, dull. Fig. 78.**

**1162 Poecilus lucublandus Say**

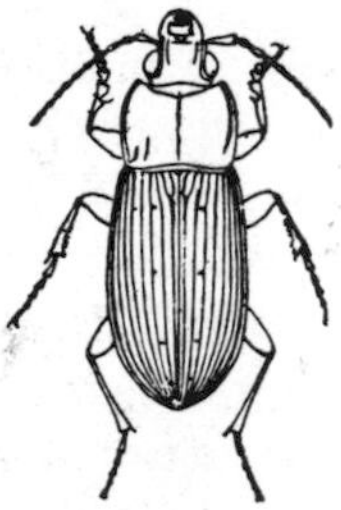

Figure 78

LENGTH: 10-14 mm. RANGE: U. S. and Can. Common.

Color highly variable, usually green or bluish; dorsal punctures 4 located on the third interval. Legs usually reddish; under surface punctured. (After Wickham)

*P. chalcites* Say (1161), length 10-13 mm., common throughout the U. S. Is green or bronzed but highly polished. It has but two dorsal punctures. The legs are black and the undersurface is not punctured.

**28a Basal impressions wide and deep; thorax with prominent margins; striae deep. Fig. 79.**

**1167 Lophoglossus tartaricus (Say)**

LENGTH: 16-20 mm. RANGE: Eastern U. S. Common.

Depressed, black, shining. Elytral striae indistinctly punctate. (After Wickham)

*L. scrutator* (Lec.), (1169) differs in being more highly polished and the striae less prominent, becoming very faint near apex of elytra. Its length is 15-16 mm. and range the North Central States.

Figure 79

**28b Basal impressions linear; marginal lines of thorax light. Fig. 80.**

**1178 Dysidius mutus (Say)**

Figure 80

LENGTH: 10-13 mm. RANGE: N. and E. U. S.

Subdepressed. Black, shining. Striae of elytra deep with fine punctures, intervals subconvex. (After Wickham)

*D. purpuratus* Lec. (1177) is closely related. As the name indicates it is purplish instead of black. It is 13-14 mm. long and is found in the North Central States though usually not common.

29a Elytra without dorsal punctures...........................30

29b Elytra with but one dorsal puncture. Fig. 81.

1074 *Evarthrus orbatus* (Newn.)

Figure 81

LENGTH: 15-17 mm. RANGE: North Central States and Ga.

Black; thorax as long as broad, but slightly narrowed behind; elytral striae deep with fine punctures; intervals convex.

*Eumolops colossus* (Lec.), (1061), is similar but larger (16-22 mm.), and with the thorax much narrowed behind and the elytral striae fine. It is recorded for Iowa, Nebraska and Louisiana.

30a Thorax broadest at its base, gradually narrowing to apex......31

30b Thorax broader in front than at base; often somewhat heart-shaped. Fig. 82.

1262 *Leiocnemis avida* (Say)

Figure 82

LENGTH: 8-10 mm. RANGE: Colorado to Atlantic.

Convex. Black, shining; antennae and legs reddish-brown; thoracic disk smooth at middle, densely punctate at base and sparingly so at apex; elytral striae deep. (After Smith)

A closely related species, *Bradytus latior* Kby., (1272), but slightly larger often shows a bronze reflexion from its black surface. It ranges from Northern Illinois east to the Atlantic and Canada.

31a Hind tibia of males pubescent on inner side. Apical spur of front tibia simple. Fig. 83.

1385 *Amara impuncticollis* Say

Figure 83

LENGTH: 7-9 mm. RANGE: U. S. and Canada. Abundant.

Dark bronze sometimes with a greenish tinge. Elytral striae shallow not punctured, but with a single large puncture where the scutellar stria joins the second stria. Flies freely to lights. (After Blatchley)

*A. cupreolata* Putz. (1400), is a smaller (6-7) bronzed or purplish-black species, quite oval and convex, which is very common over a wide range of our North Central States and Canada. It is readily distinguished from *impuncticollis* by the lack of the large puncture at the end of the scutellar stria.

37

**31b Hind tibia of males not distinctly pubescent on inner side; antennae and legs reddish-brown. Fig. 84.**

1281 *Percosia obesa* (Say)

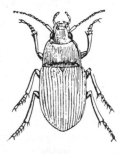

Figure 84

LENGTH: 9-12 mm.  RANGE: N.E. U. S.

Somewhat depressed.  Black, shining, elytra dull in females; antennae and legs reddish-brown; elytral striae deeper at apex, with very fine punctures.  (After Riley)

*Celia rubrica* Hald, (1378), found in Texas, Colorado and other western states as well as in the Central States, is reddish to chestnut-brown and but 6-7 mm. long.  *C. musculus* (Say), (1372), is a darker reddish-brown and still smaller (5 mm).  It seems to range over much of U. S. east of the Rockies.

**32a Front of head short, the labrum impressed**..................**33**

**32b Front of head normal**........................................**37**

**33a Three basal joints of antennae entirely glabrous.  Elytra without dorsal punctures.  Genus *Dicaelus***...........................**34**

**33b But two basal joints of antennae glabrous; each elytron with two dorsal punctures.  Fig. 85.**

1471 *Badister pulchellus* Lec.

Figure 85

LENGTH: 5.5-6.5 mm.  RANGE: Central and Eastern States.  Rare.

Head and markings on elytron black; antennae dusky with first joint yellow.  (After Blatchley)

*B. maculatus* Lec., (1473), is similar in size and structure to *pulchellus*.  The color is black except that the basal third of the elytra and a spot near the apex are orange.  It is reported from Pa. and Ind.

**34a Intervals (spaces between striae) on elytra regular and continuous**......................................................**35**

**34b Intervals on elytra broken by numerous large punctures. Fig. 86.**

1458 *Dicaelus sculptilis* Say

Figure 86

LENGTH: 17-19 mm. RANGE: Eastern half of U. S., not common.

Subconvex. Black, shining; antennae paler at tip. In low damp woods, under logs and debris. The members of this genus are our most attractive ground beetles. They are also of high economic importance in destroying harmful insects. If it were not for the aid given by the many useful insects in keeping the harmful species in check, men could not begin to compete with the insects. (After Say)

**35a Elytra black, the intervals equal in width and shape. (See *D. furvus* under 36a)...............................................36**

**35b Elytra purplish or brassy. Fig. 87.**

1454 *Dicaelus purpuratus* Bon.

Figure 87

LENGTH: 20-25 mm. RANGE: Central and Eastern States. Sometimes fairly common.

Purplish without brassy tinge, legs black, elytra with deep striae and very convex intervals. It is a grandly decorated beetle. (After Say)

*D. spendidus* Say (1452), is of similar size and shape but even more beautiful than *purpuratus*. The upper parts are purplish to rose violet and all adorned with a strong brassy iridescent sheen. It is not rare but scarce enough to give the collector a real thrill when he finds one. It belongs to the West Central States.

**36a Two bristle-bearing punctures on margin of thorax. Fig. 88.**

1465 *Dicaelus elongatus* Bon.

Figure 88

LENGTH: 15-18 mm. RANGE: Central and Eastern States and Canada.

Elongate. Black, shining thorax with deep median line and 2 bristle-bearing punctures at side in front of the middle; humeral carina reaching the middle.

*D. furvus* Dej., (1460), is readily told from the other black species by the wide and narrow intervals alternating on the elytra. The humeral carinae almost reach the apex. It is rather dull, 15-16 mm. long and ranges in the North Central States.

**36b But one bristle-bearing puncture on the margin of the thorax. Fig. 89.**

1450 *Dicaelus dilatatus* Say

LENGTH: 20-25 mm. RANGE: Central and Eastern States.

Black, dull. Elytral striae deep and faintly punctured near tip. Humeral carina reaching 2/3 to tip of elytra. (After Say)

*D. ovalis* Lec., (1464), is something like a small edition of *dilatatus.* Its length is 15-16 mm. and ranges through much of the Central and Eastern States. It is also much like *furvus* except for the alternating intervals.

Figure 89

**37a Next to last segment of labial palpi with but two bristly hairs..38**

**37b Next to last segment of labial palpi longer than the last segment and bearing several bristly hairs; first joint of antennae elongate. Fig. 90.** 1616 *Galerita janus* Fab.

LENGTH: 17-22 mm. RANGE: Central and Eastern States and Canada.

Bluish-black, densely covered with short hairs; legs, palpi, thorax and base of antennae brownish-red. A very common, rather loosely-jointed beetle, often attracted by lights. (After Blatchley)

*G. bicolor* Drury (1620), is a closely similar species of the same size but apparently more restricted in its distribution. The sides of the head are longer and less rounded behind the eyes and the pubescence near the scutellum stands erect in contrast to *janus.*

Figure 90

One or both species of these interesting beetles are almost certain to be found in spring and summer collections. They are highly valuable in destroying large numbers of caterpillars.

**38a Head prolonged behind the eyes into a neck which is dilated at posterior into a knob like part.................................39**

**38b Head not prolonged as in 38a................................40**

**39a Very slender yellowish-brown beetles. Fig. 91.**

1610 *Leptotrachelus dorsalis* (Fab.)

Figure 91

LENGTH: 7-8 mm. RANGE: Central and Eastern States.

Head, thorax and sutural stripe on elytra blackish; antennae, legs and elytra golden brownish-yellow; elytral striae deep and distinctly punctured. This and the following species do not much resemble ground beetles. Both are oddities and attract attention. This one is rather rare but is now and then caught in light traps.

**39b Slender black beetles with elytra dull red with black spots. Fig. 92.**

1612 *Casnonia pennsylvanica* L.

Figure 92

LENGTH: 7-8 mm. RANGE: U. S. and Canada.

Somewhat ant-shaped. Head, thorax and spots on elytra black; elytra and 3 basal joints of antennae dull red; elytral striae coarsely punctured on basal half.

Nature must have been experimenting when she made a beetle like this. It not only looks queer but acts the part too. It often flies to light and is fairly common.

**40a Elytra truncate at tip** ..................................... **47**

**40b Elytra obliquely sinuate at tip** ............................ **41**

**41a Tarsal claws serrate. Fig. 93.**

1484 *Calathus opaculus* Lec.

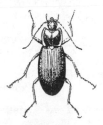

Figure 93

LENGTH: 8.5-10 mm. RANGE: much of U. S.

Head and thorax reddish-brown; antennae and legs paler; elytra darker, with very fine striae. (After Blatchley)

C. *gregarius* Dej., (1482), is a larger beetle, 10-11 mm. with shining reddish-brown upper surface. It is widely distributed and as the name suggested is gregarious in it hibernation.

**41b Tarsal claws not serrate** ................................... **42**

42a Elytra with broadly rounded humeral angles.  Side pieces of metathorax longer than wide....................................43

42b Elytra oval without humeral angles; side pieces of metathorax
scarcely, if at all, longer than wide.  Fig. 94.

1507 *Agonum hypolithum* (Say)

Figure 94

LENGTH: 13-15 mm.  RANGE: New York to Indiana.

Black shining; legs and antennae pale reddish-brown; Elytral striae moderately deep with
intervals convex.  Fairly large punctures on the
sides of alternating intervals.  (After Blatchley)

A. *caudatum* (Lec.) (1503) may be readily recognized by the prolonged elytral suture which extends into the diverging tips of the elytra.
The third joint of the elytra is nearly twice as long as the fourth.  It
is dark reddish-brown with antennae and legs paler, and measures
12-13 mm.

43a Hind angle of thorax much rounded........................45

43b Hind angles of thorax not rounded........................44

44a All the tarsi with distinct grooves on the sides; thorax and scutellum reddish-yellow.  Fig. 95.

1523 *Agonum decorum* (Say)

Figure 95

LENGTH: 8-8.5 mm.  RANGE: East of Rockies including Canada.

Head green, often bronzed: thorax, scutellum,
legs and base of antennae reddish-yellow.  Elytra
blackish, often tinged with green at margins, the
striae shallow and not punctured.  (After Blatchley)

A. *extensicollis* (Say), (1522), is a trifle larger.
Its head and thorax are both metallic green and
the elytra dull green or purplish.

It has a variety, *viridis* in which the elytra and
thorax are bright green.

**44b** Only the middle and last tarsi with grooves on the side, the front tarsi smooth. Fig. 96.

1514 *Agonum sinuatum* (Dej.)

LENGTH: 10-11 mm.  RANGE: Northeast United States and Canada.  Fairly rare.

Black, shining.  Elytral striae but moderately deep, with fine punctures.  (After Blatchley)

A. *cincticollis* (Say), (1518), is often abundant and gregarious in its range.  It is wholly black. The elytral striae are not punctured.

Figure 96

**45a** Side margins of thorax wider towards the base and reflexed; green with elytra and disk of thorax bronzed.  Fig. 97.

1566 *Agonum octopunctatum* (Fab.)

LENGTH: 7-8 mm.  RANGE: widely distributed but not very common.

Upper parts green; under parts shining greenish-black; the third interval with four (occasionally 3 or 5) punctures each in a large square impression. (After Blatchley)

This is a handsome and interesting beetle readily distinguished by the large impressions.  The adults hibernate.

Figure 97

**45b** Side margins of thorax narrow and scarcely if at all turned up.
. . . . . . . . . . . . . . . . . . . . . . . . . . . . . . . . . . . . . . . . . . . . . . . . . . . . . .46

**46a** Each elytron with 3 dorsal punctures; pubescence of antennae beginning on 4th joint.  Fig. 98.

1581 *Agonum punctiformum* (Say)

LENGTH: 7-9 mm.  RANGE: East of the Rockies in United States and Canada.  Common.

Black, shining, base of antennae, tibia and tarsi reddish-brown, femora darker.  Elytra with rather deep striae, and with fine punctures at basal end. (After Blatchley)

A. *pallipes* (Fab.), (1578), has a southern range (Texas to South Carolina, Florida).  Its size is similar to *punctiformum*.  It is often reddish-brown though sometimes black.  The legs, palpi and base of antennae are yellowish brown.

Figure 98

43

**46b** Each elytron with 4-6 dorsal punctures; pubescence of antennae beginning on third joint. Fig. 99.

1587 *Agonum picipennis* (Kby.)

Figure 99

LENGTH: 6-7 mm. RANGE: North Central and Middle States.

Slender; head and thorax black; antennae, legs and elytra brownish-yellow; elytral striae of moderate depth, not punctured; intervals nearly flat. Four to six dorsal punctures on third interval. It is often quite abundant and is gregarious in winter.

**47a** Front tibiae rather stout, broadening gradually to tip; paraglossa horn-like. Fig. 100.

1770 *Helluomorpha bicolor* Harris

Figure 100

LENGTH: 13-16 mm. RANGE: North Central States to Atlantic. Not common.

Head, thorax and legs reddish-brown, elytra darker. Elytral intervals with punctures in three confused rows.

*H. texana* Lec. (1771), more southern in its range and a bit larger is distinguished by uniform reddish-brown color and but two rows of punctures on the elytral intervals.

**47b** Front tibia slender; paraglossae membranous.................48

**48a** Spurs at end of tibiae short or normal......................49

**48b** Spurs at end of tibiae very long, and with fine teeth. Fig. 101.

1636 *Tetragonoderus fasciatus* Hald.

Figure 101

LENGTH: 4-5 mm. RANGE: California to New York.

Head and thorax dark, bronzed, elytra dull yellow or grayish marked with dark bands as pictured. Males with 3 joints of front tarsi dilated. It seems to be found only in sandy areas where its markings gives it protective coloration.

*Nemotarsus elegans* Lec. (1639), is a little larger, brownish-yellow with picious elytra, each marked with a pale spot at base and at apex. It ranges from Illinois, east and is the only member of its genus.

44

49a Head constricted back of the eyes........................50

49b Head not constricted back of the eyes; tarsi hairy above. Fig. 102.

1752 *Cymindus americana* Dej.

LENGTH: 12-15 mm. RANGE: Iowa, east to Atlantic. Not common.

Piceous, feebly shining, legs, antennae, humeral spot and narrow side margins of elytra pale reddish-brown; sides of thorax curved in front. Striae of elytra deep, finely punctured, with coarser punctures on the rather flat intervals.

*Calleida punctata* Lec. (1710), is a characteristically marked slim-bodied beetle. The head is dark blue, thorax reddish-yellow, elytra bright green, and legs yellowish. It measures 7-8 mm. and ranges from Kansas to New York.

Figure 102

50a Front tarsi of male not obliquely dilated; both head and thorax not reddish-yellow...........................................51

50b Front tarsi of male obliquely dilated; both head and thorax reddish-yellow; elytra dark blue. Fig. 103.

1642 *Lebia atriventris* Say

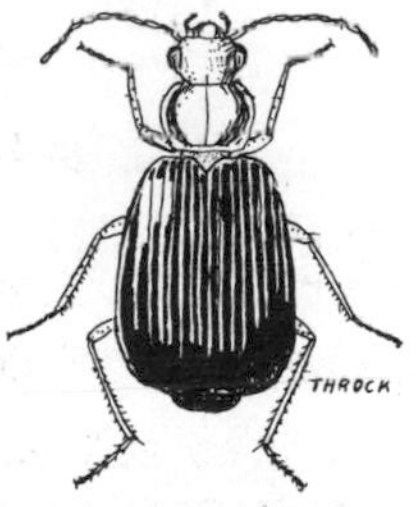

LENGTH: 6-7 mm. RANGE: general. Abundant.

Elytra dark blue; head and thorax reddish-yellow. Three basal joints of antennae pale, striae on elytra fine with fine punctures.

*L. grandis* Hentz (1641), is quite similar but larger 8-10 mm. The antennae are entirely pale and elytral striae deep. It is common and has a wide distribution.

This is an interesting genus with many characteristically marked species.

Figure 103

51a Elytra with pale stripes; mentum not toothed.................53

51b Elytra without pale stripes; mentum with a distinct tooth......52

**52a Head with lengthwise wrinkles; not over 5mm. long. Fig. 104.**
**1671 Lebia analis Dej.**

Figure 104

LENGTH: 4.5-5 mm. RANGE: general. Common.

Head black; four basal joints of antennae paler; thorax reddish-yellow with pale margins; elytra black with yellowish markings.

L. viridis Say (1655), ranges abundantly throughout the United States and Canada. It is 4.5 to 5.5 mm. long and shining green or purplish-blue throughout. Its head is smooth and the elytral striae shallow.

**52b Head practically smooth; length 6 mm. or more. Fig. 105.**
**1672 Lebia fuscata Dej.**

Figure 105

LENGTH: 6-7 mm. RANGE: Canada to the Gulf east of the Rockies.

Elytra and margins of thorax pale brownish-yellow. Head, disk of thorax and markings on elytra black or nearly so; antennae, legs and underparts reddish-yellow.

L. ornata Say (1667), ranges quite generally over the United States. It is 4.5 to 5 mm. long. Head, thorax and elytra piceous, with the margins of both thorax and elytra as well as two large basal and two small apical spots on elytra dull yellow.

**53a Head and thorax reddish-yellow; thorax with wide margins. Black stripes of elytra broad. Fig. 106.**
**1681 Lebia vittata Fab.**

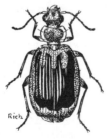

Rich.

Figure 106

LENGTH: 5.5-6 mm. RANGE: Central States and Middle States.

Head and thorax reddish-yellow; legs black; elytra and margin of thorax pale yellow. Elytra marked with black as pictured.

L. furcata Lec. (1677), ranging rather generally over the United States and Canada is much like vittata except larger (6.5-7.5 mm.) and the black stripes of elytra are more narrow.

**53b Head black, thorax reddish-yellow, its margins narrow. Fig. 107.**

1686 *Dianchomena bivittata* (Fab.)

LENGTH: 5.5-6 mm. RANGE: rather general; most common in South and West.

Elytra black each with two narrow white stripes, abdomen reddish-yellow; legs black.

*Lebia solea* Hentz (1675), is somewhat similar. Its head, thorax and legs are pale reddish-yellow; the elytra are piceous, each with a median and a marginal stripe pale yellow. It ranges abundantly over the eastern half of the United States.

Figure 107

**54a Elytra entire; mandibles without a bristle-bearing puncture in the outer groove, hind coxae contiguous** . . . . . . . . . . . . . . . . . . . . . . . . . . . .55

**54b Elytra truncate at apex; mandibles with a bristle-bearing puncture; hind coxae often separated. Fig. 108.**

1774 *Brachynus americanus* Lec.

LENGTH: 10-12 mm. RANGE: Central, Southern and Western States. Common.

Elytra bluish-black; four basal joints of abdomen pale, the others dusky. (After Blatchley)

There are about 30 species of this genus. They vary in size from 4 to 15 mm. or more. All have the narrow head and thorax, together with the legs colored reddish-yellow and the elytra dark in bluish or blackish shades. Their defense scheme of "firing" several rounds of a volatile gas at their pursuer have won them the name "bombardier beetles." Even their human enemy is disconcerted by these sounds and smoke-like puffs.

Figure 108

**55a Three basal segments of antennae glabrous; margin of elytra somewhat interrupted by an internal fold** . . . . . . . . . . . . . . . . . . . .56

**55b But two basal segments of antennae glabrous; margin of elytra without interruption** . . . . . . . . . . . . . . . . . . . . . . . . . . . . . . . . . . . . . . .59

**56a Third joint of antennae longer than the fourth** . . . . . . . . . . . . . . .57

47

**56b Third joint of antennae not longer than the fourth. Fig. 109.**

1821 *Chlaenius tricolor* Dej.

LENGTH: 11-13 mm. RANGE: rather general throughout the United States and Canada.

Elytra blackish-blue; head and thorax metallic green. Elytral striae rather deep and fine with fine punctures. (After Blatchley)

This genus has some 50 species, all greenish or bluish-black and usually covered with a fine pubescence. They are abundant in damp places under logs, stones, etc. and are attractive.

Figure 109

**57a Middle tibiae of male with a pubescent area near the tip; abdomen with a few punctures at middle and more at the sides.....58**

**57b Middle tibiae of male without a pubescent area near the tip; abdomen without punctures. Fig. 110.**

1806 *Chlaenius tomentosus* (Say)

LENGTH: 13-15 mm. RANGE: east of Rockies. Abundant.

Blackish, bluish or greenish, somewhat bronzed. Antennae black, the two basal joints pale. Elytral striae shallow with rather coarse round punctures. (After Blatchley)

*C. purpuricollis* Rand. (1808), is one of the smaller members of this genus measuring 8.5-9.5 mm. It is a dark violet-blue above and black beneath with black antennae. The elytral striae are very fine with widely spaced fine punctures. It ranges from New England, west through the North Central States.

Figure 110

**58a Episterna of metasternum long, the outer side longer than the front one. Bright green to bluish; legs pale. Fig. 111.**

1846 *Chlaenius sericeus* Forst.

LENGTH: 13-17 mm. RANGE: common throughout the United States and Canada.

Bright green or bluish, under surface black; antennae pale but darker toward tip. Striae of elytra fine with distant fine punctures, the intervals flat with many fine punctures. Under stones and debris near water. (After Blatchley)

*C. fuscicornis* Dej. (1847), is one of the larger species, with a length of 21 to 23 mm. It ranges through our Central and Southern States. Blackish with a bluish tinge, its antennae are brown, the basal joints paler.

Figure 111

**58b** Episterna of metasternum short, the outer side shorter than the front one. Fig. 112.

**1841 *Chlaenius kuntzeni* Csiki**

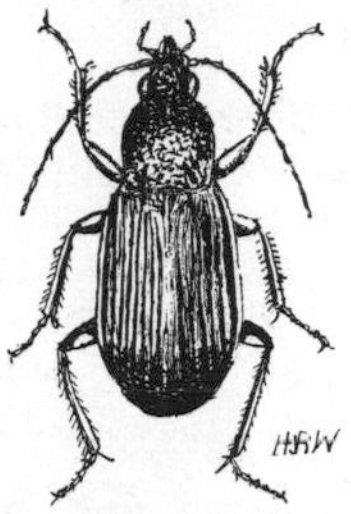

LENGTH: 13-15 mm. RANGE: Mexico and Central States. Common.

Thorax violet or purplish-blue; elytra dark bluish tinged with green; antennae brown with three basal joints paler.

*C. solitarius* Say (1830), though seldom abundant ranges through much of the western two-thirds of the United States and Canada. It is bright green above, with the underparts reddish-brown, the last ventral segment being margined with dull yellow. Its length is 12-14 mm.

Figure 112

**59a** Next to the last segment of the labial palpi with two bristles; about the same length as the last segment.  Fig. 113a...................65

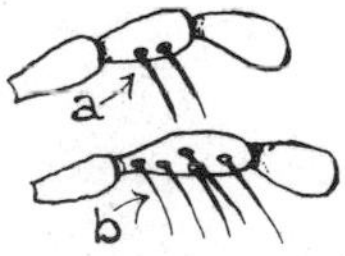

**59b** Next to the last segment of the labial palpi with more than two bristles, longer than the last segment.  Fig. 113b......................60

Figure 113

**60a** Front tibia with its outer apical side produced into a plate for digging ...................................................61

**60b** Front tibia normal; not used for digging.....................62

**61a** Mandibles large, body somewhat peduncled.  Fig. 114.

**1878 *Geopinus incrassatus* (Dej.)**

LENGTH: 13-15 mm. RANGE: Middle and North Central States.

Somewhat cylindrical. Brownish-yellow; front of head and disks of thorax and elytra often darkened. Striae of elytra fairly deep and not punctured; intervals but slightly convex.

There is but the one species of this genus in our country. It burrows in damp, sandy soil and sometimes flies to lights. It carries but little resemblance to most of the ground beetles and at a casual glance looks more like a Scarabaeid.

Figure 114

**61b Mandibles not prominent; body not pedunculate. Fig. 115.**

1882 *Euryderus valens* (Csy.)

LENGTH: 14-15 mm. RANGE: Central States to California. Not common.

Heavy, convex. Black, shining; basal margin and hind angles of thorax depressed. Striae of elytra fine, not punctured; 5 to 8 distinct bristle-bearing punctures on each of the 3rd, 5th and 7th intervals.

But four species of this genus occur in our region. There are many other small genera in this family that are seldom collected and but poorly known.

Figure 115

**62a Dilated front tarsi of male spongy pubes-cent or brush-like beneath. Fig. 116...64**

VENTRAL VIEW

Figure 116

**62b Front tarsi not spongy but with two rows of small scales beneath..............63**

**63a Mentum toothed; legs and antennae reddish-yellow. Fig. 117.**

1925 *Harpalus pennsylvanicus* DeG.

LENGTH: 13-16 mm. RANGE: general in United States and Canada. Common.

Black, moderately shining; under-surface reddish-brown; striae of elytra moderately deep. (After Riley)

This genus is a large one with well over 100 species known for the region. They are for the most part highly beneficial though a few feed on seeds.

Figure 117

**63b Mentum without a tooth; legs black. Fig. 118.**

1896 *Harpalus caliginosus* (Fab.)

LENGTH: 21-25 mm. RANGE: throughout the United States, very abundant.

Black; antennae and tarsi reddish-brown; elytra deeply striate with the intervals moderately convex. It often appears in large numbers at lights. Its habit of feeding on seeds makes its value questionable.

*H. herbivagus* Say (1956), ranging widely over the United States and Canada is one of the smaller species (8-10 mm.). It is black with reddish-brown antennae and legs.

Figure 118

50

**64a Abdomen punctate over its entire surface. Fig. 119.**

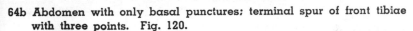

2111 *Amphasia interstitialis* (Say)

LENGTH: 9-10 mm. RANGE: North-central States to the Atlantic.

Head, thorax, antennae and legs reddish-yellow; elytra piceous; intervals of elytra subconvex, densely and rather coarsely punctate. Flies to lights; common. (After Blatchley)

*Pseudamphasia sericea* (Harris) (2112), in shape and size is much like the above. The upper side is wholly black; the legs are paler. It too is widely distributed and often very abundant at lights.

Figure 119

These two genera each have but the one species for the entire region.

**64b Abdomen with only basal punctures; terminal spur of front tibiae with three points. Fig. 120.**

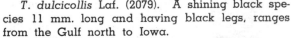

2071 *Triplectrus rusticus* (Say)

LENGTH: 9-14 mm. RANGE: Central and Eastern States. Common.

Brownish-black; base of antennae and part of hind thoracic angles reddish-brown; legs piceous. Elytral striae deep, intervals convex, the third with one to four punctures behind the middle. (After Blatchley)

Figure 120

*T. dulcicollis* Laf. (2079). A shining black species 11 mm. long and having black legs, ranges from the Gulf north to Iowa.

**65a Submentum with a distinct tooth; antennae with two glabrous segments. Fig. 121.**

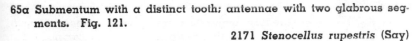

2171 *Stenocellus rupestris* (Say)

LENGTH: 4.5-5 mm. RANGE: throughout the United States especially in the southern half.

Reddish-brown, shining; head and disk of elytra usually piceous; two basal joints of antennae and the legs pale. Striae of elytra deep, their intervals convex. (After Blatchley)

*S. tantillus* (Dej.) (2195), is still smaller (3 mm.) and is black or piceous, with pale antennae and legs. It ranges in the Gulf States and North.

Figure 121

**66b** First segment of hind tarsi fully as long as segments 2 and 3 taken together. . . . . . . . . . . . . . . . . . . . . . . . . . . . . . . . . . . . . . . . . . . . . . . . . . **67**

**67a** Sutural striae long, joining the first dorsal; thorax with rather deep mid impression. Fig. 122.

2218 *Stenolophus ochropezus* (Say)

Figure 122

LENGTH: 5.5-6 mm. RANGE: much of the United States and Canada. Common.

Black or piceous, the elytra frequently iridescent; legs and base of antennae pale; striae of elytra deep; intervals flat. (After Blatchley)

S. *carbonarius* (Dej.) (2216) is larger, 7-7.5 mm. The color is black, with tibia, tarsi and first antennal joint brown. Its range includes the Central and Eastern States.

**67b** Sutural striae fine, short and not joining the first dorsal. Fig. 123.

2234 *Stenolophus plebejus* Dej.

Figure 123

LENGTH: 4.5-5 mm. RANGE: United States and Canada east of the Rockies.

Piceous black, shining; narrow margins of thorax, legs and base of antennae brownish-yellow. (After Blatchley)

S. *conjunctus* (Say) (2238) is a little fellow (3.5-4.5 mm.) which ranges widely throughout the United States and Canada. It is piceous with reddish-brown legs and antennal base. We often see it flying around our study lamp.

**68a** Thorax pale without a dusky spot; size 2.5- 4mm. . . . . . . . . . . . . . **69**

**68b** Thorax usually with a large dusky spot; size 5.5-7 mm. Fig. 124.

2256 *Agonoderus pallipes* (Fab.)

Figure 124

LENGTH: 5.5-7 mm. RANGE: Central and Southern States.

Yellowish-brown with an indefinite wide blackish stripe on each elytron (this sometimes faint or practically wanting); head black. (From U. S. D. A.)

A. *comma* (Fab.) (2261), closely similar to *pallipes* averages a little larger with wider elytral stripes.

These two species are known as the Corn Seed Beetle. In cold damp seasons they feed on the slowly germinating seed. They fly in great abundance at lights so that an example can be had readily in their season, when they are one of our most common beetles.

**69a Basal impressions well marked with a few coarse punctures, thorax dusky beneath. Fig. 125.**

2249 *Agonoderus partiarius* (Say)

Figure 125

LENGTH: 3.5-4 mm.  RANGE: Central and Eastern States to Texas.  Common.
Head black, antennae brownish, legs pale. Elytral striae deep; intervals convex.

A. *indistinctus* (Dej.), (2245), has much the same range and size. The elytra are blackish with margins and suture brownish-yellow.

**69b Basal impressions more poorly marked, with but few if any punctures; thorax pale beneath. Fig. 126.**

2247 *Agonoderus pauperculus* (Dej.)

Figure 126

LENGTH: 3-3.5 mm.  RANGE: Central and Eastern States.  Common.

Reddish-brown; elytra dusky or piceous, the margins and suture pale. Striae of elytra fine, the intervals flat.

A. *testaceus* (Dej.), (2246) with a similar range is still smaller 2.5-3 mm.  It is reddish-brown above, with pale yellow legs.  The thorax is as wide as long with much rounded hind angles.

Casey in 1914 put all the beetles on this page in the genus *Tachistodes* but they were later returned to the genus given here which now numbers around 30 species in all.  It is an important group.

# Family 4  OMOPHRONIDAE
## The Hemispherical Savage Beetles

This family until recent years was counted a tribe of the Carabidae. The members are convex rounded beetles which live near water in holes in the sand, about roots or under debris. Throwing water over a sand bank makes them come out of their burrows. Some 15 North American species are known.

1a (a, b, c) Thorax with only side margins pale; elytra with 15 striae. Fig. 127.                                      2284 *Omophron americanum* Dej.

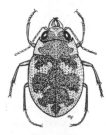

Figure 127

LENGTH: 6-7 mm.   RANGE: Northeastern United States and Canada.

Bronzed or greenish-black; head largely green, thorax and elytra with narrow, pale margins; Elytral striae with fine punctures; the intervals convex.

*Istor robustum* (Horn) (2295), with about the same size and range as *americanum*, is pale brownish-yellow with broken green cross markings. It may be recognized by its 14 shallow striae.

1b Thorax with a somewhat square green spot in center wholly surrounded by wide yellowish margins. Fig. 128.

2237 *Omophron tessellatum* Say

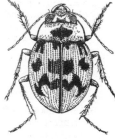

Figure 128

LENGTH: 6-7 mm.   RANGE: Middle United States and Canada.

Pale brownish-yellow.   Head with a green band across the base; thorax with center green spot; cross markings on elytra metallic-green. Elytra with 15 striae with close fine punctures.

*O. ovale* Horn (2285) is found in California, while *O. grossum* Csy. (2288) is known from Texas.

1c More broadly oval; elytral striae plain only at base. Fig. 129.

2282 *Omophron labiatum* (Fab.)

Figure 129

LENGTH: 6 mm.   RANGE: east of the Rockies.

Nearly black with pale side margins.   The punctures are only in the basal end of the striae. (After Hart)

*O. nitidum* Lec. (2283) 5-6 mm. long and ranging through our South is a shining metallic green, pale at sides.

54

## Family 5 HALIPLIDAE
## The Crawling Water Beetles

Though rather poorly equipped for swimming, these beetles prefer to spend much of their time in the water where they crawl about
over the aquatic plants or swim feebly in the open. They are usually
pale colored with dark spots. Perhaps the best way to get a larger
number of species is to stand out in a water course quietly and use
a small aquatic net to dip up the choice ones seen active down in
the water. Another scheme is to haul out on land a quantity of algae
and catch the beetles as they scramble out and back to the water.
The family is a small one but ranges widely.

1a Terminal segment of palpi large, conical, longer than the preceding.
All but the last segment of the abdomen covered by the hind
coxae................................................................2

1b Terminal segment of palpi small, awl shaped; only the first 3 segments of abdomen covered by the hind coxae; pronotum widest
at the base. Fig. 130.

Figure 130

(a) 2301 *Haliplus triopsis* Say

LENGTH: 3.5-4.25 mm. RANGE:
Maine and Ontario west to Wis-
consin and Colorado, south to
Georgia and New Mexico.

Pale to reddish-yellow with
black markings; eyes circular in
outline. Legs pale yellow; the
markings on elytra are variable.

(b) 2318 *H. ruficollis* DeGeer
LENGTH: 2.5-3 mm. RANGE:
North America, common.

Rufous to reddish-yellow marked with black; may be recognized
by paired basal impressions on the pronotum and by the deeply
grooved prosternum. (After Blatchley)

*Haliplus* is the largest genus of this interesting family in point of
number of species. *H. borealis* Lec. (2317) measuring 3 mm. and ranging through the northern half of the Central States and on into Canada,
resembles *ruficollis* but lacks its basal impressions. It is dull reddish-
yellow with five black spots on the elytra.

**2a Hind femora entirely dark brown or rufous; elytra with 10 rows of punctures and median spot, not broadly touching sutural stripe. Fig. 131.**                    **2332 *Peltodytes pedunculatus* Blatch.**

Figure 131

LENGTH: 3.5 mm. RANGE: New York to Iowa and south to Texas and Georgia.

Pale yellow marked with black; antennae and legs pale yellow, except that hind femora are black. Head closely and finely punctate. (Zimmerman considers this a synonym of No. 2336.)

*P. callosus* (Lec.) (2323) is distinguished from other members of the genus by a prominent tubercle at the place of the anterior black spot. It has a length of 3.5 mm. and is found in California, British Columbia and New Mexico. It is pale yellow and black.

**2b Hind femora never entirely dark brown or rufous..............3**

**3a Vertex with a prominent black spot. Fig. 132.**

**2337 *Peltodytes edentulus* (Lec.)**

Figure 132

LENGTH: 3.5-4 mm. RANGE: Central and Eastern United States and Canada.

Pale yellow with black markings. Head and antennae dull yellow-brown, with a crescent-shaped black spot on the vertex.

*Brychius horni* Cr. (2297) with palpi and hind coxae like the genus *Haliplus* can be distinguished from it by its quadrate pronotum, widest in front instead of being widest behind. It measures 3.5 to 4 mm. and is pale yellow marked with black. It has been found in Montana and California.

**3b Head wholly pale. Fig. 133.**

**2336 *Peltodytes duodecempunctatus* (Say)**

Figure 133

LENGTH: 3.5-4 mm. RANGE: East half of United States and Canada.

Dull yellow, with black markings as pictured. Often very common. (After Wickham)

*P. muticus* (Lec.) (2328), a widely distributed species closely resembles the above but may be distinguished by its wholly darkened femora and broadly rounded hind coxal plates.

## Family 6 DYTISCIDAE
## The Predaceous Diving Beetles

This family of some 2500 species is distributed world wide but is at its best in the Palaearctic Region. The larvae live in water and the adults spend most of their time there, when at rest suspending themselves by the posterior end to the surface film. The adults, when swimming, come frequently to the surface for fresh air which they take under the elytra. The pupa are terrestrial. The adults are strong flyers and common at lights. They prey on insect larvae and other small animal life in the water.

1a Episternum (es) of metathorax reaching the middle coxal cavity (cc). Fig. 134a.....3

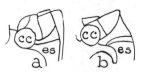

1b Episternum (es) not reaching the middle coxal cavity (cc). Fig. 134b. (After Wickham) ..............................2

Figure 134

2a Elytra blackish with greenish-yellow spots. Fig. 134½.

2351 *Laccophilus maculosus* (Germ.)

Figure 134½

LENGTH: 6 mm. RANGE: Central and Eastern United States. Common.

Head, thorax and under parts reddish yellow. Elytral markings variable.

*Canthydrus bicolor* (Say) (2341), is a small species (2.5 mm.) with yellow head and thorax and dark brown elytra, having a yellowish cross bar near middle.

*Hydrocanthus iricolor* Say (2346), is fairly common. Its head, thorax and underparts are reddish-yellow; elytra dark reddish-brown. It is 4 to 5 mm. long and is found in the Central and Eastern United States.

2b Elytra dull yellow with blackish bar behind middle. Fig. 135.

2359 *Laccophilus fasciatus* Aube.

Figure 135

LENGTH: 5 mm. RANGE: Central and Eastern United States and Canada.

Head, thorax and underparts dull brownish-yellow; elytra greenish-yellow marked in black.

*L. undatus* Aube. (2363), is recognized by its black elytra which are marked with two yellowish cross bars. It measures a scant 5 mm.

3a Spine at back of prosternum bent down into a different plane from
the sternum; less than 6 mm....................................4


3b Spine at back of prosternum not bent; length at least 7 mm.......6


4a At least 3.5 mm. long..........................................5


4b Small. 2 mm. or less in length. Fig. 136.

2394 *Bidessus lacustris* (Say)

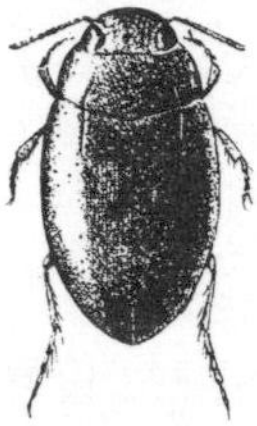

LENGTH: 1.4-1.8 mm. RANGE: likely much of United
States east of the Rockies. Common.

Head and thorax dull reddish-yellow; elytra brownish-yellow, with darker clouding. Underparts black.
(After Blatchley)

*Desmopachria convexa* (Aube.) (2374), is a tiny (1.7
mm.) brownish-red water beetle that has much the
same range as the above but is more rounded in form.

Figure 136


5a (a, b, c) Hind coxal cavities contiguous. Thorax distinctly margined. Fig. 137.                    2447 *Hydroporus undulatus* Say


LENGTH: 4-4.5 mm. RANGE: Eastern half of the
United States. Common.


Head and thorax reddish-yellow, elytra blackish with reddish-brown markings, rather variable.

Rich

Figure 137


*H. stagnalis* G. & H. (2521), measuring 3-4 mm. and with northern
range, is uniformly colored a dark reddish-brown. Each elytron has
a row of four to six coarse punctures on the basal half, with a few
distinct punctations scattered rather uniformly.

**5b As in 5a, except thorax with narrow indistinct margin. Fig. 138.**
**2454 *Hydroporus consimilis* Lec.**

LENGTH: 4.5 mm. RANGE: Northern United States and Canada. Common.

Head and thorax reddish-yellow, the latter darker at base and apex. Elytra blackish, marked as pictured with reddish-brown. (After Wickham)

Figure 138

**5c Hind coxal cavities separated; under parts black. Fig. 139.**
**2437 *Hydroporus wickhami* Zaitz.**

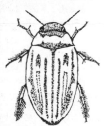

LENGTH: 3.2-3.75 mm. RANGE: Eastern half of the United States. Common.

Head and thorax reddish-brown; elytra black with reddish-brown cross bands, interrupted at suture. (After Blatchley)

*H. niger* Say, (2514), is a common widely distributed species ranging through the eastern half of our region. It measures 4.4 to 5 mm. and is black or nearly so on under parts, and above, with some rufous spots on head, thorax and elytra.

Figure 139

**6a Margin of front of head making a notch in outline at front of eye.**
**Length 7 to 16 mm.........................................7**
**6b Outline of eye not notched. Length 10 to 40 mm.................11**
**7a Hind claws of unequal length; the outer claw more sharply bent at**
**tip than inner...............................................8**
**7b Hind claws of equal length and shape. Fig. 140.**
**2557 *Agabus disintergratus* (Cr.)**

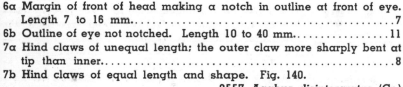

LENGTH: 7-8 mm. RANGE: much of the United States and Canada. Common.

Head and thorax reddish-yellow, markings black; elytra dull yellow with black stripes. Underparts mostly pale. (After Wickham)

*A. lugens* (Lec.), (2542), ranging throughout much of the Rocky Mountain and Pacific coast region is very common there. It measures 8.3-9.5 mm. and is black with small yellowish spots on the elytra.

Another widely distributed black species is *A. nigroaeneus* Er. (2579) ranging from Labrador to British Columbia and down into the Northern United States. It is one of the largest species (9.3-11.1 mm.).

Figure 140

59

**8a Hind tibiae with a line of cilia on the inner half of the apical angles.
Fig. 141.** 2598 *Ilybius fenestralis* (Say)

Figure 141

LENGTH: 10-11 mm. RANGE: Northeastern United States and Canada.

Black, slightly bronzed; elytra margined with reddish; antennae and front and middle legs reddish-brown, hind legs and under surface piceous.

*Matus bicarinatus* (Say), (2603), 8-9 mm. and ranging through much of the eastern half of the United States is a shining reddish-brown. The head is unusually wide.

**8b Hind tibia not as in 8a.........................................9**

**9a Side lobes of the metasternum broad and wedge-shaped.......10**

**9b Side lobes of the metasternum narrow; linear. Fig. 142.**
2610 *Coptotomus interrogatus* (Fab.)

Figure 142

LENGTH: 7 mm. RANGE: much of Canada and the United States east of the Rockies. Common.

Head, thorax and underparts reddish-brown, the thorax with a stripe of black at front and back; vertex black. Elytra pitch brown with obscure lighter markings. Often seen at lights. (After Wickham)

**10a Metasternum with a broad distinct pit-like depression on its front
border between the coxae; pronotum usually margined. Fig. 143.**
2621 *Rantus confusus* Blatch.

Figure 143

LENGTH: 12 mm. RANGE: Indiana.

Upper surface black, shining; antennae and palpi light reddish-brown; under surface piceous; tibiae and tarsi dark reddish-brown. (After Blatchley)

*R. bistriatus* (Berg.), (2623), ranges widely through Central and North Eastern United States and Canada. It measures 9-10 mm. Its elytra are blackish with margins and many lines through the disk, dull yellow. The front and vertex are dull yellow.

**10b** Metasternum flat between the coxa or sometimes with a faint longitudinal impression; thorax without margins. Fig. 144.

2692 *Colymbetes sculptilis* Harr.

LENGTH: 15-16 mm. RANGE: California, North Central and Eastern United States, Canada and Labrador.

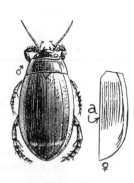

Vertex black with two paler spots; thorax, front of head and margins of elytra dull yellow; bar across disk of thorax black. Under surface black; legs reddish-brown. (After Wickham)

Our knowledge of the distribution of many species is highly fragmentary. Many of the "ranges" given here are based on actual collecting records but should be understood to be incomplete.

Figure 144

**11a** Length one inch or more; outer margin of hind tarsi not fringed with flattened hairs . . . . . . . . . . . . . . . . . . . . . . . . . . . . . . . . . . . . . . . . .12

**11b** Length but little over ½ inch at most; hind tarsi fringed on outer margin with golden-yellow flattened hairs . . . . . . . . . . . . . . . . . . . .13

**12a** Labrum distinctly notched at middle; abdominal segments reddish-brown with hind margins darker. Fig. 145.

2636 *Dytiscus fasciventris* Say

LENGTH: 25-28 mm. RANGE: North Central and Eastern United States.

Greenish-black above; thorax margined with yellow at sides and sometimes more faintly at front and back. Elytra margined with yellow. Elytra of female each with ten grooves reaching beyond the middle (a). (After Riley)

*D. marginicollis* Lec. (2639), similarly colored but 30 mm. long is very common in California and the West.

The members of this genus are sometimes known as water tigers. They are highly destructive to young fish and tadpoles.

(It has been contended that *Dyticidae* was the original spelling.)

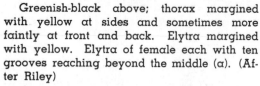

Figure 145

**12b Labrum practically truncate at middle; all margins of thorax broadly yellow. Fig. 146.**           **2646 *Dytiscus harrisi* Kby.**

LENGTH: 38-40 mm. RANGE: N.E. United States and Canada.

Elytra with yellow marginal line narrowing at apex and with a crossbar as pictured. Segments of abdomen reddish-yellow margined with piceous. (After Wickham)

The members of this genus as well as many of the other members of the family are readily taken in light traps.

Figure 146

---

**13a Hind femora reddish-brown. Fig. 147.**

**2651 *Acilius semisulcatus* Aube.**

LENGTH: 12-14 mm. RANGE: Northern United States and Canada.

Upper parts dull brownish-yellow with markings of black. Elytra with yellowish cross bar behind the middle. (After Wickham)

*Thermonectes ornaticollis* (Aube.), (2654), 11-13 mm. long, is dull yellow above with two transverse black lines on the thorax and many fine black dots on the elytra.

Figure 147

---

**13b Hind femora black. Fig. 148.**

**2653 *Acilius mediatus* (Say)**

LENGTH: 12 mm. RANGE: Northeastern United States and Canada.

Head, thorax and basal half of elytra brownish-yellow with black markings as pictured. Wavy cross bars at tips of elytra light buff. Under surface reddish-brown.

*Graphoderes cinereus* (L.) (2660), measures 13-15 mm. and ranges across the continent around our Canadian boundary. Its thorax is dull yellow with black margins. The elytra are blackish with numerous dots and marginal and sutural lines yellow.

Rich

Figure 148

## Family 7  GYRINIDAE
### The Whirligig Beetles

These highly gregarious beetles are always giving a skating carnival. Just how they maintain so much activity without some serious collisions is a mystery. Structurally, they are oddities. Flattened bodies, divided eyes and very queer antennae are characters that make them distinct. Catch one (if you can) and it gives off a milky secretion with a rather unpleasant odor. Some of them are called "apple bugs" because of this. Up at McGregor, Iowa the kids call them "penny bugs." They have been told if they put one under their pillow on going to bed, in the morning they'll find a "scent" there.

1a Scutellum distinct; length less than 8 mm.; elytra with 11 striae...3

1b Scutellum hidden; length 9 or more mm.; elytra with 9 striae or smooth...................................................... 2

2a Under surface brownish yellow.  Fig. 149.

2674 *Dineutes discolor* Aube.

LENGTH: 11.5-13 mm.  RANGE: Central and Eastern United States.

Upper parts black with bronze reflection, shining; under surface brownish-yellow to straw color; elytra with side margins at outer apical angle and tips slightly sinuate.

*Dineutes ciliatus* Forsberg (2671), may be readily told by its larger size (12-15.5 mm.). Its upper parts are black with bronze stripes near the margins and the under surface dark brown or pitchy. It ranges through the Atlantic and Southern States.

Figure 149

2b Under surface black or bronzed.  Fig. 150.

2680 *Dineutes assimilis* (Kby.)

LENGTH: 10-11 mm.  RANGE: pretty much throughout the United States and Canada.  Common.

Black above and below, much bronzed and very shiny; legs brownish-yellow. Femur without a tooth; punctures shallow and not closely placed. (After Blatchley)

*Dineutes carolinus* Lec. (2683), is a smaller species 9-10 mm. which ranges from the South Atlantic States to Texas. Its surface is black, sometimes bronzed, and rather dull.

Figure 150

63

**3a Scutellum with a distinct but very fine longitudinal ridge at base. Small. Fig. 151.**

Figure 151

**2684 Gyrinus minutus Fab.**

LENGTH: 3.5-4.3 mm. RANGE: United States, Canada, Alaska (also Central and Northern Europe and Asia). Common.

Upper parts black, sides bronzed, dull; under parts brownish-yellow; abdomen black; thorax with a fine ridge at middle.

*Gyrinus analis* Say (2700), is a common and very widely dispersed species ranging from Nova Scotia to Kansas and south to Florida and Louisiana. It measures 4.5-5.5 mm. and is bronzed above and beneath; the legs are reddish brown.

**3b Scutellum flat, under surface reddish-brown. Fig. 152.**

Figure 152

**2691 Gyrinus ventralis Kby.**

LENGTH: 4.8-6 mm. RANGE: Northern United States and Canada.

Black, highly polished, often with bluish reflections, sides bronzed. (After Blatchley)

*Gyrinus affinis* Aube. (2696), is very common in its range, apparently over much of the United States and Canada. It is shining black with faint bluish reflections. In length it is 5.6-7 mm.

## Sub-order POLYPHAGA*

**1a Antennae lamellate, bearing 3 to 7 segments at the end, each of which extends to one side into a flattened plate-like structure, (a). Legs often fitted for digging. Fig. 153. (*LAMELLICORNIA*) Super-family SCARABAEOIDEA** . . . . . . . . . . . . . . . . . . . . . . . . . . . . . . . .page 231

Figure 153

Many of these are heavy-set beetles and often quite large. The antennae are distinctive. They are widely distributed.

*It will be noted that some other families of the Polyphaga have been provided for earlier in the keys and that the full list of families ordinarily assigned to this sub-order do not appear at this place.

1b Antennae not lamellate..........................................2

2a Hind legs modified for swimming, (a). Antennae clavate or capitate, short with 6 to 9 segments. (The genus *Sphaeridium* belonging here, does not have swimming legs.) (Water Scavenger Beetles) Fig. 154. Family 8, HYDROPHILIDAE.....................page 78

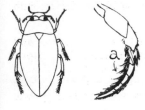

The members of this large family vary widely in size. Black or dull colors are the rule, though brighter shades are occasionally displayed.

Figure 154

2b Hind legs not modified for swimming............3

3a Elytra (a) covering less than half the length of the abdomen (b), wings folded under the short elytra when not in use; all of the abdominal segments horny on top. Fig. 155................................4

3b Elytra covering all or at least more than half of the abdomen (if short, the wings are not folded at rest or are absent); upper part of some of the abdominal segments membranous...........................6

Figure 155

4a Abdomen flexible with 7 or 8 segments visible below. (Rove Beetles) Fig. 156. Family 16, STAPHYLINIDAE......page 92

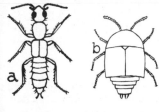

This is a very large family of usually strong-flying beetles. They range from very small to medium sizes. Most of the species are slender as in figure "a" while some are short and compact as in figure b. More than 300 species live in association with ants and are sometimes shaped somewhat like them.

Figure 156

4b Abdomen rigid with but 5 or 6 ventral segments. Small ant-like beetles.............................................................5

**5a Antennae with 10 or 11 segments. (Ant-Loving Beetles) Fig. 157. Family 17, PSELAPHIDAE**..............................page 113

These tiny beetles are usually reddish or yellowish. They live in ant colonies and are not uncommon. Their bodies are heavily chitinized.

Figure 157

**5b Antennae with but 2 segments. Fig. 158. Family 18. CLAVIGERIDAE.**

**(a) 6386 *Fustiger fuchsi* Bndl.**

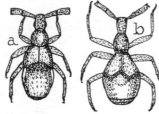

LENGTH: 1.7 mm. RANGE: Ind., Tenn., Ariz.

Dark brownish yellow; head and thorax rather deeply impressed with a netted design. Basal segment of abdomen large and wide.

**(b) 6389 *Adranes lecontei* Bndl.**

Figure 158

LENGTH: 2.5 mm. RANGE: Ind. and Miss.

Like the few other species of the genus it differs from those of the genus *Fustiger* in having no eyes. The head and thorax are elongated and slim. It is colored brownish-yellow and covered with a fine pubescence.

The members of this little family closely resemble the Pselaphidae in appearance and habits but of course have only two segments to the antennae.

**6a Small oval convex, very shiny beetles with conical tipped abdomen (a) exposed under broadly truncate elytra. Six or seven ventral abdominal segments. (The Shining Fungus Beetles). Fig. 159. Family 21. SCAPHIDIIDAE**..............................page 117

The casual observer might confuse the members of this rather small family with the Hister beetles. One glance at the antennae should clear up that question.

Figure 159

6b Not as in 6a...................................................7

7a Abdomen with seven or eight visible ventral segments. Fig. 160a.........17

7b Abdomen with less than seven ventral segments. Fig. 160b.....................8

8a First three ventral abdominal segments fused and immovable; last segment of tarsi longer than other four combined and armed with long simple claws; live in or near water but legs not fitted for swimming...................................9

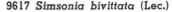

Figure 160

8b Not as in 8a...................................................10

9a Abdomen with six ventral segments; front coxae with very large trochantin; (body subdepressed). Fig. 161. Family 55, PSEPHENIDAE.

9586 *Psephenus lecontei* (Lec.)

Figure 161

LENGTH: 4-6 mm.  RANGE: Eastern U. S. and Can.

Black, often tinged with dull brown, head and thorax darkest; with fine punctures and pubescence. Uses its strong claws to attach itself to rocks and water plants, both above and within water. Only 3 other species are known for the family, all of which are confined to California in their known range.

9b Abdomen with but 5 ventral segments; front coxae rounded, without trochantin; body convex and lightly pubescent. Fig. 162. Family 57, ELMIDAE.

9617 *Simsonia bivittata* (Lec.)

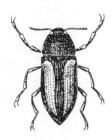

Figure 162

LENGTH: 3 mm.  RANGE: Eastern and north U. S.

Shiny black, marked with yellowish as pictured.

*Helichus striatus* Lec. (9605) belonging to another small family (56 DRYOPIDAE) and distinguished by transverse front coxae and large trochantins is blackish and measures 6 mm.  It is widely scattered.

**10a Abdomen with six ventral segments**.........................11

**10b Abdomen with but five ventral segments**.....................20

**11a Tiny flattened beetles with only rudimentary eyes or none; live in nests of small mammals, birds and bumblebees. Fig. 163. Family 11, LEPTINIDAE.**

2906 *Leptinus testaceus* Mull.

LENGTH: 2-2.5 mm.  RANGE: Europe and N. A.

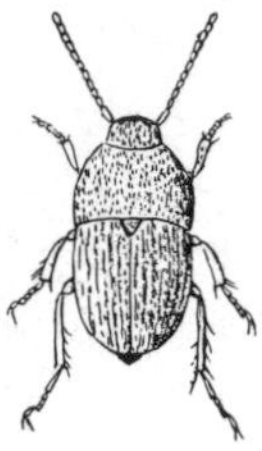

Pale yellow.  Fine regular punctures thickly set with golden hairs.  Eyes wholly wanting.

Leng's catalog shows but three species for this family.  *Leptinillus aplodontiae* Ferris (2908), measuring about 3 mm. and colored reddish-brown is associated with a rodent in California.

It is questioned whether these tiny beetles live at the expense of the owners of the nests in which they are found or prey on the mites also infesting the nests.  They are not at all common but are well worth searching for.

Figure 163

**11b Not as in 11a**..............................................12

**12a Very small oval, (from less than 1 mm. to not over 3 mm.), convex, shining, brown or blackish beetles; usually covered with erect hairs.  Eyes coarsely granulate.  (Ant-like Stone Beetles). Fig. 164.  Family 14, SCYDMAENIDAE**.................page 88

These tiny little fellows seldom get into collections unless one goes out and deliberately looks for them.  Look under bark, in damp places and in ants' nests.

Nearly 200 species have been named and described for our region.  Wickham reported 40 species for Iowa.

Figure 164

**12b Not as in 12a**..............................................13

13a Mostly large beetles, usually over 12 mm. long, either broadly flattened (a) or heavy and in this latter case with elytra short, exposing two or three segments of abdomen (b). (A rather large number of poorly known species ranging in size from 1.5-4.5 mm. have by some been assigned a family of their own.) (Carrion Beetles) Fig. 165. Family 12, SILPHIDAE.............page 82

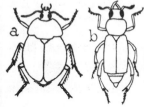

Many of these scavengers are brilliantly colored in outstanding patterns of red and black or yellow and black. They may be readily trapped by use of dead animals.

Figure 165

13b Seldom over 10 mm. in length. Cylindrical forms.............14

14a First abdominal segment cut into three parts by hind coxae. Brown cylindrical beetles with wrinkled thorax. (The Wrinkled Bark Beetles) Fig. 166. Family 67, RHYSODIDAE.

9944 *Rhysodes americanus* Lap.

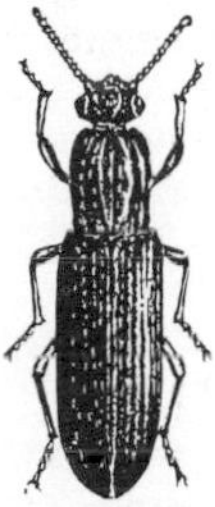

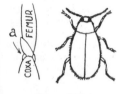

LENGTH: 6-8 mm. RANGE: Eastern half U. S.

Dark reddish-brown, shining. Deep furrows on thorax; elytral striae with large punctures. Male with distinct tooth on front femur. Found under bark of logs and trees of beech, oak and elm.

*Clinidium sculptile* Newn. (9946) is similar to the above in shape, size, color and range, but has grooved elytra but no punctures.

Figure 166

14b Not as in 14a.............15

15a Hind coxae conical. Front coxae long with distinct trochantins (a). (Soft-winged Flower Beetles) Fig. 167. Family 28, MELYRIDAE.
.............page 130

These beetles have rather soft wings and are for the most part small size. The antennae have 11 segments, though in some species appearing as 10. More species are known from the western states.

Figure 167

69

**15b** Hind coxae flat; covered with femora when at rest............16

**16a** Fourth tarsal segment equal to others; disk of thorax not separated from the flanks. (Checkered Beetles) Fig. 168. Family 29, CLERIDAE. ...........................................page 132

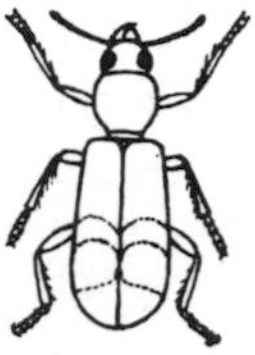

This is a comparatively large family of medium sized beetles. They are usually cylindrical, pleasingly marked, often with rather brilliant colors and often densely pubescent.

Figure 168

**16b** Fourth tarsal segment very small, scarcely if at all visible from above; disk of thorax separated from the sides by an elevated marginal line. Fig. 169. Family 30, CORYNETIDAE......page 135

These beetles are highly similar to the Clerids, the most apparent difference being in the small tarsal segment mentioned in the key.

Figure 169

**17a** Middle coxae separated from each other. Epipleura absent. No light giving organs. (Net-Winged Beetles) Fig. 170. Family 24, LYCIDAE...........................................page 124

The members of this small family have soft wings and do not look just like beetles. They fly by day and are not very abundant.

Figure 170

**17b** Middle coxae touching, distinct............................18

18a Episternum of metathorax sinuate (with S curve) on inner side. (Fig. 171a) head if at all less than half covered by prothorax. (Soldier Beetles, etc.) Fig. 171. Family 27, CANTHARIDAE..page 128

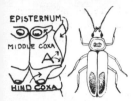

The members of this comparatively large family have leathery elytra, are usually dusky colored or yellow, and possess no light organs. The antennae are 11 segmented and often serrate.

Figure 171

18b Episternum of metathorax (See fig. 172b) not sinuate (double curved) on inner side.............................................19

19a Head more or less completely covered by the thorax; antennae usually close together at base. (Firefly Beetles) Fig. 172. Family 25, LAMPYRIDAE...................................page 126

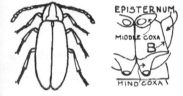

This is a large family, becoming more common as the tropics are approached. They are usually flat topped, variously colored and many, but not all species have light producing organs on the abdomen.

Figure 172

19b Head not at all covered by thorax; antennae well separated at their base. Fig. 173. Family 26, PHENGODIDAE.

7023 Phengodes plumosa (Oliv.) LENGTH: Male; 11-12 mm. RANGE: Eastern half of U. S.

Dull yellow with fine pubescence. Antennae pulmose; elytra small and diverging. Female; elongate, wormlike. (After Glover)

Zarhipis piciventris Lec. (7018) is a California species. The yellowish brown larviform females measure 30 to 50 mm. while the winged males are but 10 mm. long. They are piceous with legs, pronotum and mandibles reddish.

Z. riversi Horn (7020) is somewhat larger. The male is black with yellowish red on head, thorax and part of abdomen. The female is yellowish-brown.

Figure 173

71

20a Antennae both elbowed and club-shaped, (a). Hard, usually small, black, red and black or dark green beetles; elytra square-cut (truncate) (b) at apex exposing two segments of the abdomen (pygidium). (Hister Beetles) Fig. 174. Family 23, HISTERIDAE...page 119

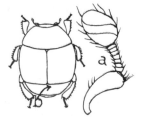

These beetles are hard oval forms (a few much flattened to live under bark), smooth and usually shining. They may be readily recognized by the antennae.

Figure 174

20b Not as in 20a.....................21

21a Femora (f) attached to end of trochanter (t) or very near the end. Fig. 175.
...................................22

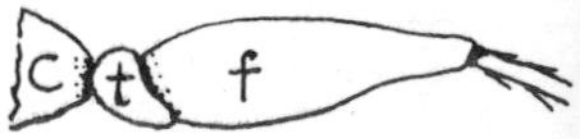

Figure 175

21b Femora attached to side of trochanter. Fig. 176..........................25

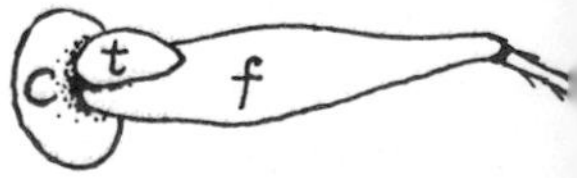

22a First segment of tarsus shorter than second.......................... 23

22b First segment of tarsus equal to or longer than the second...........24

Figure 176

23a Antennae attached on the front of the head, their basal segments close together; thorax without side margins. (Spider Beetles etc.) Fig. 177. Family 91, PTINIDAE........................page 224

These tiny beetles are usually yellowish or brownish, with small head and long antennae. They feed on dried animal and plant products.

Figure 177

72

23b Antennae attached in front of eyes on sides of head, their basal segments usually more widely separated. (Death Watch Beetles) Fig. 178. Family 92, ANOBIIDAE.....................page 225

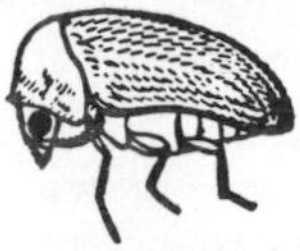

These too, feed on plant and animal products, and bore in wood thus doing considerable damage. They are small, dull colored and have the head concealed by the thorax.

Figure 178

24a First ventral segment of abdomen not longer than the others; antennae with club of 3 or 4 serrate segments. Black or brown cylindrical beetles with head usually directed downward, and hidden by thorax. (Bostrichids) Fig. 179. Family 93, BOSTRICHIDAE....................................................page 227

These are small to large beetles, blackish or reddish-brown. The legs are short and the 11 segmented antennae arise from in front of the eyes. Some 400 species are known, many of which are destructive to dry wood.

Figure 179

24b First ventral segment of abdomen longer than the others; antennal club with but 2 serrate segments; slender brown or black; head distinct. (Powder Post Beetles) Fig. 180. Family 94, LYCTIDAE...............................................,page 229

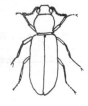

These beetles are definitely economic; their damage is not very rapid but none the less certain. They are small cylindrical beetles and usually dull colored.

Figure 180

25a Front coxae conical, projecting prominently from coxal cavity...26

25b Front coxae globular or transverse, usually projecting but little from the coxal cavity.......................................28

26a Antennae with last 3 segments enlarged to form a strong club...27

**26b** Antennae serrate (or often flabbelate [fan-like]) in the males; hind coxae transverse and dilated partly covering the femora; a hairy pad or cushion between the claws; 10 to 25 mm. long. (Cedar Beetles) Fig. 181. Family 50, RHIPICERIDAE...........page 159

Figure 181

There are only a few species—medium to large size—belonging to this family. They are brown or black and the males often have brush-like antennae.

They are found on plants, — especially on cedars, in the case of the genus *Sandalus*.

**27a** Hind coxae dilated into plates partly covering the base of femora, (occasionally small). Antennae ending in a large three segmented club. (Skin Beetles) Fig. 182. Family 64, DERMESTIDAE...page 180

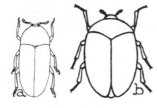

Figure 182

This important family has many species which are destructive to clothing, rugs and food products. Some species are oval (b), others are elongate; most of them are covered with scales which are frequently colored and carry a pattern.

**27b** Hind coxae flat, not dilated into plates, fourth joint of tarsi equal to the others. (See fig. 168) Family 29, CLERIDAE........page 132

**28a** Front coxae transverse: hind coxae flat......................29

**28b** Front coxae globular (oval in Cryptophagidae)...............32

**29a** Elytra covering entire length of abdomen, never truncate......30

**29b** Elytra usually truncate; tarsi more or less dilated, first segment not short; (Sap-feeding Beetles). Fig. 183. Family 69, NITIDU-LIDAE................................................................page 183

Figure 183

These small beetles are usually flattened though a few are cylindrical. The antenna has a rounded club of three (occasionally but 2) segments; the tarsi usually 5 may sometimes have only 3 or 4 segments.

74

**30a** Body covering thin and soft; antennae usually serrate, not clavate. (The Soft-bodied Plant Beetles.) Fig. 184. Family 62. HELODIDAE.
.................................................page 179

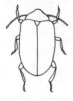

These comparatively small beetles are found on plants near water. They are often dark blackish with sometimes lighter markings.

Figure 184

**30b** Body normally hard as with most beetles; antennae with usually small club....................................................31

**31a** Tarsi slender, first segment short, small to medium beetles living in grains or under bark, usually flattened. (Grain and Bark-gnawing Beetles) Fig. 185. Family 68. OSTOMIDAE.........page 182

These beetles are common under dead bark or logs and some species are pests of stored grain and cereal products. They live a predacious life and are almost cosmopolitan.

Figure 185

**31b** Last segment of tarsi about as long as other four combined; hind coxae extending to margin of abdomen. (Tooth-necked Fungus Beetles) Fig. 186. Family 74, DERODONTIDAE.

10353 *Derodontus maculatus* (Melsh.)

LENGTH: 2.5-3 mm. RANGE: Eastern U. S.

Dull brownish yellow, elytra marked with blackish, as pictured. It is found in fungi and under bark.

The family has only a few known species. The antennae have 11 segments and the serrated thorax is characteristic. (After Sharp)

Figure 186

**32a Prosternum with a spine which fits into a groove in the metasternum. Fig. 187.** ................................... 33

**32b Without such spine** ................. 36

Figure 187

**33a The first and second abdominal segments fused; prothorax closely joined to mesothorax. (Metallic Woodborers) Fig. 188. Family 54, BUPRESTIDAE** .................................... page 169

This is a large and widely scattered family of medium to large sized beetles. Their brilliant metallic colors and iridescent sheen make them very attractive and readily recognized.

Figure 188

**33b Ventral segments not fused** ................................ 34

**34a Prothorax loosely joined to mesothorax and moving freely on it, its hind angles prolonged into a tooth. See Fig. 190** ........... 35

**34b Prothorax not movable but firmly fixed to mesothorax. Length 4 mm. or less. (Pseudo Click Beetles) Fig. 189. Family 53, THROSCIDAE.**

2049 *Throscus chevrolati* Bonv.

LENGTH: 2.5-3 mm. RANGE: Eastern and central U. S.

Reddish brown, rather densely covered with coarse yellowish pubescence. Clypeus with two parallel ridges.

*Drapetes geminatus* Say (9182), a little larger than the former (4 mm.) and widely distributed is black with a crossbar or dot of red on basal half of each elytron. The antennae are serrate in this genus instead of clubbed as in *Throscus*.

Figure 189

These "pseudo click beetles" are a small family intermediate between the click beetles and the metallic wood borers.

**35a** Prosternum with lobe in front, thorax and body "clicked" abruptly from straight to bent position throwing the insect into the air. Small to large size. (Click Beetles) Fig. 190. Family 51, ELATERIDAE. . . . . . . . . . . . . . . . . . . . . . . . . . . . . . . . . . . . . . . . . . . . . . . . . . . page 159

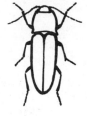

These beetles are readily recognized by their shape and habits. The family is large. The coloring and markings vary widely. The larvae are known as wire worms.

Figure 190

**35b** Prosternum without a lobe; labium hidden; cannot click as above. Small size. Fig. 191. Family 52, MELASIDAE. . . . . . . . . . . .page 168

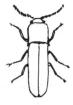

This is a small family of non-clicking click beetles. Few if any of the less than a hundred known species are at all common. Many of the species live in decaying wood or under bark. Others are taken by sweeping.

The larvae are more like those of the Buprestidae than of the Elateridae, with which family this group was once included.

Figure 191

**36a** (a, b, c) Body flattened, middle coxal cavities open behind; abdominal segments equal. (Flat Bark Beetles or Cucujids) Fig. 192. Family 72, CUCUJIDAE. . . . . . . . . . . . . . . . . . . . . . . . . . . . . . . . . . . . . . . . . . .page 186

This is an important family that varies rather widely in the structure of its members. Many are pests of stored foods. The adults are usually flattened and elongate; brown is a frequent color.

Figure 192

36b Front and middle coxal cavities closed behind. Body convex or cylindrical; abdominal segments 5, equal. (Pleasing Fungus Beetles) Fig. 193. Family 73, EROTYLIDAE.....................page 188

This is a medium sized family of medium to small beetles. Some are narrowly cylindrical, others are wider and somewhat flattened. They are usually shining and often brilliantly colored.

Figure 193

36c Body convex, ventral abdominal segments 5, the first longer than the others; front coxae oval, separated by prosternum; middle coxal cavities closed. (The Silken Fungus Beetles). Fig. 194. Family 75, CRYPTOPHAGIDAE........................page 190

This is a small family of tiny beetles which are covered with a shining silky pubescence. Their usual color is yellowish-brown. They resemble the Cucujids but are shorter and more convex.

Figure 194

# Family 8  HYDROPHYLIDAE
## The Water Scavenger Beetles

This family of some 1,000 species, many of which are tropical, is characterized in many species by the extra long maxillary palpi which serve as sense organs, and which may be mistaken for antennae. The adults live largely on decaying plants; some of the larvae utilize this same food while others are predacious. The adults are readily distinguished from the Dytiscidae by being more convex on the dorsal side and their antennae ending in a club. In swimming, the legs move alternately instead of as pairs as in the Dytiscidae. A film of air spread over the ventral side from a bubble "picked up" at the surface by the antennae, supplements that carried under the elytra in supporting respiration while the adults remain under water.

Sweeping submerged plants with a water net is a good means of collecting. Many species fly to lights.

1a Thorax narrower than elytra; elongated with surface roughened; less than 6 mm.; elytra with 10 rows of punctures..............2

1b Thorax at base as wide as elytra................................3

2a Antennae with 9 segments. Fig. 195.

2750 *Helophorus lineatus* Say

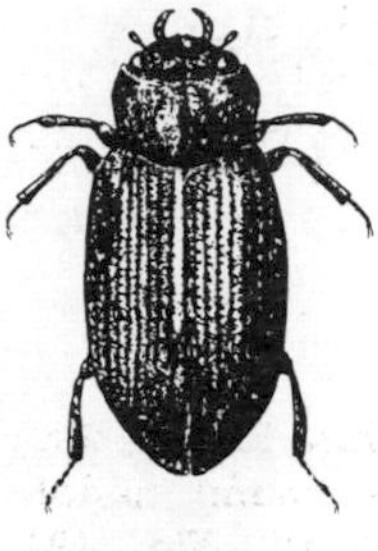

LENGTH: 2.8-3.5 mm.  RANGE: United States east of the Rockies, and Canada.

Above light brown with greenish tinge, antennae and legs pale; elytral striae with deep transverse punctures. (After Blatchley)

*H. lacustris* Lec. (2743), can be distinguished from the above by its obtuse hind thoracic angles. It is larger (4-4.5 mm.), blackish-brown and ranges in our Central States.

Figure 195

2b Antennae with 7 segments. Fig. 196.

2764 *Hydrochus squamifer* Lec.

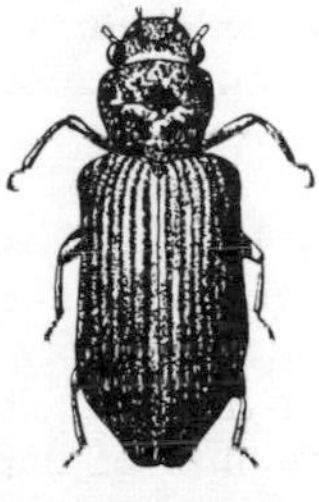

LENGTH: 3.5-4 mm.  RANGE: North Central United States.

Grayish-bronzed or coppery; head and thorax darker than elytra and tinged with greenish. (After Blatchley)

*Ochthebius fossatus* (Lec.) (2718 [19260]), is a small (1.2-2.5 mm.) rather closely related species of wide distribution. The thorax narrows markedly towards the base; the color is brownish.

Figure 196

3a First segment of middle and hind tarsi short. Fig. 197a...........4

3b First segment of middle and hind tarsi elongated.  Fig. 197b.......8

4a Metasternum elongated into a distinct spine; tarsi compressed......5

4b Metasternum not elongated; tarsi not compressed....................7

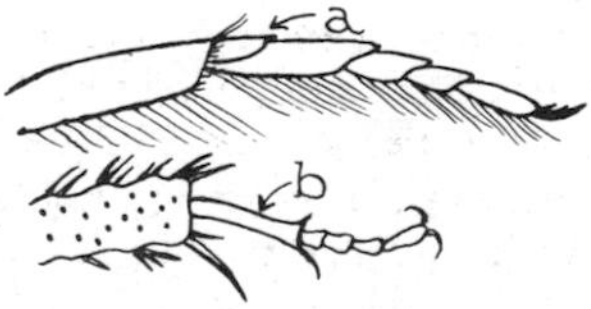

Figure 197

5a Posternum marked with grooves; metasternal spine long........6

79

**5b Prosternum with a ridge, metasternal spine short; length 13-16 mm. Fig. 198.** 2795 *Hydrochara obtusata* (Say)

Figure 198

LENGTH: 13-16 mm. RANGE: Central and Eastern States.

Black, shining; under surface dark reddish-brown, pubescent. Elytra each with 4 rows of distinct punctures, the outer row double. Spine of metasternum not reaching beyond middle coxae. Often abundant at lights and in light traps.

**6a Length 25 mm. or more; last joint of maxillary palpi shorter than the preceding. Fig. 199.**

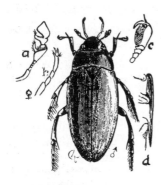

Figure 199

2789 *Hydrophilus triangularis* (Say) LENGTH: 34-37 mm. RANGE: Common from coast to coast.

Black with olive tinge, shining; under surface dark often triangular yellowish spots at sides of abdomen. Prosternal prominences (receiving front end of spine) closed in front; a, antenna; b, front tarsus of female; c, front tarsus of male; d, side view of sternal spine. (After Riley)

*Dibolocelus ovatus* G & H (2792), is similar to the above, but wider, shorter (31-33 mm.) and more convex. The prosternal prominence is open in front. It ranges through the eastern third of the United States and like the above is often attracted to lights.

**6b Length less than 12 mm.; last joint of maxillary palpi equal to the preceding or longer. Fig. 200.**

2807 *Tropisternus lateralis* (Fab.)

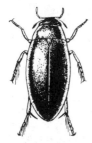

Figure 200

LENGTH: 8-9 mm. RANGE: Quite general over the entire United States. Common.

Olive-black, shining; clypeus, thorax and margins of elytra pale yellow; under surface black or piceous. Legs yellow, femora black at base. (After Blatchley)

*T. striolatus* (Lec.) (2797), is a southern species, a bit larger in size (9-10.5 mm.) than the above and readily distinguished by the yellow stripes on the disk of the elytra.

**7a** Last joint of maxillary palpi longer than the third; elytra with striae or punctures in rows. Fig. 201.

2810 *Hydrobius melaenum* Germ.

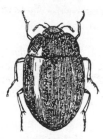

Figure 201

LENGTH: 7.5 mm. RANGE: Northeast United States.

Piceous-black, shining, with bronze reflections. Scutellar striae distinct.

*Paracymus subcupreus* (Say) (2819), colored much like the above; is small (1.5-2 mm.) but common throughout much of the United States and in parts of Canada.

**7b** Last joint of maxillary palpi shorter than the third. Fig. 202.

2835 *Enochrus orchraceus* (Melsh.)

Figure 202

LENGTH: 3.5-4 mm. RANGE: Central and Eastern United States. Often common.

Dull smoky-brown, shining, head darker with a pale space in front of each eye; under parts piceous, the tibia and tarsi paler. (After Blatchley)

*Berosus striatus* (Say) (2784), is a dull greenish-yellow water beetle 4-5 mm. long which differs from the above in having its last ventral abdominal segment notched. It is common over much of the eastern half of the United States.

**8a** Length 5 mm. or over. Scutellum elongate; antennae with 8 segments. Fig. 203.

2867 *Sphaeridium scarabaeoides* (L.)

Figure 203

LENGTH: 5.5-6.5 mm. RANGE: much of North America, also Europe.

Upper parts black, shining; elytra with reddish sub-basal spot and the apical fourth yellowish; underparts piceous. Elytra punctured but without striae.

This European import, seems to have taken seriously the admonition "don't go near the water." It is found abundantly in fresh dung of cattle and may thus be mistaken for a Hister beetle or a Scarabaeid. It and the other members of its tribe do not have swimming legs.

**8b** Length not over 3 mm.; scutellum equilateral; antennae with nine
segments. Fig. 204.

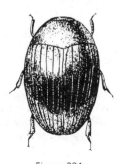

Figure 204

2876 *Cercyon praetextatus* (Say)

LENGTH: 2.5-3 mm. RANGE: East of the Rockies
in the United States and Canada.

Piceous black, shining; front angles of thorax,
and margins and tip of elytra yellowish; antennae dull yellow, the club darker. Common in
dead fish and other decaying debris. (After
Blatchley)

C. *navicularis* Zimm. (2892), is a tiny black
member of this genus which seems to be found
all over the United States and Canada. It measures 1.5-1.7 mm. and is found in damp leaves
near water pools.

# Family 12  SILPHIDAE
## The Carrion-Beetles

A number of fairly large, attractively marked and quite abundant
beetles belong to this family making it some what a favorite with collector in spite of the disgusting ways of its members.

While some feed on vegetable matter and a few are even predaceous, they, for the most part, live on decaying animals.

The family is widely scattered and numbers over 1500 species.

**1a** Front coxae somewhat transverse at base and with trochantin
(small movable piece on coxa.)...............................2

**1b** Front coxae cylindric-conic, without trochatin, the cavities closed
behind. Length less than 6 mm.............................13
   (Hatch '33 proposed a new family LEPTODIRIDAE for the small
beetles falling here.)

**2a** Front coxal cavities open behind; hind coxae touching, length over
10 mm........................................................3

**2b** Front coxal cavities closed behind; length less than 5 mm.......11
   (Hatch '29 proposed a new family LEIODIDAE for the small beetles
falling here.)

**3a** Antennae with 11 segments; antennae slender or gradually clubbed;
form rather flattened. Genus *Silpha*.........................7

**3b** Antennae with 10 segments; the last 4 forming an abrupt club; form
robust. The Burying Beetles, *Nicrophorus*.....................4

**4a** Tibia straight................................................5

**4b Hind tibiae (and frequently the middle one) curved. Fig. 205.**
**2911 *Nicrophorus americanus* (Oliv.)**

LENGTH: 27-35 mm. RANGE: Central and Eastern United States.

Black shining; vertex, disk of thorax, epipleural fold and 2 spots on each elytron orange-red; antennae black with orange-red club.

*N. marginatus* Fab. (2914), is colored much the same but is smaller (20-27 mm.) and only the first segment of the antennal club is red. The thorax is wholly black. Under dead snakes is a good place to look for it. It ranges over the entire United States and much of Canada.

Figure 205

**5a Thorax oval, wider than long with wide side and basal margins...6**

**5b Thorax a circular disk, about as long as wide. Fig. 206**
**2913 *Nicrophorus orbicollis* Say**

LENGTH: 20-25 mm. RANGE: Central and Eastern North America from Hudson Bay to Florida.

Black shining marked with orange-red on elytra and last three segments of antennal club; epipleural fold black.

The members of this genus are known as Burying or Sexton Beetles because of their habits of digging under small dead animals, reptiles or birds until the cadaver is buried. Before the process is completed eggs are laid on the animal which then furnishes the food for the rapidly developing larvae.

Figure 206

**6a Disk of thorax densely covered with golden-hairs; antennal club piceous. Fig. 207.**
**2920 *Nicrophorus tomentosus* Web.**

LENGTH: 15-20 mm. RANGE: Central and Eastern United States.

Black, shining, markings as pictured and the epipleural fold orange-red; antennal club piceous.

*Nicrophorus guttulus* Mots. (2916), ranging from Alaska to our southwestern border is known as the Yellow-bellied Burying Beetle because of the mass of golden hairs on the ventral parts of the thorax. It measures 12-20 mm. and is shining black.

Figure 207

**6b Disk of thorax without hairs; all but first segment of antennal club orange. Fig. 208          2918 *Nicrophorus pustulatus* Hersch.**

LENGTH: 17-18 mm.  RANGE: Much of North America.

Black, shining; a small basal spot and double spots at apex of each elytron and last 3 segments of antennae orange-red.

The variety *investigator* (Zett.) (2918c) which is found throughout the West from Alaska to the Mexican border is recognized by a red epipleural fold.

The variety *nigritus* (Mann.) (2918b) belongs to the South-west from Texas to California.  It is wholly black except the 3 segments of the club.

Figure 208

7a Form oval; eyes not prominent............................................8

**7b Form elongate; eyes large, prominent.  Fig. 209**
**2922 *Silpha surinamensis* Fab.**

LENGTH: 15-24 mm.  RANGE: United States east of the Rockies except the South East.

Elongate, depressed.  Black or piceous apical cross bar of elytra red, often broken into spots or occasionally wholly wanting.

If the collector wishes to use "wholesale methods" in gathering members of these two genera he has only to put dead fish or other animals in a depression and cover them with a large board so that little if any light gets in.  They are nocturnal but apparently pay no attention to the clock as long as it is dark.  A day or two later hold your nose, turn the board back and harvest your crop!

Figure 209

8a Thorax wholly black or blackish...............................10

8b Thorax partly yellow or red....................................9

**9a** Thorax bright yellow with brown or black spot at center; third joint of antennae shorter than second. Fig. 210.

2928 *Silpha americana* L.

Figure 210

LENGTH: 16-20 mm. RANGE: Central and Eastern United States and Canada.

Elytra brownish, the ridges darker. Often common at carrion and sometimes in garbage cans. When clean this is a very attractive beetle. The larvae of Silphids are flattened and wedge shaped and are often found with the adults.

**9b** Thorax marked with red or reddish-yellow; third joint of antennae as long or longer than the second. Fig. 211

2927 *Silpha noveboracensus* Forst.

Figure 211

LENGTH: 12-15 mm. RANGE: Much of the United States.

Elytra and thorax brownish or piceous; three ridges on disk of each elytron. (Redrawn from Comstock)

S. *lapponica* Hbst. (2923) measuring 12-13 mm., ranges through our West to the Missouri River or beyond. It is grayish black with head and thorax thickly clothed with yellowish hairs.

**10a** Each elytron with three distinct ridges; the outer the most prominent. Fig. 212.

2926 *Silpha inaequalis* Fab.

Figure 212

LENGTH: 10-14 mm. RANGE: United States.

Dull black. Thorax with broad depressed truncate lobe at middle. Elytra rounded at apex, longer than wide, the disk with three prominent ridges, as pictured. Both adults and larvae are abundant in carrion and hibernate together. It is often found associated with S. *noveboracensis*. (After Riley)

85

**10b With but one ridge on each elytron. Fig. 213**

**2931 *Silpha bituberosa* Lec.**

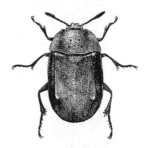

LENGTH: 10-13 mm. RANGE: From Kansas west.

Depressed. Black. This spinach carrion beetle damages spinach, squash, beets, pumpkin, alfalfa and other cultivated plants. (U. S. D. A.)

Two other members of the genus ranging from Alaska through western Canada and the United States are sometimes destructive to garden crops. The Beet Carrion Beetle *S. opaca* L. (2930) (12 mm.) is shining black; the Garden Carrion Beetle *S. ramosa* Say (2929) (12-18 mm.), is velvety black.

Figure 213

**11a Head with antennal grooves beneath. Fig. 214**

**3029 *Agathidium oniscoides* Beauv.**

LENGTH: 3.5-4 mm. RANGE: Central and Eastern United States and Canada.

Black or piceous, smooth and shining. Lives beneath the bark of fungus bearing logs. For protection it rolls itself into a tiny ball with legs hidden and does not at all resemble a beetle. The hind legs have but 4 tarsi.

*A. politum* Lec. (3042) is a more convex and smaller species (2-2.5 mm.). It is a shining reddish-brown and is often abundant within much the same range and habitat as the preceding.

Figure 214

**11b Head without antennal grooves...............................12**

**12a Antennal club with 3 segments. Fig. 215**

**3014 *Colenis impunctata* Lec.**

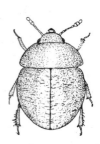

LENGTH: 1.5-2 mm. RANGE: Central and Eastern United States.

Pale reddish-brown; elytra with fine transverse lines. Its tarsi number 5-4-4. It is often found in fleshy fungi and is rather common. It does not contract itself into a ball when disturbed.

*Anisotoma basalis* (Lec.) (3026) has about the same size and range. It is piceous-black with an orange-red humeral spot. Like others of its genus it is found in fungi.

Figure 215

**12b. Antennal club with 5 segments. Fig. 216**

2998 *Leiodes valida* (Horn)

LENGTH: 3.5-6 mm. RANGE: Northern United States and Canada.

Piceous to paler, moderately shining. Antennae 11 segments. Hind tarsi with but 4 segments.

Figure 216

**13a Abdomen with six segments; head narrowed behind the eyes. Fig. 217**

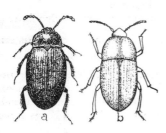

Figure 217

(a) 2951 *Catops basillaris* **Say**

LENGTH: 3-4 mm. RANGE: Central United States.

Elytra dark brown; head and thorax piceous. (After Blatchley)

(b) 2942 *Pinodytes cryptophagoides* (Mann.)

LENGTH: 2-3 mm. RANGE: General.

Shining. Chestnut-brown. One of three members of its genus, all of which are blind. They live in rotten wood, etc.

*Nemadus parasitus* (Lec.) (2965), measuring 2 mm., oval, and shining dark reddish brown is interesting since it is fairly common in the nests of the large Carpenter Ants, *Camponotus* spp.

**13b Abdomen with but 5 segments, (sometimes 4); head not narrowed behind. Fig. 218**

2977 *Colon magnicolle* **Mannh.**

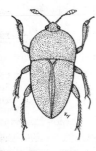

Figure 218

LENGTH: 2.5-3 mm. RANGE: Central United States and Alaska.

Piceous, somewhat dull, heavily punctured and finely pubescent. All the members of the genus have 11 segments in the antennae.

*C. pusillum* Horn (2978) likely ranges through much of our Central States but such small insects unless injurious or annoying are not readily found. It measures about 2 mm.

# Family 14 SCYDMAENIDAE
## The Ant-like Stone Beetles

Many of these little fellows live with the ants,—but that is not so strange for the ants often maintain quite variable "ranches" with all sorts of insect guests, pets, pests, etc., hanging around. It is a large family with considerably over a thousand known species. They are small, usually brownish or blackish beetles, shining and oval in shape. Some are only a fraction of a millimeter in length.

1a Fourth joint of maxillary palpi awl-shaped; neck narrow, eyes in front of middle of head. Fig. 219

3080 *Pycnophus rasus* (Lec.)

Figure 219

LENGTH: 1.6-1.8 mm. RANGE: East half of United States and Canada.

Shining. Pale reddish-brown. Thorax with well defined small pit at each basal angle. Found in ants' nests and under logs.

*Connophron fossiger* (Lec.) (3099) 1.6 mm., ranging widely, is black with elytra reddish except at tips. It is heavily clothed with long pale hairs.

1b Fourth joint of maxillary palpi obtuse; hind coxae oval; femora abruptly clubbed. Fig. 220

3216 *Scydmaenus motschulskyanus* Csiki

Figure 220

LENGTH: 1.7 mm. RANGE: East half of United States.

Dark chestnut brown with recurved yellowish pubescence. Elytra very convex. (After Blatchley)

*Acholerops zimmermanni* (Schaum) (3222) is only 1.5 mm. long. The first joint of the hind tarsi is longer than in the above. It is dark reddish-brown and is found in the central parts of the United States.

Extremes in sizes are always interesting. *Connophron fulvum* (Lec.) (3145) measures only .8-.9 mm. It is shining, pale chestnut-brown with legs and antennae lighter. The antennae are as long as the head and thorax combined and have a 3-segmented club . *Euthiodes latus* Bndl. (3207), is still smaller, measuring a scant .7 mm. Its color is brownish-yellow.

# TRIMERA

Under this heading have been placed the beetles which appear to possess but three tarsal segments. Some of these have in reality four segments, but with the third one so small that the tarsus seems to be made of only three segments. Occasionally species possessing only three tarsi and others with "apparently three" occur in several other families of beetles. They, too, are included here. It should be understood that this is an artificial arrangement, used for convenience, and that it does not constitute a phylogenetic group.

1a Elytra short (often very short and covering half of the body or much less, but occasionally in the Staphylinids nearly or quite reaching the tip of the abdomen). (See Figs. 221 and 222)........2

1b Not as in 1a.................................................3

2a Abdomen flexible and with 7 or 8 (rarely 6) segments visible below. (Rove or Short-winged Scavenger Beetles.) Fig. 221.
Family 16, STAPYLINIDAE............................page 92

Any large group of insects is almost certain to have some non-conforming species. While the Rove Beetles normally are equipped with five tarsi there are exceptions, one of which is provided for here.

Figure 221

2b Abdomen rigid; elytra short, covering about half of body; antennae usually clubbed, occasionally bead-like; tarsi sometimes with but two segments; less than 4 mm. in length. (Ant-loving Beetles) Fig. 222. Family 17, PSELAPHIDAE....................page 113

As with the Rove Beetles which they resemble, these little fellows sometimes have a reduced number of tarsi. They are often dull-yellow to brownish; the head and thorax are usually much narrower than the abdomen.

Figure 222

3a Tiny beetles having fringe of long hairs on the wings..........4

3b Wings not fringed.........................................5

4a Tarsi actually with 4 segments, the third very small and hidden within a notch in the second; wing broad. (Fringe-winged Fungus Beetles) Fig. 223                   Family 15, ORTHOPERIDAE.
3269 *Molamba ornata* Csy.

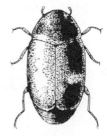

Figure 223

LENGTH: 1.3-1.5 mm. RANGE: Central United States.

Piceous, antennae and legs yellowish; thorax reddish-yellow with dark diskal spot as pictured, elytra with two spots and edge of tips, dull yellow. (After Blatchley)

*Corylophodes marginicollis* (Lec.) (3230) measures less than 1 mm. It is shining blackish with paler legs and antennae and is fairly abundant.

4b Tarsi with but 3 segments; wings narrow; fringe longer than in 3a. (Feather-winged Beetles.) Fig. 224. Family 19, PTILIDAE.
6393 *Nossidium americanum* Mots.

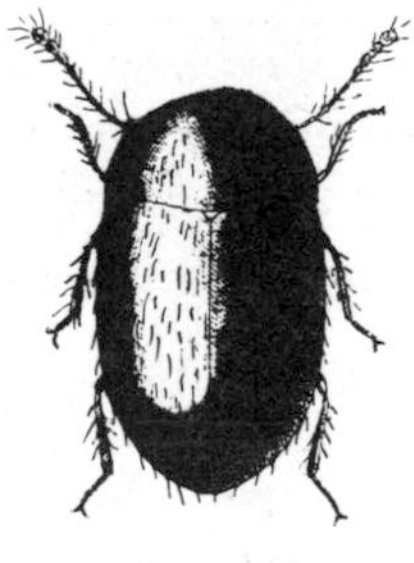

LENGTH: 1 mm. RANGE: Much of the United States.

Head and thorax shining, piceous; elytra reddish-brown, clothed with rather long yellowish hairs; legs and antennae yellow.

Some of the smallest known beetles belong to this family. The true wings when present are usually fringed with long hairs. They live in decaying wood. Other species are *Acratrichis moerens* Matth. (6432) .6-.7 mm. and ranging widely, shining black and *Limulodes paradoxus* Matth. (6475) shining reddish-yellow with grayish pubescence, 1 mm., ranging widely.

Figure 224

5a Tarsal segments actually 4, the third being very small and not readily seen.....................................6

5b Only three tarsal segments.....................................7

6a Tarsal claws toothed or appendiculate (See fig. 225A). Epimeron triangular; first ventral abdominal segment with distinctly curved coxal lines; last segment of maxillary palpus oval, or hatchet-shaped (a) (Lady Beetles). Fig. 225B.

Figure 225a

Family 85, COCCINELLIDAE........page 197

Figure 225

A large family of small to medium sized often oval beetles. Many are marked with dots or stripes in contrasting colors, often black on red. The members are for the most part predacious on aphids and scale insects; a few are plant feeders.

6b Tarsal claws simple. First ventral abdominal segment without coxal lines. (Handsome Fungus Beetles) Fig. 226
Family 83, ENDOMYCHIDAE............................page 194

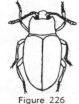

Figure 226

Frequently prettily marked red and black beetles somewhat resembling the lady beetles. Both larvae and adults are found in fungi and rotting wood.

7a Elytra truncate, exposing the last abdominal segment. 1st and 5th ventral abdominal segments longer than others. Small depressed beetles. (Monotomid Beetles). Fig. 227
Family 71, MONOTOMIDAE.

10159 *Monotoma picipes* Hbst.

LENGTH: 2-2.3 mm. RANGE: Europe and much of the United States.

Dull black or brownish; antenna and legs reddish-brown; thorax with coarse dense punctures. Elytral striae with coarse punctures and yellowish hairs. (After Blatchley)

*Bactridium ephippigerum* (Guer.) (10183) is about the same size and color but is shining and its head does not narrow behind the eyes. The punctures and striae are fewer. It inhabits the eastern half of the United States.

Figure 227

7b Elytra not truncate, entirely covering the abdomen; ventral segments about equal in length. (Minute Brown Scavenger Beetles). (See figs 473, 474)
Family 81, LATHRIDIIDAE...............................page 193

# Family 16 STAPHYLINIDAE
## The Rove Beetles

The short wing covers of these usually slender beetles together with their habit of turning up the abdomen as though about to sting, make them readily recognized. More than 20,000 species, small to large, have been named. Some members of this family rival all other beetles in strong and swift flight.

1a Hind coxae widely separated, rounded, small. Fig. 228a......................2

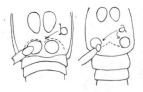

1b Hind coxae touching or at least close together. Fig. 228b..................3

Figure 228

2a Antennae 9-segmented, capitate and inserted at the side of the head. Next to last segment of abdomen with an elevated ridge. Fig. 229
3284 *Micropeplus cribratus* Lec.

Figure 229

LENGTH: 2 mm. RANGE: Southeast United States.

Blackish; sides of thorax orange-brown; elytra with wavy ridges, and the intervals coarsely punctate. Antennae pubescent. (There are but 3 tarsal segments.)

*Kalissus nitidus* Lec. (3291) Smooth and shining and has no ridges on its abdomen. It is known from Vancouver, B. C. It, too, has but three segments to the tarsi.

2b Antennae inserted between the eyes, 11 segmented, cheeks very small. Fig. 230
3832 *Stenus flavicornia* Er.

Figure 230

LENGTH: 4.6-4.8 mm. RANGE: Eastern U. S.

Shining black, thinly clothed with gray hairs; elytra wider than abdomen; thorax widest in front of middle. (After Blatchley)

This large genus numbers more than 150 American species.

*Dianous nitidulus* Lec. (3858), represents a small genus differing from the above in having large cheeks and a large red-yellow spot on each elytron. It measures 4.5 mm. and ranges widely.

3a (a, b, c) Hind coxae conical.................................4

3b Hind coxae transverse........................................23

3c Hind coxae triangular........................................13

4a Front coxae short; tarsi with but 4 segments; abdomen with margin; body punctured. Fig. 231

3872 *Euaesthetus americanus* Er.

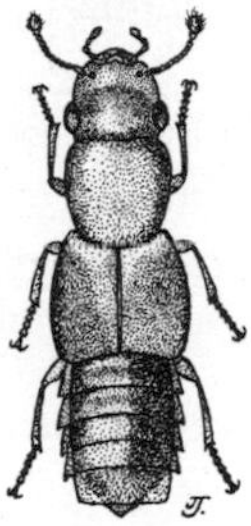

LENGTH: 1.2-1.5 mm.  RANGE: Eastern third U. S.

Piceous or dark reddish-brown, antennae and legs paler.  Abdomen as wide at base as elytra, punctate.

*Stictocranius puncticeps* Lec. (3859), has no margin on the abdomen.  It resembles the ants with which it lives.

Figure 231

4b Front coxae long.  Tarsi 5 segmented.........................5

5a Last segment of maxillary palpi obliquely hatchet-shaped and as long as the preceding one.  Abdomen not margined.  Fig. 232

3892 *Palaminus testaceus* Er.

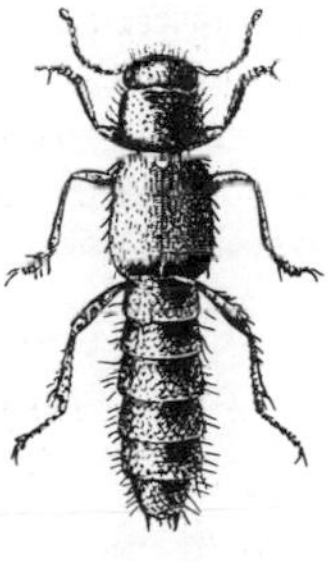

LENGTH: 3.5-4 mm.  RANGE: Eastern half U. S.

Shining, pale reddish-yellow; abdomen reddish-brown; antennae and legs pale yellow.  (After Blatchley)

*Pinophilus latipes* Grav. (3874), ranging throughout eastern U. S., has its abdomen definitely margined.  It is black with reddish-yellow antennae and legs and measures 13-15 mm.

Figure 232

5b Last segment of maxillary palpi very small and awl-shaped......6

6a (a, b, c) Prosternum shortened between and under the coxae to form an acute point which does not reach the mesosternum......7

6b Prosternum lengthened behind to reach the mesosternum, but more or less acute and not dilated under the coxae; neck very slender..11

6c Prosternum lengthened as in 6b but also greatly dilated laterally under the coxae...............................12

**7a** Antennae with long basal segment, rather strongly elbowed; (See e of fig. 233a); front tarsi not dilated.........................8

**7b** Antenna with a shorter basal segment and most flexible near its base; front tarsi of various forms............................9

**8a** Inner face of mandibles two-toothed. Fig. 233

(a) 3932 *Homoeotarsus sellatus* Csy.

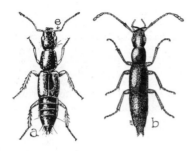

LENGTH: 8-9 mm. RANGE: Central States.

Shining, black; elytra reddish-yellow marked with black as pictured; sides of head behind eyes obliquely sloping without angles. (After Blatchley)

(b) 3926 *H. pallipes* (Grav.)

LENGTH: 8-11 mm. RANGE: Central and Eastern United States.

Figure 233

Shining, black or blackish, including elytra; legs dull yellow; head with distinct hind angles.

**8b** Inner face of mandible with 3 teeth, the 2 lower ones on a common base equal in size and larger on the left mandible. Fig. 234

3908 *Homoeotarsus bicolor* (Grav.)

LENGTH: 7-10 mm. RANGE: Central and Eastern States.

Head black; labrum, antennae, thorax, elytra and last two segments of abdomen pale reddish-brown; legs pale yellow.

*H. pimerianus* (Lec.) (3906), reddish brown to blackish, with head darker than thorax and elytra and abdomen lighter, measures 8-11 mm. and ranges from California to Indiana.

Figure 234

*H. badius* (Grav.) (3910) measuring 10-13 mm. is uniformly reddish-brown with the head slightly darker . The thorax is much narrower than the head and one-fourth longer than wide. The elytra are about one-half wider than the thorax. It is common throughout much of the eastern one-third of the United States.

**9a Labrum dentate at middle. Tip of ligula densely fringed with hairs; surface dull and closely sculptured and haired. Fig. 235**

**4094 *Lithocharis ochracea* (Grav.)**

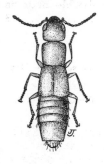

LENGTH: 3-4 mm. RANGE: Europe and North America.

Reddish-brown, antennae and elytra lighter; legs yellowish; antennae monilliform; front tarsi not dilated.

*Aderocharis corticinus* (Grav.) (4093), dark reddish brown, with antennae and legs paler and head darker, differs from the above in having its front tarsi dilated and padded beneath, and the first segment of the hind tarsi much longer than the second. It measures 6-7 mm. and ranges through the eastern half of our country.

Figure 235

The genus *Lobrathium* differs from the above in having a longitudinal fold or raised line on the elytra, and having the first and second segments of the hind tarsi each longer than the third or fourth. *L. longiusculum* (Grav.) (4045) has dull red elytra with black head and thorax. It is fairly slender (6.5-7.5 mm.), with broad neck and ranges over much of the eastern half of the United States. *L. dimidiatum* (Say) (4063), with similar ranger, is very slender, has a slim neck and measures 3.8-4.5 mm. The head and abdomen are black, while the thorax and elytra are dull red. Both of these species are fairly common.

**9b Ligula bilobed at tip; labrum not strongly toothed at middle; not closely sculptured and haired...................................10**

**10a Fourth segment of maxillary palpi conical and naked; labrum bilobed. Fig. 236.**       **3981 *Lathrobium simile* Lec.**

LENGTH: 7.5-9 mm. RANGE: Central and Eastern United States.

Shining, black; elytra and abdomen piceous; antennae and tip of abdomen reddish-brown; legs paler.

*L. collare* (Er.) (4074) with range similar to above, has head black, antennae and thorax reddish-brown; legs paler and abdomen piceous, with its tip pale. It measures 4.5-5.5 mm.

This is a large group involving many similar species.

Figure 236

10b Fourth segment of maxillary palpi compressed, linear at apex and thickly clothed with fine pubescence; thorax ovate; elytra subquadrate. Fig. 237.          3952 *Paederus littorarius* Grav.

Figure 237

LENGTH: 4.5-5 mm. RANGE: Central and Eastern United States.

Shining, reddish-yellow; elytra dark blue; antennae dark at middle, paler at each end.

*P. palustris* Aust. (3949), differs in having elytra that are shorter than wide. In coloring, range and size it is much like *littorarius*.

11a Hind tarsi rather short and thick with the basal joint at most but slightly longer than the second. Fig. 238

4216 *Scopaeus exiguus* Er.

Figure 238

LENGTH: 2-3 mm. RANGE: Eastern third United States.

Head and elytra blackish-piceous; thorax dusky yellow; abdomen blackish, paler at tip, antennae and legs pale yellow.

The subgenus *Scopaema* with four species differs in being shining black and considerably larger than the above.

11b Hind tarsi long slender the basal segment distinctly longer than the second; gular sutures practically united most of their distance. Fig. 239          4231 *Scopaeus opacus* (Lec.)

Figure 239

LENGTH: 4-5 mm. RANGE: Eastern United States.

Very slender. Dark reddish-brown, legs and antennae yellowish.

*S. duryi* Csy. (4235), piceous black with head, thorax and antennae dusky yellow has been taken in Ohio. It measures 4 mm.

**12a Fourth segment of hind tarsi bilobed; last joint of maxillary palpus small and slender. Fig. 240**

**4278 Astenus longiusculus (Mannh.)**

Figure 240

LENGTH: 3.5-4.5 mm. RANGE: Western United States.

Light reddish-brown. Very slender with head, elytra and abdomen all wider than the oval thorax.

A. *binotatus* (Say) (4265), measuring 3.5 to 4 mm. and ranging through the eastern half of the United States is reddish-yellow with the head, a large spot on elytra and on the abdomen black; antennae legs and tip of abdomen pale yellow.

**12b Fourth segment of hind tarsus not lobed beneath; antennae distinctly longer than head; neck very slender. Fig. 241**

**4243 Stilicus angularis Er.**

Figure 241

LENGTH: 3.8-4 mm. RANGE: Eastern and Southern States to Texas.

Shining, dark reddish-brown; tips of elytra pale; abdomen pisceous; legs pale yellow. (After Blatchley)

S. *dentatus* Say (4248), substantially the same size and with similar range, differs from *angularis* in having the head and thorax strigosely punctured. The abdomen is black and the antennae reddish-brown.

**13a Antennae inserted on sides of front. Fig. 242**

**4752 Habrocerus schwarzi Horn**

Figure 242

LENGTH: 1.5-2 mm. RANGE: Michigan and Connecticut.

Dark reddish-brown; elytra and tip of abdomen more reddish; legs yellowish-brown. Antennae thickly set with long hairs; a few long heavy bristles arising from anterior end and more from abdomen.

Only one other species of this genus H. *magnus* (Lec.) (4753) is known. It is found along Lake Superior.

**13b Antennae inserted on front of front**..........................14

**14a Side margin of thorax double**..............................16

**14b Side margin of thorax single**..............................15

**15a Antennae elbowed; front tarsal claws larger than others. Fig. 243**
**4564 *Acylophorus flavicollis* Sachse**

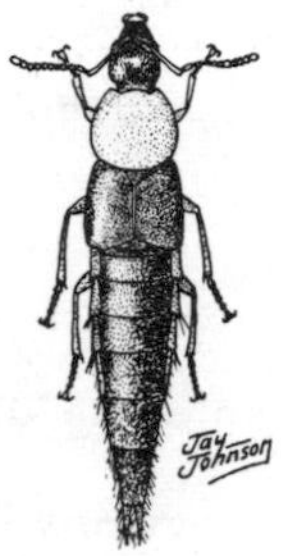

Figure 243

LENGTH: 5-6 mm. RANGE: Pennsylvania to Kansas and Texas.

Shining, black, scant pubescence on elytra and abdomen; thorax and legs reddish-yellow; antennae dusky, paler at the base.

*A. pronus* Erichs. (4565), much the same size and ranging rather commonly throughout most of the United States has antennae piceous and legs dull yellow to piceous, but otherwise closely resembles *flavicollis*.

**15b Antennae not elbowed; palpi filiform; all tarsal claws similar. Fig. 244**

Figure 244

(a) 4586 *Quedius capucinus* (Grav.)
LENGTH: 6-9 mm. RANGE: Much of North America.

Shining, black or piceous; antennae legs and sometimes the elytra dark reddish-brown; thorax broader than long; abdomen iridescent.

(b) 4621 *Q. spelaeus* Horn
LENGTH: 10-14 mm. RANGE: Colorado to Florida.

Pale reddish or chestnut brown, the elytra sometimes a bit darker; antennae reaching base of thorax; thorax wider than elytra. (After Blatchley)

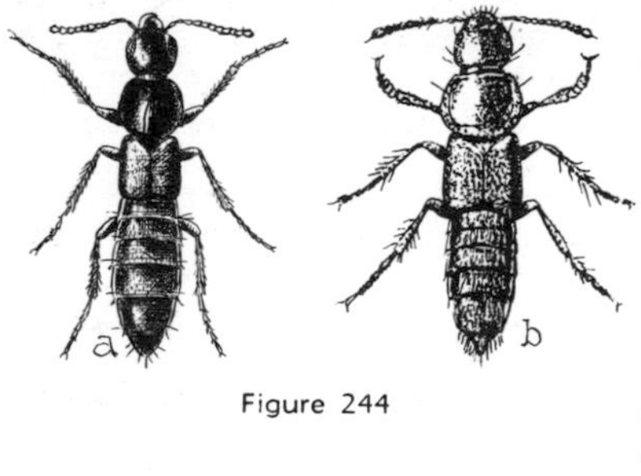

**16a Antennal bases rather widely separated**......................18

**16b Antennae with their bases close together; elytra often overlapping**........................17

**17a Elytral suture beveled and abnormal; fourth segment of maxillary palpi longer than third. Fig. 245**

4296 *Gyrohypnus obsidianus* (Melsh.)

LENGTH: 6.5 mm. RANGE: Eastern half United States. Black; legs dark reddish-brown.

*Nubobius cephalus* (Say) (4285), a widely distributed species differs from the above genus in the margins of the pronotum being rapidly deflexed. It is shining black with reddish-yellow elytra and legs. It measures 6.5-7.5 mm.

Figure 245

**17b Elytral suture normal and with a definite stria; last segment of maxillary palpi much longer than the preceding one. Fig. 246**

4351 *Baptolinus macrocephalus* (Nordm.)

LENGTH: 6-7 mm. RANGE: Alaska, Canada and N. E. United States.

Shining, reddish-brown; elytra more reddish; legs and antennae yellowish-brown. Head and elytra wider than thorax; abdomen with prominent marginal ridges.

*Parothius californicus* (Mann.) (4350), taken in California, differs from the above in the sutural striae being obsolete and the last two segments of the maxillary palpi being equal.

Figure 246

**18a Fourth segment of maxillary palpi shorter than third**...........19

**18b Fourth segment of maxillary palpi equal to or longer than the third**...................................................... 20

**19a Thorax punctured and pubescent. Fig. 247**

4552 *Ontholestes cingulatus* (Grav.)

LENGTH: 13-18 mm. RANGE: Widely distributed and common.

Heavy. Dark brown or piceous. A heavy pubescence forms irregular black spots on head thorax and abdomen, and makes gold the metasternum and tip of abdomen.

Figure 247

99

**19b Thorax smooth, middle coxae remote; suture straight. Fig. 248**

**4555 Creophilus maxillosus (L.)**

LENGTH: 12-21 mm. RANGE: United States and Canada.

Robust shining, black; second, third and sometimes fourth abdominal segments widely banded with yellowish-gray hairs; elytra marked as pictured with similar hairs. (After Knobel)

This very common and disgusting species may be readily trapped in large numbers with carrion of almost any kind. Davis '15, found both larvae and adults feeding upon the maggots of the flesh flies ever present in carrion.

Figure 248

**20a Ligula emarginate (notched); form usually robust; 11 mm. or over. Fig. 249a . . . . . . . . . . 21**

**20b Ligula entire; form slender; usually smaller than in 20a. Fig. 249b . . . . . . . . . . . . . . . . . . . . 22**

Figure 249

**21a Abdomen narrowed at tip; middle coxae slightly separated. Fig. 250.**

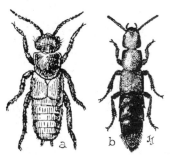

Figure 250

(a) **4533 Staphylinus maculosus Grav.**
LENGTH: 18-25 mm. RANGE: Widely distributed and very common.

Dark brown; elytra and upper part of abdomen marked with fuscous spots; base of antennae, pale; femora piceous, the edges paler. (After Knobel)

(b) **4545 S. cinnamopterus Grav.**
LENGTH: 12-14 mm. RANGE: Much of United States.

Head, thorax, elytra, tibiae, tarsi, apical margins of abdomen and entire last segment brownish-red. Antennae, femora and much of abdomen piceous.

S. *violaceus* Grav. (4546) is a very attractive species. In shape and size is much like *cinnamopterus* but is shining black with metallic violet blue head thorax and elytra.

*Thinopinus pictus* Lec. (4556) is flightless, possessing no wings. It is 15-18 mm. long, brownish-yellow, ornamented with black on the upper surface. The larvae strongly resemble the adults but differ in having no teeth on the mandibles. This "Pictured Rove Beetle" is found on the sand beaches along the lower half of California .

**21b Sides of abdomen parallel; middle coxae touching. Fig. 251**

**4551 *Ocypus ater* (Grav.)**

LENGTH: 15-18 mm.   RANGE: Europe and North America.

Shining, black; tibia, tarsi and basal half of antennae piceous.   This seems to be a water-loving species.   (After Knobel)   It is the only member of its genus.

Figure 251

**22a Femora with a row of fine spines beneath. Fig. 252**

**4514 *Belonuchus rufipennis* Fab.**

LENGTH: 6.5-7.5 mm.   RANGE: Atlantic States to Arizona.

Reddish-yellow; head, thorax and last two segments of abdomen shining black.   Antennae fuscous; piceous at base and pale at apex.

The other ten or more species of this interesting genus inhabit the Southwest.

Figure 252

**22b Femora without spines; last segment of both the labial and the maxillary palpi slender; elytra red or blue. Fig. 253**

**(a) 4429 *Philonthus thoracicus* (Grav.)**

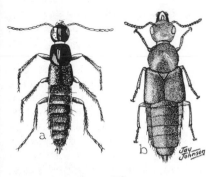

LENGTH: 7.5-8 mm.   RANGE: Central States.

Shining, piceous; thorax and elytra dull red; legs and three basal joints of antennae brownish-yellow.   All joints of antennae longer than wide.

**(b) 4447 *P. cyanipennis* (Fab.)**

LENGTH: 12-15 mm.   RANGE: Europe and North America.

Shining, black; elytra metallic-blue; antennae and tarsi

Figure 253

piceous.   Abdomen iridescent.

This genus contains well over 100 species most of which are of medium to large size.

**23a Front coxae conical, prominent or transverse** ................ **26**

**23b Front coxae globose, winged; eyes complete** ................ **24**

**24a Elytra longer than the metasternum. Fig. 254**

3293 *Trigonurus crotchi* Lec.

Figure 254

LENGTH: 3.5-4 mm.  RANGE: Pacific Coast.

Shining.  Light reddish brown, rather uniformly colored throughout.  Antennae thickened at apex and pubescent; elytra with longitudinal rows of heavy punctures.

Five other known species of this genus are also western in their range.

*Siagonium americanum* Melsh. (3298), reddish-yellow and 5-7 mm. long, ranges widely.

**24b Not as in 24a** ................................................. **25**

**25a Abdomen with a fine margin; front tibia with spines or teeth. Fig. 255.**

3307 *Eleusis pallida* Lec.

Figure 255

LENGTH: 3.5 mm.  RANGE: New York to Colorado.

Shining, reddish-brown.  It lives in the nests of ants.

*Triga picipennis* (Lec.) (3305), ranging from Quebec to Kansas, differs in having the abdomen widely margined.  It is blackish with paler antennae and legs.  It measures 3 mm.

**25b Abdomen without a margin; tarsi with but 3 segments, Fig. 256**
**3315 *Thoracophorus costalis* Er.**

LENGTH: 2-2.5 mm. RANGE: Much of North America.

Dull, dark chestnut brown; head margined. Each elytron with four ridges.

*Ancaeus exiguus* (Er.) (3308), a cosmopolitan species has five tarsal segments. It measures 2-2.5 mm. and is shining chestnut brown.

Figure 256

**29a All tarsi of four segments; antennae 10-segmented. Fig. 257**
**4824 *Oligota parva* Kr.**

LENGTH: .8-1 mm. RANGE: Throughout much of Europe and North America.

Shining. Piceous; tip of abdomen lighter. Antennae clubbed; thorax much widened behind; elytra widening still more from front to back.

This genus contains about 10 species most of which are western in their range. A closely similar genus, *Somatium*, has seven known species.

Figure 257

**31a Front of head prolonged forming a beak; labial palpi of but 3 segments. Fig. 258                    4764 Myllaena dubia (Grav.)**

Figure 258

LENGTH: 1.5-2 mm.  RANGE: Europe and North America.

Reddish-brown; legs lighter.  Antennae long and slender; abdomen with scattered, long, coarse hairs.

*M. minuta* (Grav.) (4766), ranging through two continents is but 2 mm. long.  It is dark brown with legs and apical third of antennae dull yellow.

*M. vulpina* Bnhr. (4770), is known from Indiana to West Virginia.  It is piceous and measures 2.2 mm.

**31b Head not forming a beak: labial palpi of but 2 segments; middle coxa widely separated.  Fig. 259**

**4995 Gyrophaena fasciata (Say)**

Figure 259

LENGTH: 1.5-2.5 mm.  RANGE: Eastern United States.

Pale reddish-yellow; head, apical third of elytra and fourth and fifth abdominal segments black or piceous.

*G. dissimilis* (Er.) (4999), 1.5-2.3 mm. in length is pale dull yellow with head, apical angles of elytra and abdomen blackish.

It is found in the Central and Eastern States.

*Eumicrota corruscula* (Er.) (4947) is a rather common little species (1-1.5 mm.) found on leathery fungi from Texas to New York.  It differs from the above in the antennae having a long cylindrical club of 7 loosely-jointed segments.  It is shining black with pale yellow antennae and legs.  The elytra are a bit wider and longer than the thorax and are sometimes brownish.

**32a Front tarsi with but four segments; labial palpi with 4 segments; maxillary palpi with 5 segments**..............................33

**32b Front tarsi with 5 segments; antennae with eleven segments...36**

33a Sides of anterior, dorsal, abdominal segments with dense tufts of yellow hair. (a) Fig. 260

5008 *Xenodusa cava* (Lec.)

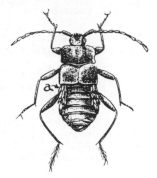

Figure 260

LENGTH: 5-6 mm. RANGE: Central and Eastern States.

Shining. Reddish-brown with scattered pubescence; antennae reaching middle of abdomen, the third segment twice as long as the second. (After Baltchley)

This and the few other species of the genus, all of which are western are found in ants nests sharing the food brought in by their hosts and in turn apparently furnishing some secretion the ants crave.

33b Not as in 33a............................................34

34a Maxillary cavity separated from the eyes by large cheeks and reaching backward beyond the eye. Fig. 261

5026 *Myrmedonia lauta* Csy.

Figure 261

LENGTH: 2.5-3 mm. RANGE: New York and Massachusetts.

Shining. Yellowish-orange; head, short; elytra and four apical segments of upper abdomen purplish-black. Legs and antennae dusky; lateral margins of abdomen dark.

*M. caliginosa* Csy. (5018), found from Iowa to New York and measuring 3 mm. is black with fuscous elytra, and reddish-yellow antennae and legs. The eyes are large.

*M. planifer* (Csy.) (5024), measuring 3-3.5 mm. and reported from North Carolina and Indiana, is dark reddish-brown, shining, with black abdomen, and legs and base of antennae pale reddish-brown. The thorax is one-half wider than long, but not as wide as the elytra.

34b Not as in 34a............................................35

105

35a Head constricted into a narrow neck (a) about a fourth as wide
   as head. Fig. 262.                    5751 *Aleodorus bilobatus* Say

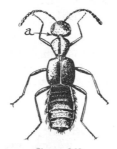

Figure 262

LENGTH: 3-3.3 mm. RANGE: Eastern half United States.

Shining. Piceous or dark brown; legs and
basal part of antennae brownish-yellow. Scutellum not carinate. Thorax heart-shaped, a bit
wider than the head. (After Blatchley)

*Falagria dissecta* (Er.) (5755), shining, black
or piceous and measuring 2 to 2.5 mm. Has
sharp ridges (carina) on its scutellum. It is scattered widely through the U. S. and Canada.

One could spend years in a systematic study of the Staphylinidae
alone without becoming too well acquainted with them. It's quite out
of the range of a book of limited scope to attempt to treat even all the
important genera of so large a family. One other in this tribe will be
mentioned.

*Meronera venustula* Er. (5743) measuring 1.6-1.8 mm. is a common
species. The head and last three segments of the abdomen are piceous,
while the base of the abdomen and the antennae are dull yellow; the
other parts are brown. It apparently ranges throughout much of the
eastern half of our country.

35b Head but slightly if at all constricted behind; maxillary palpi
   with four, labial palpi with but three segments. Fig. 263

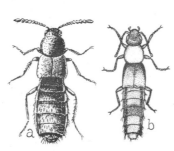

Figure 263

(a) 5250 *Atheta dentata* Bnhr.
LENGTH: 3-3.2 mm. RANGE: Proba-
bly all of United States.
Shining. Blackish piceous, with
scattered fine pubescence; elytra dull
clay-yellow; legs dusky-yellow.
*A. palustris* Kies (5314), widely
scattered in our country and Europe,
is another member of this large genus. It is black with dusky yellow
legs and measures 1.8-2 mm.
(b) 5609 *Pancota abundans* (Csy.)
LENGTH: 1.5-1.8 mm. RANGE: Missouri.
Brownish-yellow; head and mid-
dorsal line on segments 3 and 4
of abdomen black; antennae bead-
like; elytra very short; abdomen with
rather long hairs.

36a Maxillary palpi with 5 segments. Fig. 264

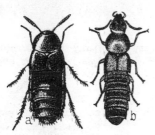

Figure 264

(a) 5766 *Aleochara lata* Grav. LENGTH: 5-7.5 mm. RANGE: Cosmopolitan.

Shining. Black; clothed with scattered gray pubescence, tarsi reddish-brown. Common in carrion.

(b) 5806 *Baryodma bimaculata* Grav.

LENGTH: 4-6.5 mm. RANGE: Much of United States and Canada.

Shining. Black; elytra paler near apex; tibiae, tarsi and tips of posterior abdominal segments d u l l brownish-red.

36b Maxillary palpi with 4 segments.............................37

37a Head prominent, narrowed at base; 1st segment of hind tarsi shorter than following two taken together. Fig. 265

Figure 265

6025 *Phloeopora sublaevis* Csy.

LENGTH: 1.8-2 mm. RANGE: Eastern half United States.

Dark brown; head and abdomen piceous; antenna fuscous, the basal part and the legs yellow. Thorax as long as wide; elytra longer and wider than the thorax.

*Amarochara fenyesi* Blatch. (5996), a brilliantly shining chestnut brown little species (1.8-2 mm.). The legs are dull yellow. Its first segment of hind tarsi is longer than the following two taken together.

37b Head retracted, not narrowed at base; ligula divided; labial palpi gradually narrowing from base to apex. Fig. 266

Figure 266

5896 *Oxypoda convergens* Csy.

LENGTH: 3-3.5 mm. RANGE: New York.

Reddish-brown; antennae, legs and elytra yellowish-brown. Thorax globular; abdomen with rather long hairs at sides; antennae bead-like.

*O. amica* Csy. (5956). This common little fellow (2-2.2 mm.) dull brownish-yellow, clothed with long shaggy pubescence; legs pale, ranges through the Central States.

38a Body slender; head with jaws directed forward...............39

38b Body broader; head inclined..............................40

39a Front coxae conical, prominent; maxillary palpi awl-shaped; mandibles toothed. Fig. 267          3318 *Pseudopsis obliterata* Lec.

LENGTH: 2 mm. RANGE: Colorado and Southern California.

Dull, brown; head and elytra darker; legs and antennae lighter; elytra with broad rounded costa; abdomen margined.

*P. sulcata* Newn. (3319), reddish-brown and measuring 2.5-3.5 mm., ranges widely in both Europe and America.

Figure 267

39b Front coxae transverse; antennae inserted on sides of front. Fig. 268          3332 *Megarthrus americanus* Sachse

LENGTH: 2.3-2.7 mm. RANGE: General, throughout North America

Dusky yellow; head black; legs dull yellow. Abdomen sparsely and rather coarsely punctate.

*M. excisus* Lec. (3330), black with sides slightly angulated, and measuring 2.5 mm. is known from our central area.

*Proteinus automarius* Er. (3322), scattered throughout Europe and our country, is blackish with dull yellow antennae and measures a strong 1 mm. Structurally, it has the last three antennal segments enlarged whereas *Megarthrus* has only the last segment larger.

Figure 268

At least three other European species belonging to this group have infiltrated into our country; *M. sinuatocollis* Boisd. (3331), *P. limbatus* Makl. (3324) and *P. brachypterus* (Fab.) (3327). Our many plants and other animals which have come from abroad are much like man in that many of them find highly useful places with us, but still others have such conflicting tastes that our country would be safer and better if they could be driven from our shores.

**40a Head margined; antennae with 11 segments. Fig. 269**
**4730 *Bolitobius cinctus* (Grav.)**

LENGTH: 4.5-7 mm. RANGE: Europe and North America.

Shining. Reddish-yellow; head, under surface, a large spot near outer apical angle of elytra and last two segments of abdomen shining black; antennae piceous, with apical and basal parts dull yellow.

*Mycetoporus splendidus* (Grav.) (4744), measuring 3-3.5 mm. and ranging through both Europe and America has thorax and elytra reddish-yellow, abdomen reddish-brown and head piceous. The two genera are separated by the maxillary palpi which is awl-shaped in this genus and filiform in *Bolitobius*.

Figure 269

Still another common member of the genus is *M. americanus* Er. (4742). It is about the same size as *splendidus* but differs in having two discal punctures on the thorax just behind the middle. It is reddish-brown to piceous. The elytra have equal length and breadth. It is known to occur from Iowa eastward.

**40b Head not margined** ........................................ **41**

**41a Mesosternum ridged (carinate) maxillary palpi filiform** ........ **42**

**41b Mesosternum not carinate. Fig. 270**
**4690 *Coproporus ventriculus* Say**

LENGTH: 2-2.5 mm. RANGE: Europe and United States.

Highly shining. Black, elytra and abdomen with a reddish-piceous tinge; antennae and legs dark reddish-brown. Upper surface finely punctate. (*C. laevis* (Lec.) (4692), is substantially the same except the upper surface is smooth.)

*Conosomus* is an important genus. The members are similar to those of *Coproporus* but highly pubescent. *C. crassus* (Grav.), (4707), piceous with pale brown pubescence and a narrow reddish part at base of thorax and elytra, 3-5 mm. is widely distributed.

Figure 270

**42a Maxillary palpi filiform. Fig. 271**

4665 *Tachinus fimbriatus* **Grav.**

Figure 271

LENGTH: 7-9 mm. RANGE: Canada and Eastern United States.

Shining. Head and thorax black; elytra pale chestnut brown; antennae black, 4 basal segments and apical one pale; abdomen, legs and under surface piceous.

*T. pallipes* Grav. (4670), common throughout Europe and America, is shining piceous black with legs, margins of thorax, base and sides of elytra and 4 basal joints of antennae, reddish yellow. It measures 5-6 mm.

**42b Maxillary palpi awl-shaped. Fig. 272**

4681 *Tachyporus jocosus* **Say**

Figure 272

LENGTH: 3-4 mm. RANGE: Europe, Siberia and much of United States.

Shining. Piceous; head black; thorax, elytra, and legs reddish-yellow; antennae dull yellow.

*T. nitidulus* Fab. (4686), 2.5-3 mm., reddish-yellow with head piceous and antennae and legs dull yellow, is a cosmopolitan species.

**43a Middle coxae touching each other.........................44**

**43b Middle coxae separated. Fig. 273**

4631 *Oxyporus major* **Grav.**

Figure 273

LENGTH: 10-14 mm. RANGE: Central and Eastern United States.

Shining. Black; elytra marked as pictured with golden yellow; tarsi pale yellowish; tibia with golden brown hairs; legs otherwise black.

*O. vittatus* Grav. (4634), has reddish-yellow legs instead of black. It is shining black or piceous with clay-yellow elytra with a black stripe on sides and at the suture. It measures 6 mm.

**44a Antennae with but 10 segments; eyes very large. Fig. 274**
3708 *Megalopsidia caelatus* (Grav.)

Figure 274

LENGTH: 4-4.5 mm. RANGE: Indiana to Florida.

Shining. Black; elytra with an oblique reddish stripe from humerus to suture at apex; legs and antenna reddish-brown; antennae shorter than head, which is wider than the thorax.

The genus *Osorius* differs in that the abdomen is not margined and the front tibia is spined. The shining blackish species *latipes* (Grav.) (3705), 4-5.5 mm. long, is rather common.

**44b Antennae with 11 segments.............................45**

**45a Front tibiae with two rows of spines; antennae elbowed. Fig. 275**
3644 *Bledius borealis* Blatch.

Figure 275

LENGTH: 6-6.5 mm. RANGE: Indiana.
Shining. Black; legs and elytra chestnut brown, antennae dusky towards apex. (After Blatchley)

*B. emarginatus* Say (3676), common along streams in the eastern half of the U. S., is black, very slender and measures 2 mm. or a little more.

**45b Tibia pubescent...........................................46**

**46a Scutellum invisible. Fig. 276.**
3498 *Trogophloeus quadripunctatus* (Say)

Figure 276

LENGTH: 3 mm. RANGE: Eastern half United States.

Shining. Black; antennae and legs piceous; knees and tarsi paler. Thorax 2/3 wider than long.

*T. arcifer* Lec. (3485), ranging rather widely and about 3 mm. long, is uniform dark reddish-brown with legs and antennae paler.

111

**46b Scutellum readily seen; head strongly constricted behind; body glabrous. Fig. 277**      **3556 *Apocellus sphaericollis* (Say)**

Figure 277

LENGTH: 2.7-3 mm. RANGE: North America.

Shining. Dark reddish-brown; head and abdomen usually darker; legs and first three joints of antennae pale. Eyes very small. Antennae longer than the head; thorax variable both in color and size.

A related species, *Thinobius fimbriatus* Lec. (3694) is a tiny (.7 mm.), slender beetle, dark reddish-brown with paler legs. It is pubescent and the head is not constricted behind.

**47a Segments 1 to 4 of hind tarsi unequal, segments 1 and 2 being elongated and equal; antennae slender; tibiae pubescent. Fig. 278**      **3412 *Olophrum obtectum* Er.**

Figure 278

LENGTH: 5-6 mm. RANGE: Central and Eastern States.

Shining. Piceous; antennae, legs and very narrow margin of thorax, reddish-brown. Head closely and coarsely punctuate.

*Lathrimaeum sordidum* Er. (3411), dull yellow with piceous abdomen and 2.7 mm. long ranges from Iowa to Virginia. Its antennae is thickened apically.

**47b Segments 1 to 4 of hind tarsi very short and equal............48**

**48a Tibiae with fine spines; mesosternum carinate (ridged). Fig. 279**      **(a) 3372 *Omalium diffusum* Fauv.**

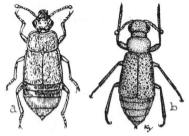

Figure 279

LENGTH: 3.5-4 mm. RANGE: Shores of Lake Superior.

Somewhat flattened, with elytra reaching beyond the middle.

**(b) 3378 *O. hamatum* Fauv.**

LENGTH: 2.3 mm. RANGE: Central States.

Dull reddish or dusky yellow, sparsely pubescent; head and tips of elytra fuscous. Hind tibiae deeply notched on the outer side.

112

48b Tibiae pubescent. Fig. 280

Figure 280

3344 *Anthobium horni* Fauv.

LENGTH: 2-2.4 mm. RANGE: Eastern
half United States.

Shining. Dull reddish-yellow. Head
finely and sparsely punctate; antennae shorter than head and thorax.
Eltyra more than twice the length of
the thorax.

*A. convexum* Fauv. (3339), 2 mm.
or a bit more in length and found in
the Central and Eastern States is dull
reddish yellow. The elytra is as long
or longer than the abdomen.

The related genus, *Arpedium*, differs in that the hind tarsal segments 1-4 are unequal instead of very short and equal as in *Anthobium*.
*Arpedium cribatum* Fauv. (3419), 4.5-5 mm., is known from Iowa eastward. It is elongate-oval in form, with thorax and elytra reddish-brown,
head black and legs and margins of the elytra and thorax paler.

## Family 17  PSELAPHIDAE
## The Ant-loving Beetles

These tiny beetles, all less than 3.5 mm., are found beneath bark,
stones, and in the nests of ants. Yellow, red, brown and fuscous are
the usual colors. The elytra are very short; the eyes are coarse or
sometimes wanting. Some 400 species are known for our country and
about 3,000 for the world.

1a Antennae arising from under two closely placed horizontal tubercules, their basal segments close together......................2

1b Antennae arising from sides of head, their bases wide apart.....4

2a Tarsi with two equal claws...................................3

**2b With but one claw on each tarsus; last segment of maxillary palpi long and hatchet shaped (a). Fig. 281.**

**6344 *Cylindrarctus longipalpis* (Lec.)**

Figure 281

LENGTH: 2 mm. RANGE: widely scattered from Florida to B. C.

Somewhat depressed, pale reddish-brown with scattered long and somewhat erect hairs; abdomen with narrow margins.

*Tychus minor* Lec. (6333) a widely distributed species measuring about 1.5 mm. differs from the above in being darker colored and in having five fovea at the base of the thorax instead of four.

Two genera of beetles similar in form and habits but possessing antennae with only two segments are now given a family of their own, CLAVIGERIDAE (see Fig. 158).

**3a Antennae with bead-like segments, not club-like; last two joints of maxillary palpi transverse (a). Fig. 282.**

**(6374) *Ceophyllus monilis* Lec.**

Figure 282

LENGTH: 3.3 mm. RANGE: Central and Eastern U. S.

Reddish brown, without punctures; antennae half as long as the body; all segments of female antennae about equal; male as pictured.

*Atinus monilicornis* (Bndl.) (6357) measuring 2.8 mm. and reddish brown; differs in the maxillary palpi which is small and has the last two segments forming a globular club. It has been taken in Va., Ohio, and Tenn.

Closely related but differing from the above two species in having clubbed antennae, *Cedius ziegleri* Lec. (6375), a bit under 3 mm. and known from Iowa eastward is fuscous-brown with appressed pubescence. *C. spinosus* Lec. (6377) is much like *ziegleri* but is smaller (2 mm. or less) and has less pubescence. It, too, is found in Iowa and eastward.

**3b Last joints of antenna gradually larger forming a distinct club (a); long bristle-like appendages on maxillary palpi (b). Fig. 283.**

6359 *Pilopius lacustris* Csy.

LENGTH: 1.8 mm. RANGE: Central U. S. and Canada.

Dark reddish-brown, elytra, legs, and antennae paler; antennae of male ¾ as long as body; of female shorter; top of head with two distinct pits between the eyes.

*Tmesiphorus carinatus* Say (6378) differs in having only short appendages on the palpi. It ranges through our Central and Eastern States and measures 2.5 mm. It is pale reddish brown.

Figure 283

Another member of this latter genus, *T. costalis* Lec., (6379) is common over a rather wide range. It is shining, piceous, and covered with short, appressed, yellowish hairs. The eyes are prominent and the antennae of the male over half as long as the body; the antennae of the female are shorter. It is 3.3 mm. long.

**4a Hind coxae conical, prominent and close together**..............5

**4b Hind coxae transverse, not prominent and widely separated**....7

**5a Antennae not elbowed; first joint not elongated; tarsi with but one claw.** .......................................................6

**5b Antennae elbowed (a). Fig. 284.**

6158 *Rhexius insculptus* Lec.

LENGTH: 1.2 mm. RANGE: eastern half of U. S.

Pale reddish-brown covered with short erect hairs; front with 3 pits; top of head ridged, antennal joints 3-8 transverse and equal. Tarsi with two unequal claws.

*Sonoma tolulae* (Lec.) (6039) from Georgia, Virginia and Pennsylvania has two equal tarsal claws. Its length is 2.1 mm. and is dark brown and covered with long dense pubescence. The antennae and legs are yellowish.

Figure 284

**6a Last joint of antennae much larger than the others. Fig. 285.**
**6082** *Melba parvula* **(Lec.)**

Figure 285

LENGTH: 1 mm. RANGE: Pennsylvania to Iowa.

Brownish yellow, shining, pubescent; thorax without punctures; top of head with foveae.

A very tiny (.7 mm.) related species is *Trimiomelba convexula* (Lec.) (6053). The first dorsal segment of the abdomen is much elongated. It is deep yellow and has been found in Florida, Pennsylvania, and Indiana.

**6b Antennal club formed gradually, the last joint not radically larger than the adjoining ones. Fig. 286.**
**6093** *Euplectus confluens* **Lec.**

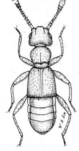

Figure 286

LENGTH: 1.2-1.5 mm. RANGE: Central and Eastern U. S.

Reddish-brown, finely pubescent. Abdomen longer than elytra; antennae reaching middle of thorax.

*Thesiastes fossulatus* (Bndl.) (6121), known to range from Iowa to Indiana is distinguished from the above by a head narrower than the thorax. It is a shining dark brown and measures 1.2 mm.

**7a Antennae with 11 segments....................................8**

**7b Antenna with but 10 segments three of which form the club. Fig. 287.**
**6319** *Decarthron brendeli* **Csy.**

Figure 287

LENGTH: 1.4 mm. RANGE: Central States and Southwest.

Piceous brown; elytra dull red; antennae and legs paler brown; antennae scarcely as long as head and thorax; eighth and ninth segments transversely oval, tenth one-half longer than wide and three times as thick as eighth, truncate at base.

*D. abnorme* (Lec.) (6317) is black. Its two large pits on the top of head are connected by grooves. It measures 1.4 mm. and is found from Canada to Florida and west to Iowa.

**8a Abdomen margined; tarsi with but one claw. Elytra with three small basal pits and thorax with two large and one small pit. Fig. 288.**

6301 *Reichenbachia propinqua* Lec.

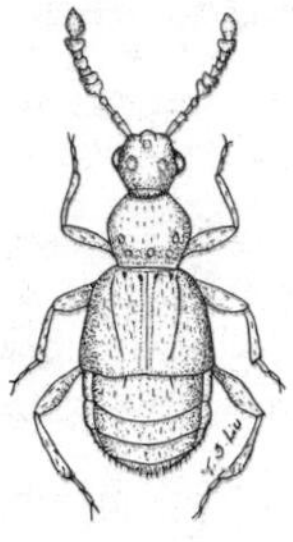

LENGTH: 1.4 mm. RANGE: Minnesota to Massachusetts.

Piceous black; elytra dark blood-red; antennae of male with fifth segment strongly dilated, the sixth a bit longer than the seventh; pubescence short and recurved.

*R. rubicunda* Aube. (6264) is common in much of its range throughout the eastern half of United States.

It is piceous black, not punctured; legs, antennae, and elytra dull red and measures around 1.5 mm. The eighth antennal segment is globular and the tenth subglobular and one-half thicker than the ninth with the eleventh one-half wider than the tenth.

Figure 288

**8b Abdomen without margin; tarsi with 2 unequal claws; body long, cylindrical and narrow; hind tibiae with a long terminal spur. Fig. 289**

6201 *Batrisodes spretus* Lec.

LENGTH: 1.7 mm. RANGE: Eastern half of U. S. Common.

Piceous black; elytra dark red, sparsely and finely pubescent. Antennae reaching base of thorax, segments 2-8 oblong; 9th longer and wider, transverse; 10th large squarish; 11th narrower than the 10th but twice as long.

*B. monstrosus ferox* Lec. (6174a) is 2.4 mm. long, reddish-brown throughout and distributed through the Central and Eastern States. It is often common.

Figure 289

# Family 21 SCAPHIDIIDAE
## The Shining Fungus Beetles

These polished oval, boat-shaped beetles may be found in fungi, decayed wood, under bark and in debris. There are about 50 species in our area.

**1a Antennae not definitely clubbed, slender scutellum very small or invisible; punctures on elytra scattered or absent................2**

117

**1b Antennae with a broad, somewhat flattened, five-jointed club; scutellum distinct; elytra with punctures in rows. Fig. 290.**

6482 *Scaphidium quadriguttatum* (Say)

Figure 290

LENGTH: 3.8-4.5 mm.   RANGE: Central and Eastern states.   Common.

Black, highly shining; elytra with transverse reddish spots; elytra with a twice curving row of coarse punctures along the basal margin.

If the red spots are lacking, this wholly black beetle is variety *piceum* Melsh. (6482d).

Another variety is *obliteratum* Lec. (6482c) in which the elytral spots are smaller, and yellow instead of red.   The disk of the elytra also lack the coarse punctures.

**2a Body oval; sutural striae reaching the base. Fig. 291.**

6515 *Baeocera falsata* Achard

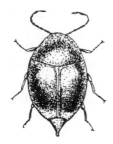

Figure 291

LENGTH: 2.7 mm.   RANGE: Central and Eastern States.

Black, highly polished; legs, antennae and tips of elytra and abdomen reddish-piceous.   No scutellum; thorax with scattered coarse punctures. (After Blatchley)

*Scaphisoma convexum* Say (6489) about 2.5 mm. long, shining black or chestnut-brown is rather common in its range of the eastern half of the United States.   It is found on fungi on logs.   The genus is distinguished by a very short third antennal segment.

**2b Body narowed; sutural striae not reaching the base. Fig. 292.**

6527 *Toxidium compressum* Zimm.

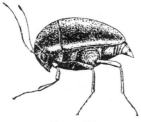

Figure 292

LENGTH: 1.4-1.7 mm.   RANGE: Central and Southeastern U. S.   Common.

Dark reddish-brown, much polished; antennae, legs and tip of abdomen paler.   Metasternum coarsely and deeply punctured.

*Cyparium flavipes* Lec. (6484) 3.5 mm. long, chestnut brown with lighter legs and antennae, resembles *Scaphidium* but has a row of small spines on the hind tibia.

# Family 23   HISTERIDAE
## The Hister Beetles

These polished, hard, usually ovoid beetles, (some live under bark and are much depressed), with truncate elytra are easily recognized. They frequent carrion where they are apparently predacious on the carrion feeders. More than 3,000 species are known, with over 500 from our area.

1a Head bent downward and usually retracted; form convex; mandibles not especially prominent...................................2

1b Head extended forward; form much flattened; mandibles conspicuous. Fig. 293.

6530 *Hololepta aequalis* Say

Figure 293

LENGTH: 7-10 mm. RANGE: eastern half of the U. S. and parts of Canada.

Fairly common under bark of logs, especially poplar, elm and tulip trees. Very flat and thin. Black, shining. Thorax punctured at the sides. (Courtesy Kan. St. Bd. Agr.)

*Hololepta yucateca* Mars. (6534) ranging from Texas to Southern California is found in decaying cacti. It is black and measures 8-10 mm.

*Hololepta vicina* Lec. (6542) belongs in the west from Washington to Southern California; inland to Arizona.

2a Prosternum distinctly lobed in front. Fig. 294 ............................3

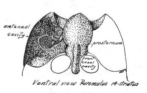

Ventral view *Paromalus 14-striatus*

Figure 294

2b Prosternum not lobed in front. Fig. 295. ................................8

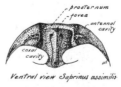

Ventral view *Saprinus assimilis*

Figure 295

**3a Antennal cavities at middle of the underside of the thorax. (See Fig. 294) Fig. 296.**

**6723 Paromalus aequalis Say**

Figure 296

LENGTH: 2.5-3 mm. RANGE: eastern half of the United States and Canada.

Common under bark on poplar and other logs. Black, shining elytra with but few or no striae; strongly flattened.

*Isolomalus bistriatus* Er. (6724) is a smaller (2 mm.), less depressed histerid which is common under bark and in fungi throughout a wide range. It is shining black with legs and antennae reddish brown.

**3b Antennal cavities beneath the front angles of the thorax, open in front. Fig. 297............................4**

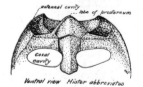

Figure 297

**4a Club of antennae rather oval, pubescent........................5**

**4b Club of antennae an inverted cone, glabrous; thorax with a lobe on each side. Fig. 298.**

**6745 Hetaerius brunneipennis Rand.**

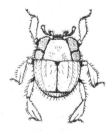

Figure 298

LENGTH: 1.5 mm. RANGE: Connecticut to Iowa.

Pale chestnut-brown shining; thorax with a lobe on each side which is separated from the disk by a groove; elytra with scattered erect fine yellowish hairs along striae. (After Wheeler)

This interesting tiny beetle like several other species of its genus lives in intimate association with ants in their nests. *H. exiguus* Mann (6748) is thus found in several of the western states. Several species of these ant-loving hister beetles are known only from California.

5a Tarsal groove of front tibiae deep, S-shaped, and plainly margined. ........................................................7

5b Tarsal groove of front tibiae straight and with margin only on inner edge. ........................................................6

6a Margin of thorax with a fringe of short hairs; elytra with a prominent red spot. Fig. 299.

**6554 Hister biplagiatus Lec.**

LENGTH: 5-6 mm.  RANGE: North Central and Eastern United States.

Black with red marks as pictured; disk of thorax smooth; pygidium with but a few fine punctures.

Figure 299

*H. bimaculatus* L. (6623) is another member of the genus marked with red, having a large diagonal orange-red spot covering much of the outer half of each elytron. It is 4.5 mm. long and is known in Europe as well as much of North America.

6b Margin of thorax not fringed with hairs; prosternum convex; mesosternum notched in front.  Fig. 300.

**6596 Hister abbreviatus Fab.**

LENGTH: 3.5-5.5 mm.  RANGE: eastern half of U. S.  Common.

Black, shining; elytra with four entire dorsal striae, fifth short and two overlapping subhumerals; dorsal striae punctured.

*H. foedatus* Lec. (6586) ranging, often abundantly, in Canada and entirely across the United States measures 4-6.5 mm.  Its subhumeral and 3 dorsal striae are entire.  The front tibia has at least six teeth.

Figure 300

*H. americanus* Payk. is a comparatively small (3-4 mm.) member of the genus, but one of the most common hister beetles and one that has a wide range.  It is black; the inner striae of the thorax are entire and the elytra possess five entire striae.  The front tibiae have three teeth, the apical one prominent and divided into two fine points.

121

**7a Body at least twice as long as wide, form cylindrical. Fig. 301.**
6657 *Platysoma basale* Lec.

LENGTH: 4.5-5.5 mm. RANGE: North Central States under bark, not common.

Black, shining; antennae reddish brown; legs piceous; disk of thorax nearly smooth; elytra with four dorsal striae entire. (After Blatchley)

*P. coarctatum* Lec. (6659) appears to be a small edition of *basale*. It measures but 2.5 to 3 mm. and has the thorax evenly punctured throughout. It seems to have a wider range and to be more common.

Figure 301

**7b Body broad and plainly depressed. Fig. 302.**
6653 *Platysoma depressum* Lec.

LENGTH: 2.5-3 mm. RANGE: Atlantic States to So. Cal. Common under bark of logs and stumps.

Black, shining; thorax with scattered coarse punctures at sides, smooth at middle; elytra with but three entire dorsal striae; front tibiae with 4 teeth; middle tibia with 3.

*Phelister subrotundus* Say (6666), a bit smaller and quite convex, is also common under bark. It has a reddish-brown cast with legs and antennae definitely that color. It too has a wide range.

Figure 302

*Phelister vernus* (Say) (6673) a widely distributed and very common species, lives under bark and logs in damp places. It is convex, oblong-oval, shining, black. The legs and antennae are reddish-brown. The elytra possess 4 full-length striae; the sutural stria and still another occur only on the apical half of the elytron; the thorax has no marginal stria. It measures 2.5 mm.

**8a Front of head without a margin. Fig. 303.....9**

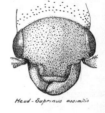

Head-*Saprinus assimilis*

Figure 303

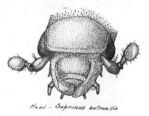

Figure 304

8b Front of head margined (Fig. 304). Prosternum with a ridge. Fig. 305.
6896 *Saprinus patruelis* Lec.

Figure 305

LENGTH: 3-4.5 mm. RANGE: North Central States.

Shining with bluish-green or bronze lustre; hind tibiae with three rows of long spines; elytra with scattered coarse punctures. Front tibiae with six teeth, the apical three coarser.

*Acritus exiguus* (Er.) (6790) has its antennae arising from the front instead of from under the frontal margin. It is only 1 mm. long, dark reddish-brown and is often common under bark throughout much of the United States.

9a Prosternum without a pit or fovea on each side close to front margin; short but distinct striae on front above the eye............10

9b Prosternum with a small but distinct fovea on each side terminating the striae (see fig. 295); no striae above eye. Fig. 306.
6836 *Saprinus assimilis* Payk.
LENGTH: 4 5.5 mm. RANGE: eastern half of U. S. Common.

Figure 306

Black, shining; sides of thorax with coarse punctures, disk smooth; coarse punctures on apical third of elytra; teeth on front tibia fine.

*S. conformis* Lec. (6838) is told from *assimilis* by its lack of a deep marginal groove, at the apex of the pygidium. It is shining black, ranges through the eastern half of the United States and is 3.5-4.5 mm. long.

*S. posthumus* Mars. (6819) 3-4 mm. in length apparently ranges widely through the eastern half of our region. It is broadly oval, black and highly polished. The thorax carries many punctures. The elytral striae are all abbreviated, with the sutural and the first being the longest; the fourth is joined to the sutural at the base by an arch. The front tibiae are armed with several fine teeth.

**10a Fourth dorsal striae but weakly arched and not joining the short sutural stria. Fig. 307.**

6827 *Saprinus lugens* Er.

Figure 307

LENGTH: 4:6 mm. RANGE: Central and Western States.

Black, somewhat shining; elytra wholly covered with coarse punctures except a large somewhat oval scutellar spot and a small subhumeral area which are smooth.

*S. fraternus* Say (6885) has "mirror spots" on the elytra similar to *lugens*. It is much smaller however (3-4 mm.) and has a distinct margin on the front of head (see fig. 304). It ranges from Newfoundland to Iowa.

**10b Fourth dorsal stria strongly arched at base, joining the sutural which is entire. Fig. 308.**

6829 *Saprinus pennsylvanicus* Payk.

Figure 308

LENGTH: 4.5-5 mm. RANGE: from Rockies east.

Bright metallic green, sometimes bronzed. Thorax smooth with a double row of coarse punctures at base. Front tibiae with coarse teeth.

*Gnathoncus communis* Mars. (6908) differs in having a flat prosternum. It is shining black with brown legs and antennae. It ranges throughout Europe and North America. It is found in fungi and measures 2.5-3.5 mm.

# Family 24    LYCIDAE
## The Net-winged Beetles

These often brightly colored and attractive insects, are not luminous like their near relatives the fireflies, and are active by day. Only about 50 species are known in our region.

**1a Under side of thorax with a prominent tubular spiracle behind and at the outer extremity of the front coxae.**........................2

**1b Under side without such spiracle as in 1a.**........................3

2a Front prolonged into a beak; antennae with third segment scarcely as long as fourth. Fig. 309.

6916 *Lycostomus lateralis* (Melsh.)

Figure 309

LENGTH: 8-10 mm. RANGE: eastern half of the U. S.

Black, apex and sides of thorax and sides of elytra to middle dull yellow.

*Caeniella dimidiata* (Fab.) (6929) measuring 10 mm. and ranging through the Atlantic States resembles *Calopteron terminale* but has comb-like antennae and a black scutellar spot.

2b Front swollen between the antennae; without a beak; antennae much flattened. Fig. 310.

6926 *Calopteron reticulatum* (Fab.)

Figure 310

LENGTH: 11-19 mm. RANGE: eastern half of U. S.

Upper surface dull orange-yellow, marked as pictured with black. Elytra at widest place but three times the width at base.

*C. terminale* (Say) (6925), widely distributed throughout the United States, is colored much like *reticulatum* except that only the apical third of the elytra is purplish-black. Its elytra attain a width four times that of the base. It measures 11-17 mm.

3a Elytra ribbed, cross-barred or netted..........................4

3b Elytra with light striae (ridges) but not as in 3a. Fig. 311.

6958 *Calochromus perfacetus* (Say)

Figure 311

LENGTH: 7-10 mm. RANGE: eastern half of U. S.

Depressed. Black, with fine pubescence; thorax marked with reddish yellow as pictured. Antennae with second segment but one third as long as third. (After Knobel)

Four other species of this genus occur in Colorado, Oregon and California.

**4a Thorax divided into cells. Fig. 312.**

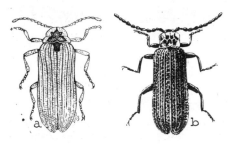

Figure 312

(a) 6939 *Eros aurora* Hbst.

LENGTH: 7-11 mm. RANGE: much of N. A. (also Europe and Siberia).

Depressed. Head antennae and under surface black; thorax and elytra bright scarlet; scutellum and depressions on thorax dusky; thorax with 5 cells, a center rhomboid one with two on each side.

(b) 6940 *E. sculptilis* (Say)

LENGTH: 5-7 mm. RANGE: Indiana and Southern States.

Black or piceous; thorax reddish-yellow often with black spot at center. Elytra with four prominent ridges running lengthwise. (After Blatchley)

*E. trilineatus* Melsh. (6942), ranging through the eastern one third of our country is wholly black except for dull yellow side margins on the thorax. The thorax has six rather weakly defined cells.

**4b Thorax without distinct cells. Fig. 313.**

6948 *Plateros sollicitus* (Lec.)

Dumse

Figure 313

LENGTH: 6-7.5 mm. RANGE: eastern one third of U. S.

Dull black; thorax reddish yellow with center spot shining black; antennae of male long, the fourth segment twice as long as the third, fifth twice as long as wide. Antennae of female shorter, the seventh joint twice as long as wide.

*P. modestus* (Say) (6945) is the same size and has much the same color and range. It can be readily separated from the above by the intervals which alternate high and low.

# Family 25  LAMPYRIDAE

## The Fireflies, Glowworms

These insects are known by everyone because of the display they make on summer nights. They prefer damp places and are inactive by day. Over 2000 species have been described.

1a Thorax completely covering head; antenae with second joint small, usually transverse...........................................2

1b Head not fully covered by prothorax; second antennal joint not transverse. Fig. 314.

7013 *Photuris pennsylvanicus* (DeG.)

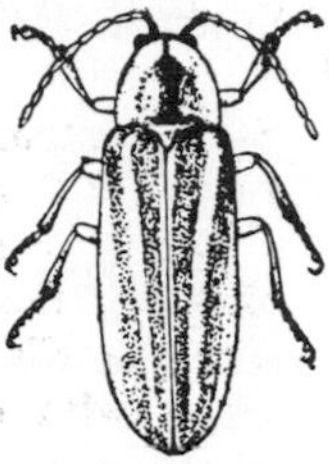

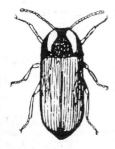

LENGTH: 11-15 mm. RANGE: eastern half of U. S.

Head and thorax dull yellow; thorax with median dark stripe on the red disk; elytra brownish with pale markings; labrum with three teeth. This is one of the most common fireflies.

*Phausis splendidula* (L.) (7009) is a European species 8-9 mm. in length which has been found in the eastern United States. It and other members of its genus have a jointed needle-like appendage on the last antennal segment.

Figure 314

2a Eyes large, larger in male than in female; light organs well developed. ........................................................3

2b Eyes small; light organs feeble; antennae much compressed, not serrate; second segment short and transverse. Fig. 315.

6975 *Lucidota corrusca* (L.)

LENGTH: 10-14 mm. RANGE: California and Arizona to Atlantic states and Newfoundland.

Black or sometimes rusty; markings as pictured on thorax, reddish and yellow; third joint of antennae longer than wide; elytra with fine prostrate yellowish pubescence. Common throughout much of its range. (After Knobel)

*L. fenestralis* (Melsh.) (6977), very common in California, ranges entirely across the United States. It measures 7-12 mm. and is black with a reddish-yellow triangle on each side of the thorax.

Figure 315

3a Thorax having somewhat of a ridge; light organs of female on the side of abdomen. Fig. 316.

6984 *Pyractomena angulata* (Say)

LENGTH: 8-15 mm. RANGE: eastern third of U. S. and Canada.

Depressed; blackish-brown with yellow and reddish markings on thorax as pictured; elytra finely granulate and punctured, each with two or three plainly evident ridges; ventral segment of female dull yellow with dusky spots. (After Knobel)

*Calyptocephalus bifaria* (Say) (6967) is an interesting species distinguished by the antennae which has comb-like projections on each side. It is black, with front and side of the thorax reddish yellow. It measures 9-10 mm. and is known from Ohio and Indiana.

Figure 316

**3b Thorax without a ridge, though often grooved; light organs of female at middle of abdomen. Fig. 317.**

6999 *Photinus scintillans* Say

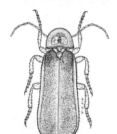

Figure 317

LENGTH: 5.5-8 mm. RANGE: Kansas to Massachusetts.

Slender; dusky brown; thorax yellowish and reddish with black center as pictured; suture and side margins of elytra pale; antennae dusky.

In some members of this family the female is always wormlike, and glows with a continuous light. The Pink Glowworm *Microphotus angustus* Lec. (7002), found in California, Colorado, Oregon and Florida is like this. The female measures 10-15 mm. while the male which is winged and has a pinkish body is about 10 mm. long.

# Family 27 CANTHARIDAE
## The Leather-winged Beetles

These beetles have much more pliable elytra than most beetles. The head is uncovered. They are predacious. Some 1500 species are known but less than 200 in the United States.

**1a Mentum small, quadrate........................................2**

**1b Mentum very long, wider in front. Fig. 318.**

7051 *Chauliognathus pennsylvanicus* DeG.

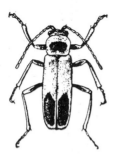

Figure 318

LENGTH: 9-12 mm. RANGE: eastern half of U. S.

Head and underparts black; thorax and elytra yellow with black markings as pictured. Very common especially on goldenrod in the fall.

*C. marginatus* Fab. (7052) is smaller and narrower. Its head is mostly yellow; the thorax has a mid-dorsal black stripe and a rather long but highly variable blackish spot on each elytron. It too is often very common, appearing earlier than the above.

**2a Elytra wholly covering the wings...............................3**

**2b** Elytra short (a) leaving the wings exposed; last segment of maxillary palpi hatchet shaped. Fig. 319.

**7169 *Trypherus latipennis* (Germ.)**

LENGTH: 6-7 mm. RANGE: eastern half of U. S. Common on catnip and many other plants.

Slender. Elytra very short as in the Staphylinids, but the wings not folded under the elytra; eyes large and prominent in the male. Dull yellow beneath, piceous above, the tips of elytra and margins of thorax dull yellow.

*Malthodes concavus* Lec. (7178) in common with the several other members of its genus, has elytra shortened but not so much so as *Trypherus*. The general color is piceous with the base of the antennae and part of abdomen yellowish. It is only 2-3 mm. long and ranges through the eastern third of our country.

Figure 319

**3a** Thorax rounded in front, partly covering the head . . . . . . . . . . . . . . 4

**3b** Thorax cut squarely in front, not at all covering the head. Fig. 320.

**(a) 7056 *Podabrus rugulosus* Lec.**

LENGTH: 7-8 mm. RANGE: eastern half of U. S. Common.

Black; front of head and sides of thorax yellow; head coarsely punctured, thorax less so.

**(b) 7062 *P. modestus* (Say)**

LENGTH: 9-13 mm. RANGE: Eastern U. S. and Canada.

Blackish front of head, margins of thorax and femora yellow.

**(c) 7066 *P. tomentosus* (Say)**

LENGTH: 9-12 mm. RANGE: Much of U. S.

Elytra black; head and thorax reddish-yellow. (After Blatchley)

All three of these species are valued for destroying aphids.

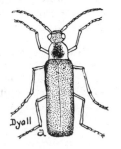

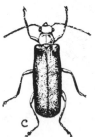

Figure 320

**4a Head short; hind angles of thorax incised. Fig. 321.**

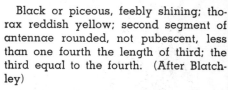

7162 *Silis latilobus* **Blatch.**

LENGTH: 4.5-5.5 mm. RANGE: North Central States.

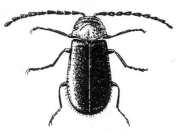

Black or piceous, feebly shining; thorax reddish yellow; second segment of antennae rounded, not pubescent, less than one fourth the length of third; the third equal to the fourth. (After Blatchley)

S. *percomis* (Say) (7152) is a bluish black species, about 5 mm. long which ranges from Canada and Massachusetts to Texas. The thorax which is wider than long is colored reddish-yellow.

Figure 321

**4b Head fairly long; hind angles of thorax rounded. Fig. 322.**

7121 *Cantharis bilineatus* **Say**

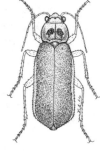

LENGTH: 6-8 mm. RANGE: eastern half of U. S.

Dull reddish-yellow; back of head, elytra, spots on thorax, all but two basal segments of antennae and tibia and tarsi black. Thorax widely margined; sparsely punctured.

C. *divisus* Lec. (7122), is a common western species ranging from Alaska to California. It measures only 6-8 mm. and is black with thorax yellow with two large black spots on the disk.

Figure 322

# Family 28 MELYRIDAE
## The Soft-winged Flower Beetles

These small beetles seem to live on the eggs of other insects. More than 100 species have been described for our region but only a few are common in general collections.

1a Antennae with 11 segments...................................3

1b Antenna with apparently 10 segments. (The second segment being small and hidden.)..............................................2

**2a Elytra marked with spots. Fig. 323.**

**7227 *Collops quadrimaculatus* (Fab.)**

Figure 323

LENGTH: 4-6 mm. RANGE: much of the U. S. especially east of the Rockies. Common.

Head, abdomen and femora, black; thorax and elytra reddish-yellow, the marking blue or bluish-black. (Courtesy Kans. St. Bd. Agr.)

*C. bipunctatus* Say (7208); about the same size (5-6 mm.), has bluish-black elytra with a reddish thorax on which are two oblique black spots. It ranges from the Missouri river to the Pacific.

**2b Elytra marked with stripes. Fig. 324.**

**7215 *Collops vittatus* (Say)**

Figure 324

LENGTH: 5-7 mm. RANGE: Much of U. S. and Canada.

Reddish with black spot on thorax and elytra marked with wide dark blue stripes. The spot on the thorax is often absent. (From U.S.D.A.)

This "Striped Collops" is a valuable predator. Both the adults and the larvae feed upon the larvae and pupae of the alfalfa caterpillar.

**3a Front tarsi simple; elytra of male prolonged at tip into a hook-like piece. Fig. 325.**

**7282 *Pseudebaeus oblitus* (Lec.)**

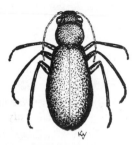

Figure 325

LENGTH: 2-2.5 mm. RANGE: Canada to Fla.

Wholly black above; legs and base of antennae pale dull yellow.

*Anthocomus erichsoni* Lec. (7276) measuring 3.5 to 4 mm. and ranging through much of the eastern half of the United States, does not have an appendage on the elytra. The head and elytra are black, the latter with a bluish tinge; the thorax is reddish yellow.

**3b Front tarsi of male with second joint prolonged covering the third; elytra of both sexes without an appendage. Fig. 326.**

7315 *Attalus circumscriptus* (Say)

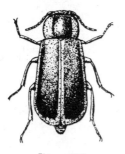

Figure 326

LENGTH: 3 mm. RANGE: South Central and Southern States west to Arizona.

Black; margins of thorax and elytra as pictured, pale dull yellow. Under surface black, the ventral segments margined behind with yellow; legs yellowish and dusky. (After Blatchley)

*A. terminalis* (Er.) (7294) differs from the above in having the head and thorax wholly black; the elytra of the male are narrowly margined with yellow but in the female they too are wholly black. It measures 2.5 mm. and ranges over much of the eastern half of the U. S.

# Family 29   CLERIDAE
## The Checkered Beetles

These beetles are often highly colored with intricate patterns. They are small to medium in size, often cylindrical and usually hairy. The adults are found under bark and on flowers; they are predacious. About 200 species are known from our region and some 2500 for the whole world.

**1a First segment of tarsi very small leaving only four visible from above; tarsal claws with teeth.................................3**

**1b All five tarsal segments visible from above.....................2**

**2a Last segment more than half the length of the entire antennae; punctures on elytra scattered. Fig. 327.**

7516 *Monophylla terminata* (Say)

Figure 327

LENGTH: 4-7 mm. RANGE: Texas and Arizona east to Atlantic coast.

Black, somewhat shining; thorax and elytra marked with yellow as pictured; abdomen of male wholly yellow, the last segment black in the female. (Courtesy N. Y. State Museum)

*Tillus colaris* Spin. (7521), 5-6 mm. long is black with a red thorax; the latter sometimes margined with black. It ranges through the Southern States. Its last antennal joint is not abnormally long.

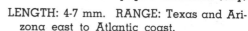

**2b** Last segment of antennae never longer than the preceding four taken together; punctures of elytra in rows. Fig. 328.

7544 *Cymatodera bicolor* Say

Figure 328

LENGTH: 6-10 mm. RANGE: eastern half of U. S.

Black, somewhat dull; thorax, legs and first two joints of antennae reddish-yellow marked with black as pictured. (After Blatchley)

*C. ovipennis* Lec. (7568), 8-11 mm. long and light brown with a paler line on elytra is native of the Southwestern States.

*C. inornata* Say (7545) is 7-9 mm. long, wholly dark brown with a coat of yellowish hairs. The antennae and the base of the femora are reddish-brown. It ranges across the eastern half of the United States and into Canada.

**3a** Eyes with a notch in front (a). Fig. 329...4

**3b** Eyes without a notch.....................7

**4a** Last three joints of antennae forming a distinct club; eyes finely granulate..........5

Figure 329

**4b** Antennae serrate, but not clubbed; eyes coarsely granulate. Fig. 330.

7577 *Priocera castanea* Newn.

Figure 330

LENGTH: 6.5-10 mm. RANGE: eastern half of the U. S. and Canada.

Head, thorax and legs dark chestnut-brown shining; elytra reddish brown marked as pictured with black and yellow. (After Blatchley)

*Cleronomus melanopterus* (Dury) (7580) with a length of 8 mm., colored black with pinkish marked thorax is known from Ohio.

**5a** Last segment of maxillary palpi slender.......................6

133

**5b Last segment of maxillary palpi slightly broader than next to last segment; antennal club triangular. Fig. 331.**

**7629 *Trichodes nutalli* Kby.**

Figure 331

LENGTH: 8-11 mm. RANGE: Eastern half of U. S. and Canada and Colorado.

Dark blue, purplish or greenish blue; elytra darker blue, marked as shown with reddish-yellow. A very attractive beetle.

*T. ornatus* Say (7627), a somewhat similarly marked and colored beetle, ranges through most of the Western States. It is 6-7 mm. long and metallic blue with 3 yellow bars across the elytra.

**6a Hind tarsus slender and elongated; thorax with impressed line at middle and with a deep subapical groove. Fig. 332.**

**7585 *Thanasimus dubius* (Fab.)**

Figure 332

LENGTH: 7-9 mm. RANGE: eastern half of the U. S.

Head, thorax and base of elytra dull red. Antennae and legs red to pitch black; elytra mostly black with cross bands of whitish hairs. (Courtesy N. Y. State Museum)

*Enoclerus cupressi* Van Dyke (7599) living in California serves a useful purpose in destroying the Cypress Barkbeetle. It is black with triangular orange spots on the elytra and is 7 mm. long.

**6b Hind tarsi broadly dilated; thorax usually smooth. Fig. 333.**

**7605 *Clerus ichneumoneus* (Fab.)**

Figure 333

LENGTH: 8-11 mm. RANGE: eastern half of U. S.

Head, thorax and elytra brick red; median band on elytra as pictured, yellowish margined with black; antennae, legs and much of under parts black. Several common closely related species are similarly marked. (After Blatchley)

*C. nigrifrons* (Say) (7594) and *C. rosmarus* (Say) (7597) have the abdomen black. In the first the elytral punctures are finer than in *rosmarus* which has red antennae.

**7a** Elytra bright red; antennae with 3 segments in club.  Fig. 334.

**7694 *Zenodosus sanguineus* (Say)**

Figure 334

LENGTH: 4.5-6.5 mm.  RANGE: northeastern half of U. S. and Canada.

Head, thorax, and under parts brown, elytra crimson or blood-red, rather dull.  There is but this one species in the genus.  These beautiful beetles are found under bark and sometimes in moss.

**7b** Elytra black, sometimes marked in yellow; antennal club small, spherical and with but two segments.  Fig. 335.

(a) **7689 *Isohydnocera tabida* (Lec.)**

LENGTH: 5-7 mm.  RANGE: northeastern half of U. S. and Canada.

Bluish black, antennae and legs pale reddish-yellow.

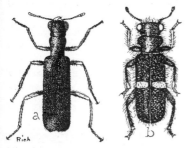

Figure 335

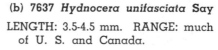

(b) **7637 *Hydnocera unifasciata* Say**

LENGTH: 3.5-4.5 mm.  RANGE: much of U. S. and Canada.

Bluish-black; elytra with bar of dense white hairs as pictured.  (After Blatchley)

*H. scabra* (Lec.) (7661), dull brownish gray and 4-5 mm. long; inhabits the Pacific coast.

## Family 30   CORYNETIDAE
### The Bone-Beetles

The members of this little family of less than 50 species are similar to the Clerids.  They feed on cereal and animal products and become pests in this way.  They were formerly with the Cleridae; some would put them back there again under the subfamilies Korynetinae and Enopliinae.

**1a** Last three segments of antennae large, flat and dilated; six segments of abdomen visible.  See (a), fig. 336....................2

1b **Antennae ending in a small compact club; but five segments of abdomen visible. Fig. 336.**

**7728 Necrobia ruficollis (Fab.)**

LENGTH: 4-5 mm. RANGE: it and the other members of its genus mentioned here seem to be scattered world wide.

Red; head, antennae, and abdomen black, elytra metallic blue or green marked at base as shown with red. (After Blatchley)

*Necrobia rufipes* (DeG.) (7727) and *N. violacea* (L.) (7729) differ from *ruficollis* in being wholly blue or green above. In *rufipes* the base of antennae and legs are red but in *violacea* they are dark. These are known as "Ham Beetles." When ham is scarce they gladly congregate in other meat supplies, cheese, spoiled fish or dead animals in the field.

Figure 336

All three species have coarsely granulated eyes; only the last three of the 11 segments forming the antennae are in the club; the claws are toothed at their base. These three species likely constitute the only serious offenders within the family.

2a Notch of eye in front.........................................3

2b **Notch of eye on inner side. Fig. 337.**

**7696 Phyllobaenus dislocatus Say**

LENGTH: 4-6 mm. RANGE: eastern half of the U. S. and Canada.

Black, with yellowish legs, antennae and markings on elytra; elytra with coarse deep punctures. (After Blatchley)

*Neichnea laticornis* (Say) (7698) with a length of 5-7 mm.; black with mid-stripe on head and sides of thorax orange yellow, is found from Canada to North Carolina and west to Illinois.

Figure 337

3a **First segment of antennae not smaller than second; visible from above. .......................................................4**

**3b** First segment small and hidden from above by overlapping second segment. Fig. 338.

7719 *Orthopleura damicornis* Fab.

Figure 338

LENGTH: 4-9 mm.  RANGE: widely scattered.

Black; thorax reddish yellow, often clouded at front and back.  Elytra sometimes with indistinct pale cross bar at middle.  (After Blatchley)

The eyes are coarsely granulate; the antennae have 11 segments, all but two of which are in the club. The elytra have many coarse punctures.

**4a** Thorax widest behind the middle then rather abruptly constricted. Fig. 339.

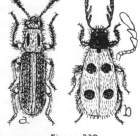

Figure 339

(a) 7716 *Cregya oculatus* Say

LENGTH: 4-6.5 mm.  RANGE: eastern half of the U. S.

Black, shining; thorax and elytra yellow, marked as pictured, with black; legs yellow.  (After Blatchley)

(b) 7702 *Pelonides quadripunctata* Say

LENGTH: 5-7 mm.  RANGE: throughout the North and South Central States.

Black, elytra bright red with 2 black spots as pictured on each wing cover. The antennae have but 10 joints. (After Blatchley)

**4b** Thorax not as in 4a.  Fig. 340.

7708 *Chariessa pilosa* Forst.

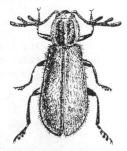

Figure 340

LENGTH: 7-13 mm.  RANGE: Canada to Texas and Florida.

Black, rather dull; thorax reddish with black markings; elytra with dense fine punctures. (Courtesy N. Y. State Museum)

*C. elegans* Horn (7706), is a western species 11-12 mm., pale red with bluish-black elytra.  It ranges from Oregon to California and Texas.

# HETEROMERA

1a Front coxal cavities closed behind. Abdomen with five ventral segments in part grown
   together. Fig. 341a.........2

1b Front coxal cavities open behind. (See fig. 341b or c)....4

Figure 341

2a Tarsal claws comb-like (pectinate) (a), body usually elongate and
   rather soft. (The Comb-clawed Bark Beetles). Fig. 342. Family
   86, ALLECULIDAE.....................................page 208

Figure 342

These mostly medium sized beetles hide under bark
and are also found on flowers and leaves. They are
plain colored, usually brown. Over 100 species are
known but only a few of them usually are seen in
the average collection.

2b Tarsal claws simple..........................................3

3a Next to last segment of tarsi spongy. (Lagriid Bark Beetles). Fig.
   343. Family 88, LAGRIIDAE.

   **12497 *Arthromacra aenea* (Say)**

Figure 343

LENGTH: 9-14 mm.

RANGE: Eastern United States and Canada.

Convex, slender. Above briliant green, blue
coppery or dark brown with metallic sheen; antennae reddish-brown; under parts dark bronze.

The genus *Satira* differs in having large prominent eyes, distinct striations on elytra and head
constricted at the base. *Satira gagatina* Melsh
(12502), 6.5-8 mm. is piceous and rather widely
distributed.

3b Next to last segment of tarsi not spongy. (Darkling Beetles). Fig. 344. (Many Tenebrionids strongly resemble fig. 343. They should be checked carefully for the tarsal characters.) Family 87. TENE-BRIONIDAE. . . . . . . . . . . . . . . . . . . . . . . . . . . . . . . . . . . . . . . . . . . . .page 209

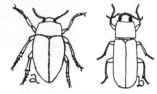

Figure 344

Some species are very common everywhere, but the family really comes into its own west of the Missouri river. The adults are usually active at night. The larvae often resemble wireworms.

4a Head not strongly and suddenly constricted at base. . . . . . . . . . . . .5

4b Head strongly constricted at base, being suddenly narrowed behind. . . . . . . . . . . . . . . . . . . . . . . . . . . . . . . . . . . . . . . . . . . . . . . . . . . .7

5a Middle coxae large; body long and narrow. (Oedemerid Beetles) Fig. 345. Family 36, OEDEMERIDAE. . . . . . . . . . . . . . . . . . .page 142

Figure 345

Only a few species of this family of some 800 (world-wide), seem at all common in our area. Some are dull colored, others are bright, sometimes metallic. Some of them are crepuscular or nocturnal in their visit to flowers.

5b Middle coxae not prominent. . . . . . . . . . . . . . . . . . . . . . . . . . . . . . . .6

6a Mesosternum long; epimera of metathorax visible. (Melandryid Bark Beetles). Fig. 346. Family 90, MELANDRYIDAE. . . . .page 222

Figure 346

Several members of this small family are common under bark. They are easily confused with the Tenebrionids and should be checked carefully.

6b Mesosternum quadrate; epimera of metathorax covered. (Flat Bark Beetles). Fig. 347. Family 72, CUCUJIDAE. . . . . . . . . . . . . page 186

Figure 347

The members of this fairly sizable family are so varied that the family appears several places in the key. The beginner can readily recognize some members at sight; if at all in doubt the specimen should be checked carefully. It is only the males of some species which have the 5-5-4 formula for their tarsae.

7a Side pieces of prothorax not separated from the pronotum by a suture. Base of prothorax narrower than elytra. . . . . . . . . . . . . . . 8

7b Lateral suture of prothorax distinct; base of prothorax as wide as elytra. Antennae filiform. Fig. 348. . . . . . . . . 13

Figure 348

8a Hind coxae large and prominent. . . . . . . . . . . . . . . . . . . . . . . . . . . . . 9

8b Hind coxae but slightly prominent, if at all. . . . . . . . . . . . . . . . . . . 10

9a Tarsal claws simple; head horizontal. (Fire-colored Beetles). Fig. 349. Family 43, PYROCHROIDAE. . . . . . . . . . . . . . . . . . . . . . . page 153

Figure 349

The members of this small family often have a red or reddish thorax contrasting with the blackish elytra.

9b Front vertical. Claws toothed or cleft. (See Fig. 350A) (Blister Beetle.) Fig. 350B. Family 39, MELOIDAE. . . . . . . . . . . . . . . . . . . . . . . . . . page 148

Figure 350a

Figure 350 b

9b Front vertical. Claws toothed or cleft. (See Fig. 350A) (Blister Beetle.) Fig. 350B. Family 39, MELOIDAE. . . . . . . . . . . . . . . . . . . . . . . . . . page 148

These beetles are usually so well known and so characteristically shaped as to be readily recognized. The colors are generally somber though a few display more brilliant colors and metallic hues.

HOW TO KNOW THE BEETLES

10a Anterior coxae globular, not prominent. (Flat Bark Beetles). See
    fig. 347. Family 72, CUCUJIDAE.....................page 186

10b Anterior coxae conical, prominent...........................11

11a Eyes usually with a notch in their edge (emarginate), finely gran-
    ulated; hind coxae touching or very close. (Pedilid Beetles). Fig.
    351. Family 44, PEDILIDAE.........................page 154

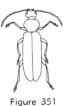

These almost always black cylindrical beetles,
usually are ornamented with yellow or red on the
thorax. There are not many species but some are
quite common.

Figure 351

11b Eyes entire (not notched), rather coarsely granulated; hind coxae
    usually separated...............................................12

12a Second joint of tarsi lobed beneath; tibia without spurs; last joint
    of labial palpi large and often dilated. (Euglenid Beetles)  Fig. 352.
    Family 46, EUGLENIDAE.

8484 *Zonantes fasciatus* (Melsh.)

LENGTH: 2-2.5 mm.  RANGE: Eastern half U. S.

Black. Legs, antenna, palpi and tips of elytra
dull yellow; elytra marked with reddish-yellow as
pictured; with long coarse but thinly scattered pubescence. On flowers and foliage.

*Phomalis brunnipennis* (Lec.) (8487) with length
of 2 mm. or less is dark brown. The head, thorax
and middle and hind legs are piceous with short
dense yellowish-gray pubescence. It is widely scattered but not common.

Figure 352

12b Not as in 12a. (Ant-like Flower Beetles). Fig. 353. Family 45,
    ANTHICIDAE. ....................................page 155

These little mostly brown or blackish beetles
are ant size and shaped somewhat like ants.
They are often very abundant in flowers,
particularly in the spring and early summer.
Several species have a forward projecting
process (a) from the thorax, but many others
do not have it at all.

Figure 353

13a Hind coxae not plate-like. (Melandryid Bark Beetles). Fig. 354. Family 90, MELANDRYIDAE.........................page 222

Figure 354

These beetles are usually black or brown and are found in dry fungi or under bark. The last segment of the palpi is usually hatchet-shaped.

13b Hind coxae plate-like, abdomen usually pointed. (See fig. 355a)..14

14a Prothorax with a sharp marginal ridge at sides (Tumbling Flower Beetles). Fig. 355. Family 37, MORDELLIDAE.........page 143

Figure 355

These usually small black or brown beetles are often prettily marked with black or white and ornamented with a close fitting silky pubescence. Their tumbling about when disturbed and their wedge shape make them easily recognized.

14b Prothorax rounded, without a sharp edge. (Rhipiphorid Beetles). Fig. 356. Family 38, RHIPIPHORIDAE..................page 147

Figure 356

These beetles, usually somewhat larger than the Mordellids are often neatly marked with black and yellow.

## Family 36   OEDEMERIDAE
### The Oedemerid Beetles

Some sixty species of this family are known in our region; 800 world wide. They are elongate and soft bodied. They often visit flowers, flying in the twilight or at night. Some may be also found under debris or on decaying stumps and logs.

1a Front tibiae with one spur; brownish yellow with black at tip of elytron. Fig. 357.

7763 *Nacerda melanura* (L)

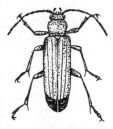

LENGTH: 8-12 mm. RANGE: throughout our country (also Europe and Asia, its original home). Dull yellow above marked on elytron as pictured, with blue-black; under parts dusky; four elevated lines on each elytron. It breeds in coniferous timber and causes considerable damage.

Figure 357

1b Front tibiae with two spurs; claws toothed at base. Fig. 358.

7739 *Asclera puncticollis* (Say)

LENGTH: 6.5-8 mm. RANGE: Central States.
Dull black; thorax entirely red and smooth except 3 fovea and a row of punctures near the base. Elytra each with three longitudinal ridges.
*Copidita thoracica* (Fab.) (7769), 5-7 mm. with thorax reddish-yellow; elytra purplish or blue and other parts piceous, ranges through the Central and Southern States.

Figure 358

## Family 37  MORDELLIDAE
### The Tumbling Flower Beetles

Few insects do a better job living up to their name than these. For the most part rather small wedge or spike shaped beetles, they live as adults feeding among flowers but when disturbed kick and tumble in all directions. We have a good 150 species; the world some 800.

1a Abdomen with last segment prolonged, cone-shaped, (see "a" fig. 361); tarsal claws cleft......................................................2

143

1b Abdomen not prolonged at tip; tarsal claws not cleft. Fig. 359.
7943 *Anaspis rufa* Say

Figure 359

LENGTH: 3-4 mm. RANGE: widely distributed.

Thorax one-half wider than long; head yellow or sometimes dull; abdomen and antennae fuscous or dull yellow.

*Pentaria trifasciatus* Melsh. (7931), has its fourth tarsal segment of front and middle legs as long as third instead of very small as in the above. The elytra are yellow with base, tips and wide middle cross-band, black.

2a Hind tibiae with only a small subapical ridge; eyes finely granulate. . . . . . . . . . . . . . . . . . . . . . . . . . . . . . . . . . . . . . . . . . . . . . . . . . . . . . . .5

2b Hind tibiae and tarsi with oblique ridges on their outer face; eyes coarsely granulate. . . . . . . . . . . . . . . . . . . . . . . . . . . . . . . . . . . . . . . . . . . . .3

3a Hind tibiae with but two oblique ridges on outer face, which are equal in length and parallel. . . . . . . . . . . . . . . . . . . . . . . . . . . . . . . . . . . .4

3b Hind tibiae with three short, oblique parallel ridges. Fig. 360.
7886 *Mordellistena sexnotata* Dury

Figure 360

LENGTH: 3 mm. RANGE: Iowa to Ohio.

Brownish yellow, marked as pictured with dark brown; first segment of hind tarsi with two oblique ridges and the second segment with but one.

*M. pubescence* Fab. (7910), (3 mm.) is characterized by four oblique ridges on the hind tibiae. It is black with a brownish pubescence. The elytra are marked with a humeral lunule and two bands of yellow pubescence. It has a wide range.

*M. marginalis* (Say) (7901), measuring 3-4 mm., is black with head and thorax reddish-yellow (frequently the head has a black spot and the thorax some black markings). It ranges widely and is often abundant.

**4a (a, b, c)** First segment of hind tarsi with two oblique ridges and second segment with one ridge. Fig. 361.

7848 *Mordellistena vapida* Lec.

Figure 361

LENGTH: 2-3.5 mm.   RANGE: eastern half of the U. S.

Clay yellow with scattered long yellow pubescence; elytra often darker at apical third.

*M. lutea* (Melsh.) (7837), (2.8-3.2 mm.) and ranging throughout the eastern half of the United States is characterized by converging instead of parallel ridges on the hind tibiae. It is brownish yellow and thickly covered with yellow pubescence.

**4b** First segment of hind tarsi with three oblique ridges; second segments with two ridges; head black; elytra with a humeral spot. Fig. 362.

7858 *Mordellistena scapularis* (Say)

Figure 362

LENGTH: 4 mm.   RANGE: western two-thirds of the U. S.

Black; elytra marked with reddish humeral spot as pictured. In *M. splendens* Smith (7883), the ridges on the tibiae are unequal and the first segment of hind tarsus has 4 ridges. It is very slender, 6 mm. long, piceous, clothed with a silvery pubescence and ranges from Iowa to Florida.

**4c** As in 4b except that head is red or reddish and elytra without a distinct humeral spot. Fig. 363.

7859 *Mordellistena comata* (Lec.)

Figure 363

LENGTH: 2.8-3.3 mm.   RANGE: much of the U. S.

Body black; head mostly or wholly reddish; thorax brick-red, often with an oblong black spot near its base; legs in part dull yellow.

*M. aspersa* (Melsh.) (7860) a widely distributed species, differs from the above, having its head and thorax black. It is a bit smaller and is covered with a brownish-gray pubescence.

145

5a Anal style long and slender; scutellum triangular..............6

5b Anal style short and blunt; scutellum notched behind. Fig. 364.

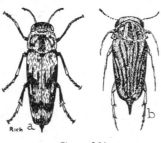

Figure 364

(a) 7804 *Tomoxia bidentata* (Say)
LENGTH: 10-13 mm. RANGE: over
much of the U. S.

Brown, marked with pattern as pictured with ash-gray pubescence.

(b) 7805 *T. lineela* Lec.
LENGTH: 5-7 mm. RANGE: Much of
the U. S.

Brown with markings of ash-gray
as pictured. (Courtesy N. Y. State
Museum)

*Glipa hilaris* (Say) (7807), (9-13
mm.), ranges widely over the United
States. It is black with a pattern of
ash-gray pubescence. Two brownish
yellow pubescent bands, each margined with gray cross the elytra.

6a Elytra with four yellowish pubescent spots. Fig. 365.

7814 *Mordella octopunctata* Fab.

Figure 365

LENGTH: 6-7 mm. RANGE: much of the U. S.

Fairly common. Black, marked as pictured with
yellowish pubescence; under parts spotted with ash-gray pubescence. (Courtesy N. Y. State Museum.)

*M. discoidea* Melsh. (7827) 2-3 mm. long and ranging through the Central and Southern States is black
with legs, antennae and top of head yellow. The
elytra have a large humeral spot, a band back of the
middle and the tips yellow; the yellow thorax has a
center spot of black.

6b Elytra with numerous spots and patches of yellowish pubescence.
Fig. 366.

7819 *Mordella serval* Say

Figure 366

LENGTH: 4-4.5 mm. RANGE: Central and Eastern States.

Piceous brown; thorax and elytra mottled as
pictured with yellowish pubescence; front legs
and antennae dull yellow.

*M. marginata* Melsh. (7817), 3-4.5 mm. long and
common over a wide range, is black with variable markings of silver hairs on thorax and
elytra.

# Family 38 RHIPIPHORIDAE
## The Rhipiphorid Beetles

The members of this small family are wedge shaped and rather closely resemble the Mordellids. The antennae are often fan shaped in the males and usually serrate with the females. The adults are found on flowers and under bark or under dead logs; the larvae seem to parasite other insects.

1a Elytra not much shorter than abdomen, often falling away and leaving the membranous wings uncovered; lobe at base of thorax covering scutellum; claws two-toothed. Fig. 367.

7956 *Macrosiagon limbatum* (Fab.)

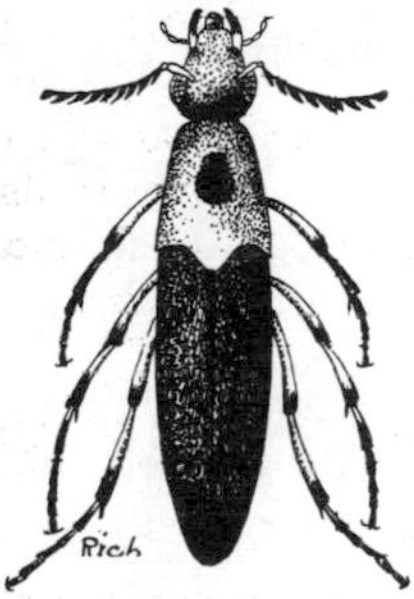

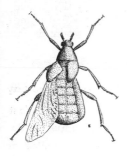

Figure 367

LENGTH: 6-10 mm.  RANGE: Eastern half of U. S.

Head, thorax, under surface, femora and middle and hind tibiae reddish yellow; thorax with oval black spot on disk. Elytra either entirely black or with pale yellow at centers.

*M. dimidiatum* (Fab.) (7950) with about the same range and size, differs in that the front coxae are not separated by a narrow prosternum, and the insect is black with pale yellow elytra which are blackened at the tips. It may be often found on the flowers of Mountain Mint.

1b Elytra very small; thorax not covering the scutellum. Fig. 368.

7967 *Rhipiphorus fasciatus* (Say)

LENGTH: 4-6 mm.  RANGE: Central to north eastern U. S.

Black. Legs and elytra yellowish. Vertex prominent with a median carina. Thorax conical with a median impressed line, densely punctate. Elytra widely separated and only 1/3 as long as abdomen.

*Rhipidius pectinicornis* Thunb. (7970½) with poorly developed mouth parts and the adult female being larviform, parasites the German Cockroach.

Figure 368

*Pelecotoma flavipes* Melsh. (7946) at the other extreme has full length elytra. It is black with yellowish antennae and legs. It ranges throughout the eastern United States and measures 4.5 mm.

147

# Family 39  MELOIDAE
## The Blister Beetles

Many of these medium to larger beetles produce *cantharidine* which blisters human skin and has been used medicinally. The antennae · of the males often have some curiously enlarged segments. The adults are usually plant feeders but the larvae which pass through several stages frequently feed on the eggs of other insects. Black, gray and brown are the common colors. More than 200 species are cataloged by Leng while around 2500 species are known for the whole world.

**1a Elytra short and overlapping, leaving much of the large soft abdomen exposed; no inner wings. Fig. 369.**

8148 *Meloe americanus* Leach

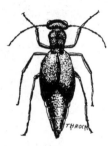

Figure 369

LENGTH: 15-24 mm.  RANGE: eastern half of U. S.

Bluish black and shining throughout. Thorax about equal in length and width, coarsely and deeply punctured.

These "oil beetles" of which there are some 15 species known to our country are clumsy insects, and are usually found in early spring or late autumn. *M. impressus* Kby. (8142) is somewhat smaller and dull black.

*M. angusticollis* Say (8147), 12-15 mm. long and widely distributed, has dark blue head and thorax with elytra and abdomen violet tinted. The thorax is about one-half longer than wide, but only two-thirds the width of the head.

**1b Elytra of normal length; wings usually present..................2**

**2a Mandibles projecting beyond the labrum, acute at tip; upper blade of claw serrate................................................9**

**2b Mandibles not reaching beyond the labrum, obtuse at tip; antennae not thickened towards tip......................................3**

**3a Antennae of moderate length; tarsal claws cleft to base..........4**

**3b Antennae rather short; tarsal claws with a short strong tooth. Fig. 370.**

8116 *Tegrodera erosa* Lec. Soldier Beetle.

LENGTH: 16-30 mm. RANGE: the desert areas of our Southwest.

Head and prothorax red, the latter dusky; other parts shining black except the reticulations on the elytra which are golden.

*T. latecincta* Horn (8117), having much the same range, is distinguished by the greater areas of black on the elytra. Both species are pests in alfalfa fields.

Figure 370

**4a Antenna heavy at apex, segments spherical (moniliform).........5**

**4b Antenna filiform..............................................6**

**5a Labrum with a deep notch. Fig. 371.**

7990 *Pomphopoea sayi* Lec.

LENGTH: 15-18 mm. RANGE: middle U. S. and Canada.

Elytra glabrous, bronzed; legs and under parts blue-black. Taken on flowers of serviceberry, apple, etc.

*Pyrota engelmanni* (Lec.) (7973), ranging from Indiana to the Southwest, is dull yellow with six black spots on the thorax and three black bars on the elytra. It attains a length of 20 mm.

Figure 371

*Pomphopoea aenea* (Say) (7993) is a rather handsome beetle. It is 10-16 mm. long. The head, thorax and under surface are greenish and covered with long gray hairs; elytra bronzed; antennae black; legs reddish-yellow with black knees. It is found on blossoms of apple and related plants and ranges widely.

149

**5b Labrum with only a shallow notch. Fig. 372.**

**8066** *Lytta nuttalli* **(Say). Nuttall's Blister Beetle.**

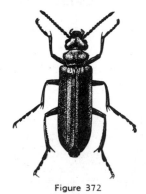

LENGTH: 16-28 mm. RANGE: Rocky Mt. region.

Metallic green often with purplish sheen; beautiful but very destructive. (U.S.D.A.)

Several other members of this genus are troublesome throughout the west. The "Infernal Blister Beetle" *L. stygica* (Lec.) (8088) 9-14 mm., ranges in spring along the West Coast while the "Green Blister Beetle" *L. cyanipennis* Lec. (8067) 13-18 mm. is a western pest of leguminous crops. Both of these are green or bluish. *L. inseparata* Horn (8078) 15-20 mm., which destroys sugar beets in California, is black.

Figure 372

**6a First antennal segment much enlarged. Fig. 373.**

**(a) 8042** *Epicauta murina* **Lec. Ash-gray Blister Beetle.**

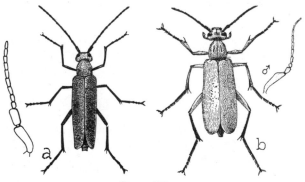

LENGTH: 8-15 mm. RANGE: Middle and eastern U. S. and Canada.

Black, densely clothed with grayish hairs; thorax

Figure 373

slightly longer than broad, both first and second joints of male antennae much thickened as pictured. A common garden pest. (U.S.D.A.)

**(b) 8036** *E. albida* **(Say). Two-spotted Blister Beetle.**
LENGTH: 14-20 mm. RANGE: west of Missouri river.

Gray or yellowish, the thorax marked with two nearly parallel lines; antennae of male as pictured. A serious pest of sugar beets, and garden crops. (U.S.D.A.)

*E. torsa* (Lec.) (8041), black, thinly clothed with grayish pubescence, 11-15 mm. long, should be readily determined by the somewhat S-shaped first antennal segment of the males. In the females the second antennal segment is a bit longer than the third. It has been taken from Texas eastward.

**6b First antennal segments of moderate length; mandibles short.....7**

7a (a, b, c) Elytra wholly black. Fig. 374.

8033 *Epicauta pennsylvanica* (DeG.). Black Blister Beetle.

LENGTH: 7-13 mm. RANGE: most of U. S.

Dull black throughout. Thorax quadrate with front angles rounded. Very common on goldenrod and other autumn plants. (U.S.D.A.)

*E. atrata* (Fab.) averaging smaller than the preceding may be readily distinguished by its red head. It seems to largely limit its attention to *Coreopsis palmata* on which it may be usually found.

Figure 374

*E. puncticollis* (Mann.) (7997), 7-11 mm. in length and ranging throughout our Pacific coast states has a bluish sheen.

7b Elytra clay-yellow with black stripes. Fig. 375.

8018 *Epicauta vittata* Fab. Striped Blister Beetle.

LENGTH: 12-18 mm. RANGE: Central and N.E. U. S. and Canada.

Under parts black, head, thorax and elytra clay-yellow; each elytron with 2 black stripes; head wider than thorax.

This "old fashioned potato bug" is a serious pest to gardens. (U.S.D.A.)

The Three-lined Blister Beetle *E. lemniscata* Fab. (8019) is distinguished from the former by a third black strip on the elytra. It ranges throughout our Southern States.

Figure 375

*E. ferruginea* (Say) (8004) is smaller, 4-9 mm., and principally western in its wide range. Clay-yellow hairs (sometimes gray) cover the black elytra. The other parts are black.

7c Elytra in part at least, gray.....................................8

151

8a Elytra with numerous fine black spots. Fig. 376.

8017 *Epicauta maculata* (Say). Spotted Blister Beetle.

LENGTH: 10-14 mm. RANGE: west of Missouri River.

Entirely black but so covered with ash gray hairs that only numerous spots on the elytra show black. It is a pest of sugar beet, potato and clover. (U.S. D.A.)

*E. pardalis* Lec. (8016), 10 mm. in length, is black with many white spots and short lines on its upper surface. It ranges throughout the West and into Mexico.

Figure 376

8b Elytra wholly gray or black, entirely margined with gray as pictured. Fig. 377.

(a) 8024 *Epicauta cinerea* (Forst.). Gray Blister Beetle.

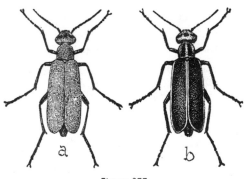

Figure 377

LENGTH: 10-18 mm.

RANGE: Central and N.E. U. S. and Canada.

Robust. Black, clothed with gray hairs throughout. (U.S.D.A.)

(b) 8024a The Margined Blister Beetle with elytra mostly black, and a black spot on thorax is designated by Leng as a variety, *marginata* (Fab.) of the preceding. S o m e would count the two as distinct species. Relationships of this sort may be accurately determined only by careful breeding experiments. Regardless of name of species status, they are both serious garden pests. (U.S.D.A.)

*E. trichrus* (Pall.) (7998) 8-11 mm., is black with fairly thick black pubescence with gray hairs making a marginal stripe and often one on the suture of the elytra. The head may be red back of the eyes, or with a small red spot in front, or it may be wholly black. It ranges from Texas to the Atlantic and into Canada.

9a Outer lobe of maxilla bristle-like and prolonged.  Fig. 378.

8191 *Zonitis vittigera* Lec.

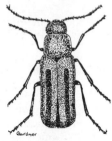

Figure 378

LENGTH: 9-11 mm.  RANGE: Central and Western States.

Reddish-yellow; elytra usually with broad discal black stripe; antennae, tibia and tarsi blackish.

Z. *immaculata* Say (8185), similar in shape and size but wholly pale greenish-yellow, seems to confine itself to flowers of the tar weed, *Grindelia squarrosa*.  It ranges largely west of the Missouri river into the Rocky Mt. area, but is found in prairie areas of Iowa and Minnesota.

Z. *punctulata flavipennis* (Uhler) (8180a) measuring 8-11 mm., is orange-yellow, thinly covered with yellow hairs.  Much of the underparts and of the antennae and tarsi is blackish.  The front of the head is flattened and finely punctate.  The sides of the thorax are straight or nearly so, its disk with scattered coarse punctations.  The typical form (8180) is brownish-yellow with a black stripe on each elytron.

9b Outer lobe of maxilla not prolonged.  Fig. 379.

8158 *Zonitus bilineata* Say

Figure 379

LENGTH: 7 9 mm.  RANGE: Middle and eastern U. S.

Robust, dull brownish-yellow; elytra yellowish-white each with a median blackish stripe not fully reaching base or apex.

Z. *rufa* Lec. (8163), similar in size and shape, is reddish-brown throughout.  It is a native of Texas.

## Family 43  PYROCHROIDAE
### The Fire-colored Beetles

These medium sized soft bodied beetles usually have some "fire color" on them, hence the name.  They are often found under bark.  The family is small with less than a score of species known for our region.

1a Eyes very large, almost touching. Fig. 380.

8225 *Dendroides canadensis* Latr.

Figure 380

LENGTH: 9-13 mm. RANGE: Widely distributed in U. S. and Canada.

Reddish yellow; head, antennae and elytra, piceous; the antennal branches are much longer in the male.

*D. concolor* Newn. (8226) ranging throughout the eastern half of the United States and Canada and about the same size, is pale brownish-yellow throughout.

1b Eyes normal in size and well separated. Fig. 381.

8221 *Neopyrochroa femoralis* Lec.

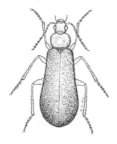

Figure 381

LENGTH: 14-17 mm. RANGE: Widely distributed.

Head and thorax yellowish-red, elytra bluish-black with scattered sub-erect pubescence, shining; under surface, tibiae, tarsi and palpi blackish.

*N. flabellata* Fab. (8220) attains the same size. It is reddish throughout except the elytra and most of the antennae which are black. The thorax is wider than in the above.

Two other genera belong to this small family. *Ischalia costata* (Lec.) (8218) 5 mm., is dull brownish-yellow; the elytra have a pale stripe on the sides and the tips are pale. The antennae are simple.

*Schizotus cervicalis* Newn. (8224) 7 mm., is blackish; front of head, the thorax and sutural and marginal lines on the elytra reddish. The antennae bear branches.

## Family 44 PEDILIDAE
### The Pedilid Beetles

These rather small, usually black elongate cylindrical beetles number some 50 known species in North America. They were formerly included with the Anthicidae. They may be frequently found on the flowers of various plants, sometimes under leaves and, of course, are often taken in the sweeping net.

154

1a **Neck wide; eyes large. Fig. 382.**

8250 *Pedilus labiatus* (Say)

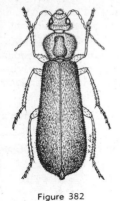

LENGTH: 6-8 mm.   RANGE: Eastern two-thirds of U. S.

Piceous black, feebly shining; palpi, clypeus and labrum and first two segments of antennae pale yellow; thorax marked as pictured with reddish-yellow.

*P. lugubris* (Say) (8251) 6-8 mm., is wholly black except the first two antennal segments and the labrum which are reddish-brown. It ranges through Central Canada and the United States.

*P. terminalis* (Say) (8245) (5-7 mm.) has a wholly red thorax.

Figure 382

1b **Neck narrow; less than 5 mm. long.   Fig. 383.**

8278 *Macratria confusa* Lec.

LENGTH: 4-4.5 mm.   RANGE: Iowa to Conn.

Dark gray thickly covered with yellowish silky hairs; antennae and legs dull yellow.

*Stereopalpus mellyi* Laf. (8824) (7-8 mm.) ranges from Iowa to the Atlantic. The head is the same width as the thorax. The color is fuscous, modified with a dense grayish pubescence.

Figure 383

# Family 45   ANTHICIDAE
## The Ant-like Flower Beetles

The members of this fairly large family are mostly small sized beetles. They are often abundant on flowers and may be taken in large numbers with the sweeping net. Several species have a peculiar horn-like structure projecting forward on the thorax.

1a **Thorax with horn-like part projecting forward over the head.   See Fig. 384.** ..................................................2

1b **Thorax normal, not as in 1a.** ...................................3

2a Elytra pale with dark cross bar back of middle, horn broad with fine teeth on its sides. Fig. 384.

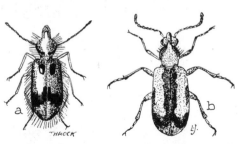

Figure 384

(a) 8304 *Notoxus monodon* Fab.

LENGTH: 2.5-4 mm. RANGE: coast to coast; abundant.

Dull brownish-yellow; thorax and elytra with piceous marks as pictured; elytra pubescent with both long and short hairs.

(b) 8302 *N. anchora* Hentz

LENGTH: 3-3.5 mm. RANGE: Atlantic coast west to Colorado.

Reddish-yellow with darker markings as pictured. (Courtesy N. Y. State Museum).

*N. constrictus* Csy. (8309), a similar species is known as the Fruit *Notoxus* in California and is common in orchards.

*Mecynotarsus candidus* Lec. (8322) (2 mm.) differs from Notoxus in having the tarsi longer than the tibiae. It is uniform dull yellow and widely distributed.

2b Elytra dark with oblique pale spots. Fig. 385.

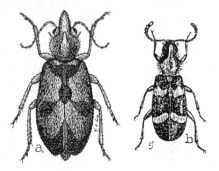

Figure 385

(a) 8285 *Notoxus talpa* Laf.

LENGTH: 3.5-4 mm. RANGE: the Rockies and eastward.

Thorax, antennae and legs dull reddish-brown; head, undersurface and elytra piceous; elytra with paler, somewhat pinkish spots as shown.

(b) 8289 *N. bifasciatus* Lec.

LENGTH: 3-4 mm. RANGE: Canada to Arizona.

Shining, piceous; legs and antennae reddish brown; elytra with pale bars as pictured. (Courtesy N. Y. State Museum.)

*N. bicolor* Say (8283) (3.5 mm.) ranging in the eastern third of the United States has its head fuscous, thorax, legs and undersurface reddish-yellow and elytra purplish-black with prostrate gray pubescence.

3a Sides of mesosternum more or less abnormally dilated...........4

3b Sides of mesosternum straight, slightly oblique and coming to a point; not dilated..............................................6

4a Thorax much constricted or narrowed behind the middle.........5

**4b Thorax not narrowed except slightly so, near its base; femora club shaped. Fig. 386.**

8387 *Anthicus floralis* (L.)

Figure 386

LENGTH: 3-3.5 mm. RANGE: A European species scattered world wide.

Reddish-brown, shining; head, abdomen and apical two-thirds of elytra piceous.

*A. rixator* Csy. (8390), a closely related species ranges through the Southwest.

**5a Antennae long and slender; constriction of thorax not extending across its upper side. Fig. 387.**

8359 *Anthicus sturmii* Laf.

LENGTH: 2.5-3 mm. RANGE: Iowa to Conn.
Dark reddish-brown, covered with fine pubescence. Elytra piceous, the basal third reddish and marked with a crossband of longer gray pubescence. Sub-basal impressions of elytra distinct.

*A. formicarius* Laf. (8347) (3-4 mm.) ranging rather widely is reddish-brown. It differs from the above in having the last joint of the maxillary palpi small and hatchet-shaped instead of large and dilated as in the preceding.

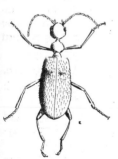

Figure 387

*A cinctus* Say (8348) measures 3-4 mm. in length. It is shining, dark reddish-brown; the elytra are black with a reddish base; a pale transverse band in front of the middle, is broken at the suture. The thorax is narrower than the head and much longer than wide. It belongs to the Central States.

*A. obscurus* Laf. (8353) measuring 3 mm. or less, is shining black. Pale coarse hairs cover the basal third of elytra; other parts have fine pubescence.

The thorax is constricted near its base and is widest at its middle. Its known range is from Indiana eastward.

157

**5b Antennae thick, bead-like; constriction of thorax extending across the dorsal surface. Fig. 388.**

8334 *Tomoderus constrictus* (Say)

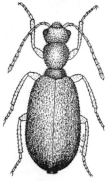

LENGTH: 2.5-3 mm. RANGE: Iowa to Florida and New York. Common.

Dark reddish-brown to piceous, shining; legs paler; elytra more piceous at apex.

*Dilandius myrmecops* Csy. (8331), looks very much like an ant. It is almost 3 mm. long, black with very short pubescence. The elytra have two light brown cross bars and an oblique band of silvery hairs.

Figure 388

**6a Thorax evenly convex, moderately large. Fig. 389.**

8417 *Anthicus cervinus* Laf.

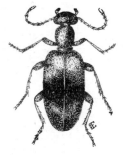

LENGTH: 2.4-2.7 mm. RANGE: Eastern half U. S. Common.

Reddish-brown, feebly shining with scant fine pubescence; antennae and legs dull yellow; elytra marked as pictured with piceous.

*A. pubescens* Laf. (8454) (2.7-3 mm.) and ranging through the eastern half of the U. S., has its thorax wider than long and elytra more than twice as wide as the thorax. It is black or dark brown with yellowish hairs.

Figure 389

**6b Thorax abruptly sloping and flattened in front; head triangular. Fig. 390.**

8342 *Amblyderus pallens* (Lec.)

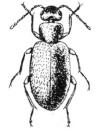

LENGTH: 2.7-3 mm. RANGE: Eastern half U. S.

Dull pale yellow throughout and covered densely with short coarse yellowish pubescence.

Blatchley calls attention to its protective coloration, being scarcely visible in its natural sandy habitat. (After Blatchley)

Figure 390

158

# Family 50  RHIPICERIDAE
## The Cedar Beetles

These members of a small family are characterized by the fan-shaped antennae of the males (usually serrate in the females). They are found under bark and logs but are rather rare at best.

1a Tarsi not lobed; antennae serrate, moderately long. Fig. 391.

8543 *Zenoa picea* (Beauv.)

LENGTH: 11-15 mm.  RANGE: Indiana to Florida.

Dark reddish or blackish-brown. Elytra each with four raised lines and a short oblique raised line on each side of the scutellum. Found under bark and in logs in dry woods. (After Horn)

Figure 391

1b Tarsi with distinct lobes; antennae flabellate in male, serrate in female; short. Fig. 392.

8546 *Sandalus niger* Knoch

LENGTH: 21-24 mm.  RANGE: North and South Central States.

Black, somewhat shining; elytra about twice the width of thorax, with faint ridges.

*S. petrophya* Knoch (8544), with a length of 12-17 mm. and ranging through the eastern one-third of the United States is dark reddish-brown to black. The male is noticeably smaller than the female.

A new family, SANDALIDAE has been erected for the genus *Sandalus* because of the larval characters. Many changes like this will doubtless be made as the study of immature insects is pursued further.

Figure 392

# Family 51  ELATERIDAE
## The Click Beetles

Some 8000 species are included in this large family. The larvae are slender, hard-shelled and are known as wireworms. The adults are of many colors, some beautifully marked, and vary much in size. Their ability to snap themselves into the air and presently land on their feet has given them the names of Snapping beetles, Skipjacks, etc.

1a Prothorax with deep antennal grooves on under side, made by the separation of prosternal sutures......................................2

1b Without antennal grooves on under side of thorax as in 1a.......4

2a All or nearly all of the prosternal suture forming the antennal groove; third and fourth antennal segments of equal length..............3

2b Antennal groove shortened behind; front tarsi in grooves at rest. Fig. 393.                    8564 *Lacon rectangularis* (Say)

LENGTH: 8–10 mm. RANGE: Eastern half of United States.

Dull sooty brown, sparsely clothed with short stiff whitish hairs. Antennae paler; legs reddish-brown. Elytra with rows of rather distant medium sized punctures, intervals wider than the striae, flat. (After Blatchley)

Two other species of this genus are known, one found in the Southern States and the other in California.

Figure 393

3a Front tarsi when at rest in deep grooves. Elytra spotted with brown and yellow scales. Fig. 394.        8560 *Adelocera marmorata* (Fab.)

LENGTH: 15-18 mm. RANGE: Central, eastern and southern states.

Dark reddish-brown, dull marked as pictured with dull yellow scales. Gregarious under the bark of dead trees.

Similar in color but smaller (9-12 mm.) and having its elytral punctures in rows instead of scattered, *A. impressicollis* (Say) (8554) is widely scattered throughout the United States.

Figure 394

**3b** Tarsal grooves shallow, head and sides of thorax densely covered with golden scales. Fig. 395.    8561 *Adelocera discoidea* (Web.)

LENGTH: 8-11 mm.  RANGE: Eastern half of United States.

Black, feebly shining, head and margins of thorax covered with golden scales.  Elytra and body coarsely and densely punctured.

Figure 395

**4a** Claws with one or more bristles at the base; two large velvety oval "eye-spots" on pronotum. Fig. 396.
    8571 *Alaus oculatus* (L.) The Eyed Click Beetle

LENGTH: 25-45 mm.  RANGE: Eastern United States west to Rockies.

Black shining, sprinkled with silvery-white scales.

This is one of the beetles your friends keep bringing to you.  It is fairly common and never fails to arouse interest.  The larvae, big husky wireworms, feed in decaying logs and the adults may be found there.  Others fly to lights.

There are seven species of the genus.  In the West *Alaus melanops* Lec. (8574) (28-35 mm.) a dull black species with less white markings, is prevalent. *Alaus lusciosus* Hope (8569) about 45 mm. long with round eye-spots is native of Arizona while *Alaus myops* (Fab.) (8572) 24-40 mm. and duller than *oculatus* is native of our Southern States.

Figure 396

**4b** No bristles at base of claws......................................5

**5a** Anterior of front with a margin................................6

**5b** Anterior of front without a margin.........................11

**6a (a, b, c) The claws pectinate (with comb-like teeth). Fig. 397.**
9036 *Melanotus fissilis* (Say)

Figure 397

LENGTH: 13-17 mm. RANGE: the entire United States.

Dark smoky brown with scattered pubescence. Third joint of antennae more than twice as long as the second but shorter than the third. The members of this genus are very difficult to separate. Their larvae are some of our most destructive wire worms. (After Forbes)

*Melanotus castanipes* (Payk.) (9015) is larger (18-21 mm.) and seems to be pretty much distributed through the Northern Hemisphere. It is dark reddish-brown. Its second and third antennal joints are about equal.

**6b Claws not pectinate; the coxal plates gradually expanded inward...7**

**6c Claws not pectinate; the coxal plates suddenly and strongly expanded inward. .................................................8**

**7a Front margined, prosternal groove single and closed in front. Fig. 398.**
8668 *Athous scapularis* (Say)

Figure 398

LENGTH: 9-11 mm. RANGE: middle and eastern United States.

Dull black with fine scattered pubescence; thorax and elytra marked with reddish-yellow as pictured. (After Blatchley)

*Athous brightwelli* Kby. (8662) is larger 11-18 mm. and may likely be found throughout much of the United States east of the Rockies. It is pale dull brown with scattered yellowish hairs.

**7b Front not margined; clypeus truncate. Fig. 399.**

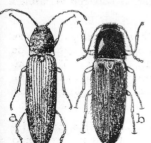

(a) 8639 *Nothodes dubitans* (Lec.)

LENGTH: 11-13 mm. RANGE: Central and eastern United States.

Dull blackish-brown, often with a bronze sheen; rather thickly clothed with yellowish hairs; elytral intervals densely punctate. This is the only species of its genus. (After Blatchley)

(b) 8650 *Pheletes ectypus* (Say)

LENGTH: 9-11 mm. RANGE: Eastern U. S.

Thorax shining black; elytra sooty brown. (U.S.D.A.)

Figure 399

*P. californicus* Mann. (8647) a rather closely related species is the Sugar Beet Wireworm in its larval state. The adult is brown and 9-11 mm. in length. Its range is in the Southwest.

**8a Prosternal suture if present bent outward; second and third tarsae lobed. Fig. 400.** 8834 *Hypnoidus choris* (Say)

LENGTH: 3-5 mm. RANGE: Central and eastern United States.

Black with scattered yellow hairs; elytra marked with yellow as pictured. It seems to prefer sandy localities. (After Blatchley)

*Oedostethus femoralis* Lec. (8850) 4-6 mm. long and ranging widely in the United States and Canada is wholly black with scattered yellow hairs. Its claws are toothed whereas those of the preceding are simple. It is the only member of its genus.

Figure 400

*H. obliquatulus* (Melsh.) (8848) 2.3-2.7 mm., is rather dull piceous with an oblique yellowish band at middle of each elytron and an oval yellow spot at the tip. It is known from Iowa and points on eastward.

**8b Prosternal suture straight or bent slightly inward..................9**

**9a (a, b, c) Fourth tarsal segment lobed, first antennal segment longer than usual. Fig. 401.**

**(a) 8601 Conoderus vespertinus (Fab.) Tobacco Wireworm**

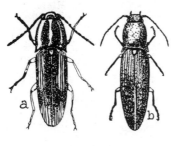

Figure 401

LENGTH: 7-10 mm. RANGE: widely scattered.

Usually yellowish marked with brown or occasionally marked with nearly black. Scutellum always light. Elytra with punctate striae. The larvae feed on beans and cotton.

**(b) 8596 Conoderus lividus (De G.)**

LENGTH: 14-17 mm. RANGE: Central and Southern States.

Dull brown with a dense covering of short prostrate pubescence; legs yellow. Striae with numerous oblong punctures.

*C. auritus* (Hbst.) (8607) 5-7 mm. long, varies in color from red to piceous with varying black marks on elytra and thorax. The legs and two basal joints of the antennae are yellow. The thorax is about as wide as long. It and the following are both common and belong to the Central and Eastern States.

*C. bellus* (Say) (8609) 3.5-4 mm., is black, with hind angles and median on thorax reddish; elytra dull-red, irregularly marked with two or three black crossbars; antennae and legs yellow.

**9b Fourth tarsal segment heart shaped. Fig. 402.**

**8614 Aeolus melillus (Say)**

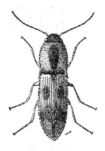

Figure 402

LENGTH: 6-7 mm. RANGE: Much of U. S.

Dull reddish-brown, with blackish markings as pictured. The spot on the thorax is sometimes reduced to a small point. (After Forbes.)

*A. amabilis* (Lec.) (8613), marked and colored much like the above but only about one-half as long; ranges through the Eastern States.

**9c None of the tarsal segments lobed or greatly widened...........10**

**10a Third joint of antennae triangular; elytra marked with pale yellow and black as pictured. Fig. 403.** (a) 8939 *Ampedus sayi* (Lec.)

LENGTH: 11-13 mm. RANGE: Central States.

Black stripe on suture of elytra broad; third joint of antennae distinctly narrower than fourth.

(b) 8935 *A. linteus* (Say)

LENGTH: 7-9 mm. RANGE: Eastern half of United States and Canada.

Head and thorax roughly punctate; black sutural margin narrow. (After Blatchley).

In these two species the legs are black. *A. nigricollis* (Hbst.) (8934) with a length of 8-10 mm. and range much the same as *linteus* is distinguished by its yellow legs.

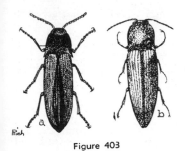

Figure 403

**10b Third joint of antennae not triangular. Dark reddish-brown or blackish, marked with dull yellow as pictured. Fig. 404.**

8955a *Ampedus obliquus areolatus* (Say)

LENGTH: 4.5-5 mm. RANGE: Eastern United States and Canada.

Covered with rather long yellowish hairs. Thorax usually yellowish. Elytral striae shallow with large punctures.

A striking species is *Ampedus sanguinipennis* (Say) (8950) with black thorax and elytra scarlet to dull red. It measures 7-9 mm. and ranges pretty much over the eastern half of our country.

Figure 404

**11a Antennal grooves large, front convex and turned down in front...13**

**11b Antennal grooves small; front concave or flattened.............12**

165

**12a Tarsi lobed or widened. Fig. 405.**

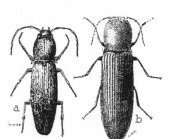

**(a) 8814 *Hemicrepidius memnonius* (Hbst.)**

LENGTH: 15-22 mm. RANGE: Eastern half United States.

Pale brown to blackish, legs paler. Elytral striae with coarse shallow punctures, intervals convex.

**(b) 8813 *H. decoloratus* (Say)**

LENGTH: 9-15 mm. RANGE: much of the United States.

Figure 405

Black, often somewhat bronzed; legs paler.

*H. bilobatus* (Say) (8817) is a rather slender click beetle, 13-16 mm. long. It is shining, chestnut-brown with the antennae and legs paler. The elytra have coarsely punctured striae, the intervals having two rows of rather fine punctures. It occurs in the Central States.

**12b Tarsi normal. Fig. 406.**        **8853 *Melanactes piceus* (DeG.)**

LENGTH: 23-32 mm. RANGE: widely scattered.

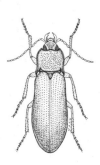

Black, shining; elytral striae very shallow with fine punctures. What is supposed to be the larvae of this species is a large wire worm which displays marked phosphorescence at night.

*M. consors* Lec. (8857), ranging through the Central States and having a length of 21-24 mm. is distinguished by its deeper striae and coarser punctured thorax.

Figure 406

*M. densus* Lec. (8854) with a length of 20-22 mm. is abundant throughout much of California. It is highly polished and wholly black. The elytra have rather deep striations.

**13a Coxal plates with their hind margin toothed at their widest place..14**

**13b Coxal plates with their hind margin rounded at the widest place. Fig. 407.**

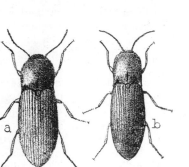

Figure 407

(a) 8885 *Agriotes mancus* (Say) The Wheat Wireworm

LENGTH: 7-9 mm. RANGE: Central and eastern United States and Canada.

Dull brownish yellow with scattered short yellow pubescence. Its wireworm larva is a serious pest of corn and small grains. (After Forbes)

(b) 8893 *Agriotes pubescens* Melsh.

LENGTH: 8-10 mm. RANGE: Central and eastern United States and Canada.

More slender than the preceding. Sooty brown densely covered with grayish-yellow pubescence. Striae with fine punctures; intervals flat, with fine wrinkles. (After Forbes)

*A. insanus* Cand. (8887) is shaped like *pubescens* but differs in that the side margins of the thorax are distinct for their whole length, and segments two and three of the antennae are each shorter than the fourth, instead of equal. It is smaller (7-8 mm.).

*A. oblongicollis* (Melsh.) (8897) which is also brown, differs from all three above in having its hind coxal plates suddenly dilated to more than twice as wide at the inner third as at the outer end. It is 6-9 mm. long.

**14a Color wholly black. Fig. 408.**

8785 *Ludius pruininus noxius* (Hyslop)

Figure 408

LENGTH: 12-14 mm. RANGE: Northwest United States.

Striae moderately deep, punctured; intervals flat. Its larva is known as the Great Basin Wireworm. (After Walton)

*Ludius inflatus* (Say) (8780), a heavy set click beetle 8-11 mm. long, ranges entirely across our country. It, too, is black and somewhat flattened and is known as the Dryland Wireworm. The larvae feed on potatoes, small grain and corn.

**14b Elytra mostly yellow. Fig. 409.**

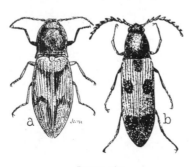

Figure 409

(a) **8796 Ludius hieroglyphicus (Say)**
LENGTH: 11-13 mm.  RANGE: Central and eastern United States.

Bronzed, and densely clothed with fine grayish-yellow pubescence; elytra dull yellow marked with blackish bands as pictured. (Courtesy N. Y. State Museum)

(b) **8706 Ludius vernalis (Hentz)**
LENGTH: 8-11 mm.  RANGE: widely scattered through the United States and Canada.

Thorax and markings on elytra black. Antennae serrate. Striae punctate, intervals flat. This genus is a large one, including many rather common and destructive species. (After Blatchley)

# Family 52  MELASIDAE
## The Melasid Beetles

This small family (sometimes known as Eucnemidae) was formerly made a part of the family Elateridae.  The larvae are often more like the Buprestids than like wireworms.  Members of this family are not very common, but are found in maple, beech and similar wood.

**1a Last segment of maxillary palpi pointed; antennae somewhat separated at their base. Fig. 410.**

**9127 Isorhipis obliqua (Say)**

LENGTH: 4-7 mm.  RANGE: much of the United States and Canada.

Black; elytra marked with yellow as pictured.  Antennae and legs reddish-brown.  Striae densely and roughly punctured.

*Melasis pectinicornis* Melsh. (9125), dull black and thinly covered with short gray pubescence ranges from Connecticut to Florida and west to Texas.  It measures 6-8 mm.

*M. rufipennis* Horn (9126), measuring 8-12 mm., black with reddish elytra and antenna is destructive to trees in the Pacific Coast states.

Figure 410

168

1b Last segment of maxillary palpi dilated; antennae close together at their base. Fig. 411.

9164 *Sarpedon scabrosus* Bonv.

LENGTH: 6-8 mm. RANGE: United States and Canada.

Black; front margins of thorax reddish; antennae of male bipectinate, of female biserrate. (After Horn)

*Deltometops amoenicornis* Say (9133), piceous with scant gray pubescence and measuring 3-5 mm. is found in much of the eastern half of the United States.

Figure 411

*Microrhagus triangularis* (Say) (9157) differs in having an antennal groove on the underside of the thorax, which *Sarpedon* lacks, and in being much smaller (3-4 mm.). It is black with brownish legs and antennae and is found from Georgia north into Canada.

# Family 54  BUPRESTIDAE
## The Metallic Woodborers

Engineered much like the click beetles, the some 8000 species belonging to this family appear as though covered with metal; a sort of "robot insect." They are often bronzed or with other metallic lusters. They are destructive borers in woody plants. They may be found sunning themselves on tree trunks, fence posts, etc. and are frequently so much alert as to be difficult to capture.

1a Hind coxal plates distinctly dilated near the base (a), the outer end cut by prolongation of the abdomen; fourth tarsal joint not lobed. Fig. 412. .........................................5

1b Hind coxal plates scarcely if at all dilated internally or near their base.................2

Figure 412

2a Thorax lobed at base, insertion of antennae narrowing the front.....3

169

**2b Thorax cut straight (truncate) at base; front not narrowed by antennae. Fig. 413.** 9272 *Acmaeodera pulchella* Hbst.

LENGTH: 5-10 mm. RANGE: general.

Cylindrical, heavy, covered with coarse punctures and brownish hairs. Blackish bronze marked with yellow, markings variable. Rather common on flowers especially New Jersey Tea.

*A. tubulus* (Fab.) (9286) a smaller species 5-8 mm. differs in having no yellow on the sides of thorax and with scattering whitish hairs. Its distribution is rather general east of the Rockies. It too is found on flowers, *Crataegus* seeming to be a favorite.

Figure 413

Several species of this genus do severe damage to trees in our western forests.

**3a Antennae at rest in grooves. Body broad. Fig. 414.**
**9574 *Brachys ovatus* (Web.)**

LENGTH: 5-6.5 mm. RANGE: general.

Flattened. Blackish or purplish bronzed marked with bands of whitish prostrate hairs. The larvae feed within oak leaves. (Courtesy N. Y. State Museum)

*Taphrocerus gracilis* (Say) (9578) differs as a genus from the preceding in having the body elongated. This species is a shining blackish-bronze. Its length is 3.5-5 mm. and ranges widely throughout our country.

Figure 414

**3b Antennae without a protecting groove.........................4**

**4a Inner prong of tarsal claws (c) turning in and almost touching. Fig. 415.** (a) 9513 *Agrilus ruficollis* (Fab.)

LENGTH: 5.5-8 mm. RANGE: United States and Canada east of Rockies.

Bluish-black; head and thorax coppery-red. Surface of elytra granulate. This is a serious pest of blackberries and raspberries and is known as the Red-necked Cane Borer.

**(b) 9548 *A. vittaticollis* Rand.**

LENGTH: 6-7 mm. RANGE: Central and eastern United States.

Head and thorax coppery-red; elytra black. Tarsal claws as pictured. (After Brooks)

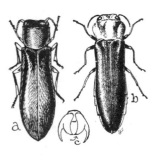

The Oak Twig-girdler, *A. angelicus* Horn (9526) a shining brassy species of California cuts many twigs from oak trees by girding them after its egg is laid in the branch. Its length is 6-7 mm.

Figure 415

**4b** Inner prong of bifid claw not turning in (c). Fig. 416.

(a) 9491 *Agrilus bilineatus* (Web.)

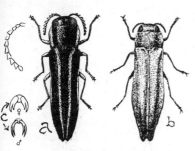

LENGTH: 6-9 mm. RANGE: East of Rockies.

Greenish-black, marked as pictured with dense yellow pubescence. Surface of elytra granulate. Feeds on oak, honeylocust and chestnut. (U.S. D.A.) Its common name is Two-lined Chestnut Borer.

(b) 9504 *Agrilus anxius* Gory.

LENGTH: 7-12 mm. RANGE: general.

Figure 416

Olive-green bronzed. Elytra clothed with granulate scales. This Bronze Birch Borer is highly destructive to shade and forest trees. (U.S.D.A.)

**5a** Prosternal spine coming to an acute angle with acute tip behind the front coxae; epimera of metathorax partly covered by the abdomen. ...................................................................... 6

**5b** Prosternal spine obtuse behind the front coxae; epimera of metathorax uncovered, triangular.................................... 7

**6a** Clypeus small and flattened but not narrowed by insertion of antennae. Fig. 417.

9387 *Melanophila fulvoguttata* (Har.) The Hemlock Borer

LENGTH: 9-11 mm. RANGE: middle and northern United States.

Blackish bronze with greenish reflections at anterior end. Upper surface with transverse punctures. Elytra each with three white or yellowish spots. An enemy of hemlock, spruce and white pine. (Courtesy N. Y. State Museum)

*Anthaxia quercata* (Fab.) (9396) of wide general distribution, is shining bluish or purplish, with bright green areas and a broad brownish stripe on each elytron.

Figure 417

It measures 4-6 mm. and is a pest of oak. The genus differs from the preceding in that the mentum is horn like instead of leathery in front.

171

**6b Clypeus reduced in length by insertion of antennae; scutellum large. Fig. 418.**

**9466 *Chrysobothris femorata* (Oliv.) Flatheaded Apple Tree Borer**

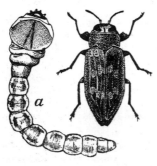

Figure 418

LENGTH: 7-16 mm. RANGE: United States and Canada.

Somewhat flattened. Dark bronze with sheens of green, copper or brass. Third joint of antennae slightly longer than the next two. The name comes from the larva (a). (U.S.D.A.)

The Pacific Flatheaded Borer *C. mali* Horn (9439) (6-11 mm.) may be distinguished from the above by a short lobe on the front margin of the prosternum.

A readily recognized but somewhat smaller species (6-11 mm.) is *C. sexsignata* (Say.) (9405). It is black above with a faint bronze sheen and green on its under parts. Each elytron is marked with three round brassy spots. The elytra are wider than the thorax. It occurs in central and eastern United States.

**7a Mesosternum and metasternum closely united; 19 mm. or more in length. Fig. 419.** **(a) 9316 *Chalcophora virginiensis* (Drury)**

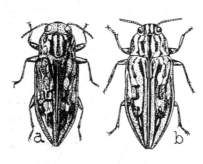

Figure 419

LENGTH: 23-30 mm. RANGE: Eastern half of United States and Canada.

Dull black, slightly bronzed. Impressions on thorax and elytra as pictured, often brassy. The larvae 1½ inches in length live under the bark of pine trees. (Courtesy N. Y. State Museum)

**(b) 9321 *C. liberta* (Germ.)**

LENGTH: 19-25 mm. RANGE: general.

Bright coppery or brassy; antennae, legs and markings on head, thorax and elytra blackish-brown. The adults feed on the buds and leaves while the larvae bore within the stems of hard pine. (Courtesy N. Y. State Museum)

7b Mesosternum separated from metasternum by a distinct suture. Usually not over 10 mm. in length..................................8
8a Mentum wholly horny, tarsi broad, shorter than tibiae. Fig. 420.

(a) 9333 *Dicerca divaricata* (Say)
LENGTH: 15-21 mm. RANGE: general.

This rather common flat brassy beetle is recognized by its elongated and diverging elytral tips. Thorax with median impressed line and elytra with numerous irregular impressed lines and short elevated black spots as pictured. In the West it is known as the Flat-headed Cherry Tree Borer. (U.S.D.A.)

(b) 9337 *D. punctulata* (Schon.)
LENGTH: 10-14 mm. RANGE: Central and eastern United States.

Blackish bronze with coppery sheen. The transverse ridges extending from eye to eye on front are characteristic. (Courtesy N. Y. State Museum)

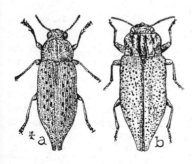

Figure 420

In this same group belongs *Trachykele blondeli* Mars. (9330), the Western Cedar Borer, a most beautiful iridescent and gold beetle (14-17 mm.). It ranges throughout the mountain states.

8b Mentum membraneous in front.................................9
9a Elytra marked with yellow. Fig. 421.

(a) 9374 *Buprestis rufipes* (Oliv.)
LENGTH: 18-25 mm. RANGE: Eastern half of United States.

Above green with brassy sheen; marked with yellow as pictured. Underparts green. Feeds on maple and beech.

(b) 9377 *B. fasciata* Fab.
LENGTH: 23 mm. RANGE: general.

Flattened. Brilliant green, marked with golden yellow on elytra. It seems to feed on maples and poplars. (Courtesy N. Y. State Museum)

*B. arulenta* L. (9361) is another striking species bluish-green with suture and margins banded with gold. It is a native of our western mountain regions where it lives in many of the conifers. Adult beetles are occasionally found in the East where they have emerged from western lumber.

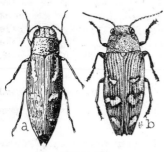

Figure 421

9b Without yellow markings on elytra. Fig. 422.

9370 *Buprestis maculativentris* Say

LENGTH: 15-23 mm. RANGE: general.

Black with brassy sheen. Front angles of thorax and a row of spots on sides of abdomen, reddish yellow. (Courtesy N. Y. State Museum)

*B. adjecta* (Lec.) (9362) a short robust species measuring 13-18 mm. and wholly metallic green is a native of the West. The tips of the elytra are double-toothed.

Figure 422

*B. laeviventris* (Lec.) (9373) 14-20 mm., is dark brown or black with spots or broken lines of yellow or orange on the elytra; a marginal line at the anterior of the thorax as well as the front of the head are also yellow-orange. Its range is in the mountains of the West.

*B. connexa* Horn (9371) 15 mm. long, a brilliant green beetle with bronze sheen on upper parts, has somewhat the same distribution.

# TETRAMERA

1a Tarsi in reality with five segments; the fourth very small and hidden between prongs of third. Fig. 423 .......................... 8

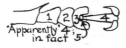

Figure 423

1b Only four segments. Fig. 424 ............. 2

Figure 424

2a First 4 ventral abdominal segments fused, only the fifth being free moving. ........................................ 3

2b Ventral segments of abdomen not grown together............... 5

174

3a Tibiae dilated and armed with rows of spines for digging; antennae short. (Variegated Mud-loving Beetles). Fig. 425.
Family 58, HETEROCERIDAE..........................page 178

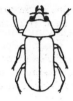

Look for these rather dull grayish beetles along water courses. They are often found flying around lights on warm evenings.

Figure 425

3b Tibiae normal, not used for digging; antennae normal...........4

4a Antennae inserted under a frontal ridge. (Cylindrical Bark Beetles.) Fig. 426. Family 78, COLYDIIDAE.....................page 192

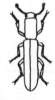

These small beetles are found under bark or sometimes in the ground or in fungi. They are carnivorous.

This is a very small family; Leng's catalog and supplements show only 4 genera with a total of 6 species. They were formerly included in the family Endomychidae.

Figure 426

4b Antennae inserted on the front. (Mycetaeid Beetles.) Fig. 427. Family 82, MYCETAEIDAE.

10718 *Phymaphora pulchella* Newn.

LENGTH: 3.5-4 mm. RANGE: Eastern United States and Canada.

Black and red, as pictured. (After Wickham)

*Rhanis unicolor* (Ziegl.) (10717), similar in size and range, is shining, reddish-brown. The elytra are sometimes black with reddish shoulders.

Figure 427

5a Front coxae globose...........................................6

175

**5b** Front coxae oval, separated, small depressed beetles. (Hairy Fungus Beetles) Fig. 428. Family 77, MYCETOPHAGIDAE.....page 191

The common name tells their story. These tiny little fellows are hair covered and are found in fungi. Perhaps less than 200 species are known.

Figure 428

**6a** Head not at all covered by the prothorax, body oval, depressed...7

**6b** Head covered at least in part by the prothorax; last segment of tarsi usually very long; body cylindrical (Minute Tree Fungus Beetles). Fig. 429. Family 96, CISIDAE.........................page 230

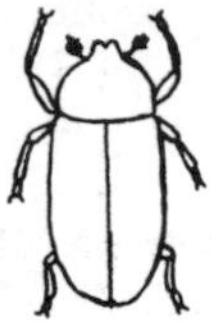

These very small blackish or brown beetles are found under bark and in fungi.

Figure 429

**7a** Tarsi slender. (Handsome Fungus Beetles) Fig. 430. Family 83, ENDOMYCHIDAE ......................................page 194

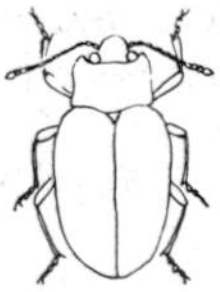

Some species in this family resemble Lady Beetles for they are often red and black. About 1000 species are known, but less than 50 species within our region (U. S. and Canada).

Figure 430

**7b** Tarsi more or less dilated and spongy beneath. (Pleasing Fungus Beetles.) Fig. 431. Family 73, EROTYLIDAE............page 188

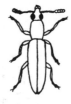

These vary in size and in shape from narrow cylindrical to rather oval forms. They are smooth, shining and often brightly colored.

Figure 431

8a Body elongate; antennae almost always long, often as long as the body or longer. Base of antennae usually partly surrounded by eyes. (Longhorned Wood-boring Beetles.) Fig. 432. Family 101, CERAMBYCIDAE .....................................page 249

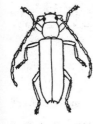

Many collectors think the members of this large family are the most attractive of all beetles. They vary widely in size and form but may usually be readily recognized.

Figure 432

8b Body usually short, more or less oval; antennae short, not at all surrounded by eyes.........................................9

9a Small (less than 3 mm.) shining, very compact, rounded, convex beetles; elytra wholly covering abdomen; last three segments of antennae enlarged forming a club. (Shining Flower Beetles.) Fig. 433. Family 84, PHALACRIDAE.......................page 195

These tiny shining oval beetles are very abundant and represent many species. They are usually blackish in color.

Figure 433

9b Not as in 9a.................................................10

177

10a Front prolonged into a broad quadrate beak. Elytra exposing tip of abdomen (a). (Seed Weevils.) Fig. 434. Family 103, BRU-CHIDAE ............................................page 303

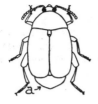

These small rounded usually dull colored beetles develop within the seeds of many species of legumes. The key characters make their identification easy.

Figure 434

10b Front not prolonged into a beak. Abdomen usually wholly covered with elytra. Larvae and adults live on leaves of plants. (Leaf Beetles.) .Fig. 435. Family 102, CHRYSOMELIDAE.....page 272

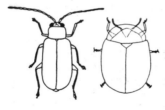

This is such a large family that many shapes, sizes and colors are represented. The adults are often brightly colored and possess unique and pleasing patterns. They are more compactly built and have shorter antennae than the Long-horned Wood-borers.

Figure 435

# Family 58   HETEROCERIDAE
## The Variegated Mud-Loving Beetles

Here is a small family of somewhat flattened grayish beetles which burrow in sand and mud and are often so mud-covered as to require cleaning before accurate determinations are possible.

**1a Thorax with a pale median stripe. Fig. 436.**

9653 *Heterocerus auromicans* Kies.

LENGTH: 3.5-4.5 mm. RANGE: general.

Blackish, sparingly clothed with golden short recumbent scale-like hairs. Elytra marked with yellow as pictured; femora and tarsi reddish-yellow, tibiae black.

Figure 436

**1b Thorax without a median pale stripe. Fig. 437.**

(a) 9650 *Heterocerus collaris* Kies.
LENGTH: 2.5-4 mm. RANGE: general.

Sooty-brown to black, covered with brownish hairs, sides of thorax and elytra marked with pale yellow as pictured; legs reddish-yellow.

(b) 9652 *Heterocerus pusillus* Say
LENGTH: 2-2.5 mm. RANGE: general.

Dull yellow marked with sooty-brown or sometimes colored entirely with either one of these colors. Legs pale.

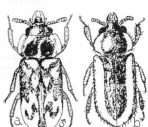

Figure 437

# Family 62   HELODIDAE
## The Soft-bodied Plant Beetles

These beetles are usually oval in shape; they are small and very soft. They are found on plants in swamps and other water courses and sometimes in damp debris.

**1a Tarsi with 4th segment very small; antennae of male as pictured. Fig. 438.**   9716 *Ptilodactyla serricollis* (Say)

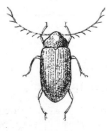

LENGTH: 4-6 mm. RANGE: Eastern half of United States.

Chestnut brown to blackish with thin pubescence; legs and antennae pale. (After Blatchley)

*P. angustata* Horn (9715). A closely related species is known from Florida.

Figure 438

179

1b Fourth tarsal segment as large as others. Fig. 439.

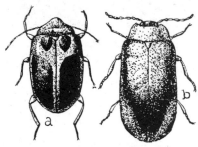

Figure 439

(a) 9687 *Helodes pulchella* Guer.

LENGTH: 3.5-5 mm. RANGE: Eastern half United States.

Yellow marked with black. Thorax finely punctate, elytra densely punctured. (After Blatchley)

(b) 9697 *Cyphon collaris* (Guer.)

LENGTH: 3.5-4 mm. RANGE: Eastern half United States.

Black shining, with fine pubescence. Marked with reddish-yellow as shown including base of antennae and tibia and tarsae. (After Blatchley)

## Family 64   DERMESTIDAE
### The Skin Beetles

Some members of this family are likely to be found in any insect collection as volunteers. Unless watched closely their larvae may wreck a good collection. Over 500 species are known in all. They are small to medium sized and usually covered with dull or brilliant colored scales.

1a Tarsi without lobes, claws without tooth.........................2

1b Tarsi with lobe beneath second and third segments; claws with a tooth at base. Fig. 440.          9718 *Byturus unicolor* Say

Figure 440

LENGTH: 3.5-4.5 mm. RANGE: general.

Pale brown or reddish-yellow, occasional blackish; thickly pubescent. Feeds on the flowers of raspberry and blackberry. The white larva is known as the Raspberry Fruit Worm.

At least two other similar species of the genus feed upon the flowers and fruit of raspberries.

2a Length 5 mm. or less; head with a distinct simple eye...........3

**2b Length 6 or more mm.; no simple eye. Fig. 441.**

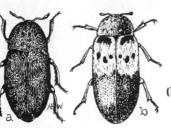

Figure 441

(a) **9725 Dermestes caninus Germ.**

LENGTH: 7-8.5 mm. RANGE: general.

Black with mottled design on thorax and elytra in pubescence of black, gray and reddish-brown.

(b) **9737 D. lardarius L. The Larder Beetle**

LENGTH: 6-8 mm. RANGE: cosmopolitan.

Black with gray hairs on elytra as pictured. Beneath black with scattered yellowish pubescence. It is sometimes a serious household pest and multiplies rapidly.

*D. marmoratus* Say (9724) 7-11 mm. in length, black with white markings at base of elytra and yellowish hairs on underparts, is found in most of the Western States.

*D. talpinus* Mann. (9730) 5-7 mm., black above, clothed with bluish-gray, clay-yellow and black hairs and underparts mostly white, is principally western in its range.

**3a With distinct antennal grooves or pits; body covered with small colored scales. Fig. 442.**

(a) **9829 Anthrenus scrophulariae (L.) The Carpet Beetle**

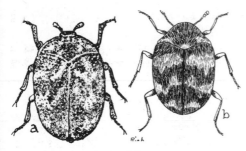

Figure 442

LENGTH: 2.5-4 mm.
RANGE: cosmopolitan.

Sutural stripe and apical spot on elytra, red. Remainder of pattern as pictured, black and white. Scales on under side orange and white. The larvae are known as Buffalo moths. It and the following are serious household pests.

(b) **9835 A. verbasci (L.) The Varied Carpet Beetle**

LENGTH: 2-3 mm. RANGE: cosmopolitan.

Body black but thickly covered with yellowish-brown and white scale as pictured. Under parts with grayish-yellow scales.

181

3b **Without antennal grooves; antennae 11 jointed (a); 9 jointed (b).
Fig. 443.**

(a) 9742 *Attagenus piceus* (Oliv.) **Black Carpet Beetle**

LENGTH: 3.5-5 mm. RANGE: Europe and America.

Black, elytra sometimes reddish-brown, with scattered pubescence. A very serious museum pest. It is a very fortunate insect collection that has this species represented only by pinned specimens.

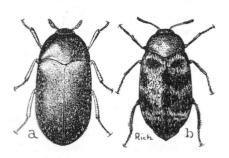

Figure 443

(b) 9785 *Trogoderma versicolor* **Creutz.**

LENGTH: 2-3.5 mm. RANGE: cosmopolitan.

Black, elytra marked with reddish and gray hairs as pictured. Eyes emarginate (notched).

# Family 68   OSTOMIDAE

## The Ostomid Beetles

These cylindrical or often flattened beetles range from small to medium sizes. Many are black or brown; some have brilliant metallic shades. Almost 700 species are known.

1a **Form elongate, thorax emarginate at apex; head large. Fig. 444.**

(a) 9977 *Tenebroides mauritanicus* (L.) **The Cadelle**

LENGTH: 9-10.5 mm. RANGE: cosmopolitan.

Blackish throughout, antennae a gradually widening club. Eighth joint of antennae equal to ninth.

(b) 9994 *Tenebroides corticalis* (Melsh.)

LENGTH: 7-8 mm. RANGE: Eastern half of United States.

Black, rather dull, antennae and legs lighter. Eighth joint of antennae smaller than the ninth. (U.S.D.A.)

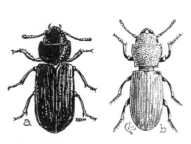

Figure 444

1b Form oval, with flattened margins.   Front coxal cavities closed (a);
   open behind (b). .Fig. 445.          (a) 9998 *Calitys scabra* Thunb.

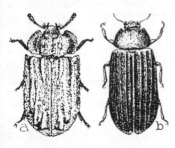

LENGTH: 9-10 mm.  RANGE: Europe and North America.

Reddish.   Thoracic margins wide. Lives on fungi on logs. (Courtesy N. Y. State Museum.)

(b) 10007 *Ostoma quadrilineata* Melsh. LENGTH: 5-6 mm.  RANGE: Central States.

Black, feebly shining, antennae and legs lighter.   Four narrow ridges on each elytron with 3-4 rows of punctures on each interval.   Under bark. (After Blatchley)

Figure 445

# Family 69   NITIDULIDAE
## The Sap-Feeding Beetles

These small beetles feed on decaying plant materials and are found in garbage, where sap is escaping from plants, under dead bark and sometimes in ants' nests. They are usually black, brown or grayish. This family is cosmopolitan and numbers over 2500 species.

1a Labrum united with the front; black usually marked with yellow
   or reddish. Fig. 446.            (a) 10137 *Glischrochilus fasciatus* (Oliv.)

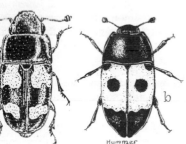

LENGTH: 4-7 mm.  RANGE: general.

Shining black marked with yellowish as pictured. Spots variable in size.  This beetle is often abundant in and under garbage pails. (Courtesy N. Y. State Museum)

(b) 10138 *G. sanguinolentus* (Oliv.) LENGTH: 4-6 mm.  RANGE: Eastern half United States and Canada.

Shining black; elytra bright red with humeral and discal spots and tips black; abdomen and metasternum red.

Hummer

Figure 446

1b Labrum free; not shining black.................................2

2a Elytra wholly covering abdomen or at most exposing but one segment........................................................3

**2b** Elytra exposing 2 or more segments of abdomen..............6

**3a** Tarsi distinctly widened; tips of elytra usually truncate...........4

**3b** Tarsi not widened; elytra entirely covering abdomen.............5

**4a** Labrum with two lobes. Fig. 447.      10085 *Epuraea duryi* Blatch.

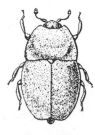

Figure 447

LENGTH: 3.5-5 mm.  RANGE: Eastern United States.

Flattened.  Shining pale yellow with scattered pubescence.  (After Blatchley)

A smaller member (2.5-3 mm.) of this genus is *Epuraea obtusicollis* Rttr. (10089).  Its color is dark reddish-brown to blackish with paler margins to elytra and thorax.  It is widely distributed.

**4b** Labrum but feebly notched.  Fig. 448.

10065 *Nitidula bipunctata* (L.)

Figure 448

LENGTH: 4.5-6 mm.  RANGE: Europe and North America.

Blackish, marked with a red spot on each elytron; covered with a fine pubescence.  Common on old bones and skins.  (After Smith)

*Stelidota geminata* (Say) (10098) 2-2.5 mm. is widely distributed and common.  It is dark reddish-brown with two indistinct cross-bars on the elytra.  Its abdomen is entirely covered by the elytra.

**5a** Mentum covering base of maxilla; thorax and elytra with wide flat margins.  Fig. 449.      10101 *Prometopia sexmaculata* (Say)

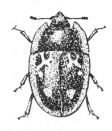

Figure 449

LENGTH: 5-6 mm.  RANGE: East of Rockies.

Piceous, marked on elytra and margins with pale reddish-brown as shown.  Feeds on sap in spring.  (After Blatchley)

Another species common to the two continents is *Omosita colon* (L.) (10069).  It is blackish with dull yellow margins on elytra and thorax and 4 or 5 dull yellowish spots on elytra.  It measures 2-3 mm.

**5b Mentum not covering the maxilla. Fairly large. Fig. 450.**

10109 *Phenolia grossa* (Fab.)

Figure 450

LENGTH: 6.5-8 mm. RANGE: Eastern half United States and Canada.

Piceous, somewhat dull; elytra with indistinct reddish markings as shown. Common beneath bark and in fungi.

*Lobiopa undulata* (Say) (10105) with perhaps much the same range, differs from the above in the front extending into lobes over the base of the antenna. It is piceous with dull yellowish margins and spots on elytra. It measures 4-5 mm.

**6a Form elongate, resembling the rove beetles. Fig. 451.**

10035 *Conotelus obscurus* Er.

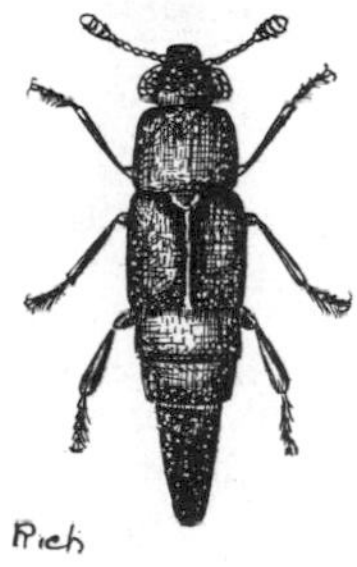

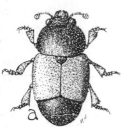

Figure 451

LENGTH: 3.5-4.5 mm. RANGE: Eastern half of United States.

Dull black, with scattered pubescence; antennae and legs brownish-yellow, the club darker. Common in flowers of Wild Morning-glory, Hollyhock, and Dogwood.

Ranging through the Southwest, also black and measuring 3 mm. *C. mexicanus* Murr. (10037) seriously attacks the buds and flowers of several species of fruit trees and shrubs as well as cotton. It is popularly known as the Fruit Bud Beetle.

**6b Not elongate. Fig. 452.**     **(a) 10039 *Carpophilus pallipennis* (Say)**

LENGTH: 3-4 mm. RANGE: West half of United States.

Reddish or yellowish-brown; elytra lighter than head and thorax. It is common in the flowers of cacti. (After Forbes)

**(b) 10042 *Carpophilus hemipterus* (L.)**

Figure 452

LENGTH: 4 mm. RANGE: cosmopolitan.

Blackish, marked as pictured with dull yellow, legs pale. It is known as the Dried Fruit Beetle. Both adults and larvae are serious pests especially in fruit drying areas. (After Smith)

*C. dimidiatus* (Fab.) (10043), the Corn Sap Beetle, differs from *hemipterus* in having a squarish thorax with distinct front angles. It is lighter in color, a bit smaller and is cosmopolitan.

# Family 72   CUCUJIDAE
## The Flat Bark Beetles

The some 1000 species of this family are highly variable in size, shape, markings and habits. They are often flattened to live under bark but some are serious pests in grain products.

1a Front coxal cavities open behind. Fig.
   453a ............................. 4

1b Front coxal cavities closed behind. Fig.
   453b ............................. 2

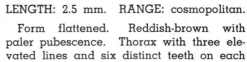

Figure 453

2a Third joint of tarsi lobed beneath, antennae long, slender, filiform.
   Fig. 454.                    10276 *Telephanus velox* Hald.

LENGTH: 4-4.5 mm.  RANGE: Eastern half of United States.

Pale brownish-yellow with darker brown markings as pictured. Rather thickly clothed with fairly long pubescence. Common in debris and under stones. Slow to get started but a swift runner.

Figure 454

2b Antennae clubbed; tarsi not lobed............................ 3

3a Last three joints of antennae enlarging abruptly into the club. Fig.
   455.                    (a) 10194 *Oryzaephilus surinamensis* (L.)

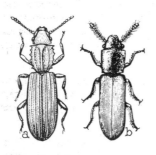

Figure 455

**The Saw-toothed Grain Beetle**

LENGTH: 2.5 mm.  RANGE: cosmopolitan.

Form flattened. Reddish-brown with paler pubescence. Thorax with three elevated lines and six distinct teeth on each edge. Much too common in stored grain and grain products.

(b) 10200 *Cathartus quadricollis* (Guer.)
**The Square-necked Grain Beetle**

LENGTH: 2-3 mm.  RANGE: cosmopolitan.
Reddish-brown, feebly punctate. Another common pest of grain products. (U.S.D.A.)

**3b Antennae gradually widening into a club of 3 or 4 segments. Fig. 456.**  10204 *Cathartus advena* (Waltl.)

Figure 456

LENGTH: 1.7-2 mm.  RANGE: cosmopolitan.

Subconvex.  Pale reddish-brown, shining, with fine pubescence.  Rows of coarse punctures on elytra.  Feeds and breeds in stored grain and fruit products.

C. *rectus* Lec. (10205) may be distinguished from the above in that the front angles of the thorax are not toothed.  It is similar in size and color and is widely distributed.

**4a Bright red; head widest behind the eyes.  Fig. 457.**  10221 *Cucujus clavipes* Fab.

Figure 457

LENGTH: 10-14 mm.  RANGE: throughout much of North America.

Much flattened.  Scarlet red above, darker beneath; antennae and eyes black.  An attractive beetle and beneficial in that both adult and larva feed on bark beetles and wood borers, the tunnels of which they invade.  (After Riley)

The western form is variety *puniceus* Mann. (10221a).

**4b Head widest across the eyes.....................................5**

**5a Thorax toothed at sides; first antennal segment about as long as the head.  Fig. 458.**  10273 *Brontes dubius* Fab.

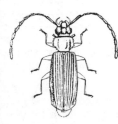

Figure 458

LENGTH: 4-6 mm.  RANGE: much of United States.

Much flattened.  Brownish-black, sometimes quite pale brown.  Sides of elytra and the head and thorax usually paler.  Antennae thickly pubescent.  Very common under bark.  (Courtesy N. Y. State Museum)

B. *debelis* Lec. (10274) differs from *dubius* in being darker in color and in being more slender with less serrate thorax.

187

**5b Thorax without teeth at sides; first joint of antennae much shorter than head. Fig. 459.** 10261 *Laemophloeus minutus* (Oliv.)

Figure 459

LENGTH 1.5-2 mm. RANGE: cosmopolitan.

Flattened. Reddish-brown. Popularly known as the Flat Grain Beetle, it may be recognized by its small size and long antennae. It infests both dried fruit and cereals.

A related species, the Rust-red Grain Beetle *L. ferrugineus* (Steph.) (10258) with cosmopolitan distribution, is often found with the above which it resembles closely.

## Family 73    EROTYLIDAE
## The Pleasing Fungus Beetles

There are in all more than 2000 species known for this family. Many of them are shining and have a metallic sheen over their black, blue, green and bright red parts.

**1a Form subcylindrical, very elongate; front coxal cavities open behind; club of 5 or 6 segments.**............................................2

**1b Form not very slim; front coxal cavities closed behind; club of 3 or 4 segments.**...............................................3

**2a Abdomen entirely black. Fig. 460.**

10292 *Acropteroxys gracilis* Newn.

Figure 460

LENGTH: 8-10 mm. RANGE: Eastern half United States.

Head in part or wholly red; thorax yellowish-red with broad greenish-black stripe extending its entire length as pictured. Feeds on ragweed and related plants. (After Wickham)

Longer and wider and with much the same range *A. lecontei* (Cr.) (10293) has the head wholly black and only a large spot at center of thorax.

**2b Abdomen mostly red. Fig. 461.**

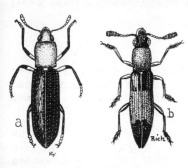

Figure 461

(a) 10282 *Languria mozardi* Latr. LENGTH: 5-8 mm. RANGE: Eastern half United States.

Shining. Head and thorax wholly red; elytra bluish-black; tarsi, antennae and apical half of femora black. The larva infests the stems of clover and is known as the Clover Stem Borer.

(b) 10287 *Languria trifasciata* Say LENGTH: 6-8 mm. RANGE: Eastern half United States.

Shining. Marked with red and bluish-black as pictured; antennae in part reddish-yellow.

**3a Mentum not transverse, 4th tarsal segment very small..........4**

**3b Mentum transverse, 4th tarsal joint readily seen. Fig. 462.**

10348 *Megalodachne heros* (Say)

Figure 462

LENGTH: 18-22 mm. RANGE: much of United States.

Shining. Black, with red markings. (After Blatchley)

*M. fasciata* (Fab.) (10347) which is colored and marked much like *heros* is readily distinguished by its smaller size (9-15 mm.) and by rows of fine punctures on elytra which the former lacks. Its range is even more general.

Both of these very attractive beetles hibernate gregariously under bark.

**4a Body oval. Fig. 463.**

10319 *Tritoma humeralis* Fab.

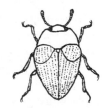

Figure 463

LENGTH: 3-4 mm. RANGE: Europe and United States.

Black with reddish-yellow spot on humerus of each elytron. (After Wickham)

*T. sanguipennis* (Say) (10308) about 4 mm. long has its elytra wholly dark red with thorax black while *T. angulata* Say (10314) has thorax and elytra wholly black. Both range widely.

**4b Body more elongate.........................................5**

**5a Eyes with large fascets. Fig. 464.**

10301 *Ischyrus quadripunctatus* (Oliv.)

LENGTH: 7-8 mm.   RANGE: Eastern half of United States.

Reddish-yellow with black markings; underparts black, with sides of abdomen yellow. Elytra with rows of distinct punctures. Feeds on fungi. Like several other species of the family it gathers in large numbers to hibernate under bark or beneath logs. If you happen to hit the "jack pot" collecting is simple.

Figure 464

**5b Eyes with fine fascets. Fig. 465.**

10334 *Triplax thoracica* Say

LENGTH: 3.5-5 mm.   RANGE: general.

Head and thorax yellow; elytra and apical half of antennae black. Underparts reddish-yellow. Beneath bark and in fleshy fungi. (After Blatchley)

*T. festiva* Lac. (10327) a widely distributed species especially in the South is a bit larger than the preceding. The ground color is black, but attractively marked with thorax, scutellum and broad median band reddish-yellow.

Figure 465

# Family 75   CRYPTOPHAGIDAE
## The Silken Fungus Beetles

These also live on fungi, decaying organic matter and sometimes with the ants. They are small. Almost 1000 species are known.

**1a Antennae inserted under sides of the front and widely separated at base.................................................2**

**1b Antennae inserted on the front and close together at base. Fig. 466.**

10463 *Anchicera ephippiata* Zimm.

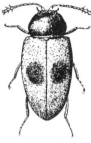

LENGTH: 1.5 mm.   RANGE: widely distributed.

Convex. Head and thorax blackish; elytra reddish-yellow marked with blackish dot or disk, often extending into a cross-bar; legs reddish-yellow. (After Blatchley)

*A. ochracea* Zimm. (10471), of about the same size and shape is dark reddish-brown to blackish with legs and antennae lighter. It is shiny, has a wide range and is said to hibernate under mullein leaves.

Figure 466

190

2a Tarsi with 2nd and 3rd segments lobed beneath, the latter the larger; 4th segment very small. Fig. 467.

10365 *Toramus pulchellus* Lec.

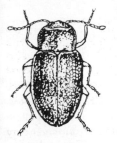

LENGTH: 1.5 mm. RANGE: Eastern half of United States.

Convex. Brownish-yellow to piceous; legs and basal half of antennae lighter. Elytra with two yellowish bands as pictured. (After Blatchley)

*Telmatophilus americanus* Lec. (10360) a widely distributed species is larger (2.5-3 mm.) and densely pubescent. It is reddish-brown to piceous with yellowish to ash-gray pubescence.

Figure 467

2b Tarsi slender and without lobes, hind tarsi of males with but 4 segments. Fig. 468.

(a) 10384 *Cryptophagus acutangulus* Gyll.

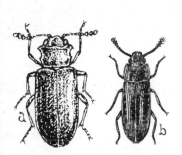

LENGTH: 2.5 mm. RANGE: Europe and North America.

Subdepressed. Pale brownish-yellow, head and thorax darker. Abundant; often found in cereals and sacked sugar. (After Blatchley)

(b) 10374 *Pharaxonotha kirschi* Reit. (Mexican Grain Beetle)

LENGTH: 4.5-5 mm. RANGE: Mexico and occasionally in the United States.

Shining, deep brown; antennae long. A pest of stored grain. (U.S.D.A.)

Figure 468

*Henoticus serratus* (Gyll.) (10418) is another cosmopolitan species. It measures about 2 mm. and is dark reddish-brown with scattered yellowish hairs. The apical angles of the thorax are not thickened as in *Cryptophagus*.

# Family 77   MYCETOPHAGIDAE
## The Hairy Fungus Beetles

The tiny members of this small family live under bark and in fungi. They are densely punctured above and covered with hair.

1a Eyes elongate, sinuate in front, antennae gradually enlarging. Fig. 469.

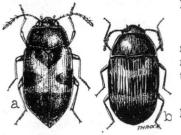

Figure 469

(a) 10490 *Mycetophagus punctatus* Say LENGTH: 4-5.5 mm. RANGE: Eastern half United States.

Subdepressed. Blackish above with reddish-yellow markings. Antennae reddish becoming blackish at apex. (After Blatchley)

(b) 10491 *Mycetophagus flexuosus* Say LENGTH: 3-4 mm. RANGE: United States.

Above black with reddish-yellow markings. (Size and arrangement of markings are variable). Feeds on sap and fungi.

1b Eyes rounded, not sinuate; segments 9-11 of antennae enlarged abruptly. Fig. 470. 10509 *Typhaea stercorea* L.

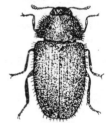

Figure 470

LENGTH: 2.5-3 mm. RANGE: cosmopolitan.

Dull reddish-yellow, elytra occasionally blackish. Antennae shorter than head and thorax, the club 3 jointed. A pest of cereal products. (After Forbes)

*Lithargus sexpunctatus* Say (10512) about the same size and widely distributed is characterized by three yellow spots on each elytron. The ground color is piceous.

*L. didesmus* Say (10517) 2-2.2 mm. in length, is shining, piceous; each elytron with yellow crossband back of the middle and a yellow humeral spot. It differs from *sexpunctatus* in lacking the basal impressions. The pubescence stands in irregular patches. It is found in many of the states east of the Missouri river.

*Thrimolus minutus* Csy. (10519) is a very little, dark brown or clay-yellow species measuring only .7-.9 mm. The head is large and transverse; the thorax much wider than long, has its hind angles broadly rounded in contrast with the other genera of the family.

# Family 78  COLYDIIDAE
## The Cylindrical Bark Beetles

These long slim beetles seem to be related to the Cucujids. They live under the bark of trees. Many of them are predacious. Around 1000 species have been described.

**la Last joint of palpi needle-shaped. Fig. 471.**

10598 *Cerylon castaneum* **Say**

LENGTH: 2-3 mm.  RANGE: general.

Depressed.  Shining.  Dark reddish-brown; elytra with punctured striae.

*Philothermus glabriculus* Lec. (10604) is a common species throughout the eastern half of the United States.  In size and color it is much the same as the preceding but its antennae have 11 segments 2 of which make the club instead of 10 and 1.

Figure 471

*Bothrideres geminatus* (Say) (10592) 3-4.5 mm., dark reddish-brown, is common and ranges from Texas to our east coast.  It differs from *Cerylon* in being slender and in the palpi not being needle-shaped.

**lb Last joint of palpi not needle-shaped. Fig. 472.**

10580 *Colydium lineola* **Say**

LENGTH: 4-7 mm.  RANGE: United States and Canada.

Black moderately shining; legs and antennae paler.  Thorax with deeply impressed center line; alternate intervals of elytra finely ribbed.  (After Blatchley)

*Bitoma quadriguttata* Say (10541) is widely distributed, about 3 mm. long, blackish-brown with 3 dull reddish spots on each elytron, and found beneath bark and under logs.  The first tarsal joint is much shorter than in the preceding species.

Figure 472

*Coxelus guttulatus* Lec. (10551) 4-5 mm. long, black with reddish-brown legs, antennae and margins of thorax and elytra, ranges from Indiana eastward.  It differs from *Colydium* in having the first joint of the tarsi short.  There are but two segments in the antennal club.

## Family 81   LATHRIDIIDAE
### The Minute Brown Scavenger Beetles

These beetles are very small, usually reddish-yellow, or occasionally black.  They are found in decaying leaves and under stones.

1a Glabrous; front coxae separated. Fig. 473.

10642 *Enicmus minutus* (L.)

LENGTH: 1.5-2 mm. RANGE: cosmopolitan.

Usually brown; sometimes yellowish or blackish. Disk of thorax granulate.

*Coninomus constrictus* Gyll. (10633), 1.3-1.8 mm. has elytra without tubercles and the antennal club but 2 segments. It is cosmopolitan.

Figure 473

*Holoparamecus kunzei* Aube (10614) dull reddish-yellow and around 1 mm. in length, is known entirely across our continent. It is unlike the above two species in having the front coxal cavities open behind.

1b Pubescent; front coxae touching. Fig. 474.

10701 *Melanophthalma distinguenda* Com.

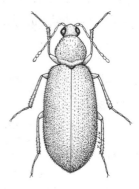

LENGTH: 1.5-1.8 mm. RANGE: cosmopolitan.

Dull brownish-yellow the elytra usually darker; long conspicuous pubescence yellowish.

*Corticaria serrata* (Payk.) (10685) is more elongate than the above and has but five ventral segments in the male. It is dull reddish-brown or reddish-yellow, measures about 2 mm. and is cosmopolitan.

*C. elongata* Gyll. (10693) 1.4-1.8 mm., is also common and cosmopolitan. It is light brownish- or reddish-yellow with rather long pale pubescence; the thorax is squarish and wider than long.

Figure 474

# Family 83 ENDOMYCHIDAE
## The Handsome Fungus Beetles

These fungus feeders range in size from 1 to 25 mm. They are usually strikingly colored and some are highly brilliant. The tarsi are 4 segmented throughout.

1a Thorax black; elytra red with 2 black spots. Fig. 475.

10753 Endomychus biguttatus Say

LENGTH: 3.5-4 mm. RANGE: general.

Shining. Black throughout except elytra which are red with black spots as pictured. Hibernates in adult stage. Common.

*Rhymbus ulkei* (Crotch) (10744) likely scattered over much of the eastern half of the U. S. measures less than 2 mm. and has reddish-brown thorax and elytra. Its rounded body, which is covered with pubescence distinguishes this genus from *Endomychus*.

Figure 475

1b Not colored as in 1a. Fig. 476. 10726 *Aphorista vittata* (Fab.)

LENGTH: 5-6 mm. RANGE: general.

Shining. Brownish-red marked with black as pictured. Common in fungi. (After Blatchley)

*Mycetina perpulchra* Newn. (10727) with a length of 4 mm. and ranging through the U. S. is shining black with thorax reddish-yellow, occasionally with blackish stripe on disk. Two reddish-yellow spots are on each elytron.

Figure 476

## Family 84  PHALACRIDAE
### The Shining Flower Beetles

The little over 100 American species of this family are tiny, highly convex, shining beetles. They and their larvae live on or in flowers. Sweeping is likely the surest way to get them.

1a Antennae inserted under the sides of the front, their base concealed from above; front and hind tarsi equal in length; scutellum large. Fig 477. 10764 *Phalacrus simplex* Lec.

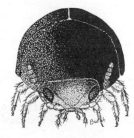

LENGTH: 2-2.3 mm. RANGE: Central and Western United States.

Red-brown or blackish; legs and antennae paler.

*P. politus* Melsh. (10773), measuring around 2 mm. is somewhat shining and black with paler legs and antennae. The antenna is slender, its third joint equalling the fourth and fifth combined.

Figure 477

195

**1b** Antennae inserted at sides of front with base visible from above; hind tarsi longer than others; scutellum not large...............2

**2a** Apex of prosternal spine with an acute free edge, and bearing a transverse row of spinules; second joint of hind tarsi not usually long. Fig. 478.       **(a)** 10829 *Stilbus apicalis* (Melsh.)

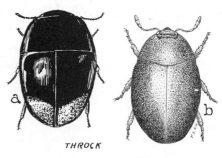

THROCK

Figure 478

LENGTH: 2-2.3 mm. RANGE: U. S.

Strongly convex. Shining. Dark chestnut-brown to blackish. Under parts reddish-brown; legs and antennae paler.

**(b)** 10844 *S. nitidus* (Melsh.)

LENGTH: 1.3-1.5 mm. RANGE: Eastern half United States.

Very shining. Pale reddish-yellow; elytra rounded at apex.

*Erythrolitus rubens* (Lec.) (10867) widely distributed, about 2 mm. long, is a shining pale reddish-yellow species, with basal joint of hind tarsi longer than those of the second leg.

**2b** Apex of prosternal spine inflexed, without a free sharp edge. Fig. **479.**       10780 *Olibrus semistriatus* Lec.

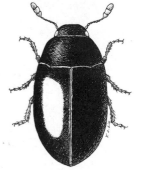

Figure 479

LENGTH: 1.8-2.2 mm. RANGE: Eastern half United States and Canada.

Shining. Dark chestnut-brown above; under parts, including legs and antennae, pale reddish-yellow.

*Acylomus ergoti* Csy. (10813), measuring around 2 mm. and shining black or chestnut brown, ranges through the Central and Eastern States.

*A. piceous* Csy. (10812) is much like *ergoti* in size, but differs in being distinctly narrowed behind the base of the elytra. It is piceousbrown and is eastern in its range.

# Family 85 COCCINELLIDAE
## The Lady Beetles

There are some 3000 known species of Lady Beetles. Some are very small; not any are large. Many are marked with spots on a colored background, but some possess a solid color. A few species eat plants, but for the most part they are preditors and are valued for the help they thus give. They are noticed by everyone and are favorites with many collectors.

**1a** Middle coxae narrowly separated; body glabrous, elongate, oval; femora of the long legs extending beyond the sides of the body; eyes not covered by thorax...................................15

**1b** Middle coxae widely separated; the femora usually not extending beyond the sides of the body; eyes partly covered by the thorax..2

**2a** Body compact, usually oval; epipleura narrow; usually flat and horizontal........................................................3

**2b** Body loosely jointed, usually rounded in form; epipleura wide and concave.........................................................8

**3a** Body pubescent.................................................6

**3b** Body glabrous.................................................4

**4a** Front tibiae with a strong spine on outer edge near middle; eyes with a small notch in front margin. Fig. 480.

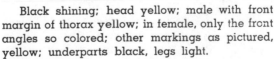

10972 *Brachyacantha ursina* (Fab.)

LENGTH: 3-4 mm. RANGE: Eastern half of United States; often common.

Black shining; head yellow; male with front margin of thorax yellow; in female, only the front angles so colored; other markings as pictured, yellow; underparts black, legs light.

*B. quadripunctata* Melsh. (10979), measuring 3 to 3.5 mm. is shining, black with yellow head in male, but in female, there is only a yellow V on an otherwise black head. It ranges from Iowa to Florida.

Figure 480

**4b** No spines on front tibiae; eyes without notch....................5

**5a Side margins of elytra marked. Fig. 481.**

Figure 481

10930 *Hyperaspis undulata* (Say)
LENGTH: 2-2.5 mm. RANGE: most of the United States, also in Canada.

Black, shining; male marked as pictured, with yellow; female with head and front margin of thorax, black.

*H. lateralis* Muls. (10874) The Lateral Lady Beetle, 3 mm., is shining black with front margin of thorax, humeral margin and an apical and larger median spot on elytra, yellow to red. It ranges from Montana to Mexico.

**5b Side margins of elytra wholly black. Fig. 482.**

Figure 482

10879 *Hyperaspis signata* (Oliv.)
LENGTH: 2.3-3.5 mm. RANGE: Eastern half of United States.

Black, shining with many punctures; male with head and narrow apical and side margins of thorax yellow; female with head and thorax wholly black. Spot on disk and sometimes a smaller one near apex of elytra yellow. (U.S.D.A.)

*H. quadrivittata* Lec. (10936), has two yellow stripes on margins of the black elytra. It ranges widely, especially in the West, and measures 2.5 mm.

**6a Elytra and thorax marked with yellow or red. Fig. 483.**

(a) 11115 *Scymnus terminatus* Say

Figure 483

LENGTH: 1.5-1.8 mm. RANGE: Eastern half of United States.

Piceous; head, narrow side margins of thorax, legs and apex of elytra reddish-yellow. Abdomen yellow except at base or sometimes wholly piceous. (U.S.D.A.)

(b) 11024 *S. caudalis* Lec.

LENGTH: 2-2.3 mm. RANGE: Colorado and eastward.

Black; head, sides of thorax, tibia and tarsi and often spot at tip of elytra dull reddish; femora piceous.

(c) 11128 *Cryptolaemus montrouzieri* Muls.

LENGTH: 3-3.5 mm. RANGE: California.

Shining. Black; head, thorax, tips of elytra, and abdomen reddish. Introduced from Australia to California to combat mealy bugs.

**6b Elytra and thorax wholly black**...............................7

**7a Pubescence distinctly apparent; tarsal claws bifid. Fig. 484.**

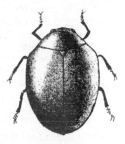

Figure 484

10998 *Stethorus punctatum* (Lec.)
LENGTH: 1.2-1.5 mm. RANGE: Eastern half of the United States.

Shining. Black; legs and antennae, except base of femora yellow. Distinguished from *Scymnus* by much shorter clypeus.

*Scymnus tenebrosus* Muls. (11055) with a length of 1.8-2.5 mm. and ranging through the eastern third of the United States is uniformly black, shining, with legs red or reddish-brown.

*S. nanus* Lec. (11079), also wholly black with reddish legs is much smaller, measuring only 1.3-1.5 mm. It seems to range from coast to coast.

**7b Apparently without pubescence unless examined with high magnification. Tarsal claws single pointed. Fig. 485.**

10989 *Microweisea misella* (Csy.)

Figure 485

LENGTH: .8-1 mm. RANGE: much of the United States.

Wholly black. It is valued in the West as a predator of the San Jose Scale.

*M. suturalis* Sz. (10995) less than 1 mm. long is shining black with brownish-red elytra, though black at the suture. It is valued in Southern California for feeding on San Jose Scale and red spiders.

**8a Upper surface pubescent**.......................................9

**8b Upper surface glabrous**.......................................10

**9a Fascets of eyes coarse; wholly black above. Fig. 486.**

11134 *Rhizobius ventralis* (Er.)
LENGTH: 2-2.5 mm. RANGE: California.

Shining or velvety black; abdomen reddish. (U.S.D.A.)

This Black Lady Beetle was introduced from Australia in 1892 and plays an important role in destroying mealybugs and soft scales in the orchards of California.

Figure 486

**9b Fascets of eyes fine; upper surface red and black. Fig. 487.**
**11129 *Rodolia cardinalis* (Muls.)**

Figure 487

LENGTH: 2.5-3.5 mm. RANGE: California and Florida.

Red with variable black markings; (the males usually have more black than red while the opposite condition is true of the females). The thick pubescence often grays and obscures the pattern. (U.S.D.A.)

This is the widely publicized Vedalia Lady Beetle, which has figured so favorably in keeping the Cottony Cushion Scale in check. It was first brought from its native Australia in 1888.

**10a Frontal plate not covering the base of the antennae............11**

**10b Frontal plate broadly dilated, covering the base of the antennae and subdividing the eyes; upper surface glabrous; front tibia with a small tooth, on outer margin near base. Fig. 488.**
(a) 11217 *Chilocorus stigma* Say   Twice-stabbed Lady Beetle.

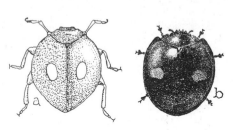

Figure 488

LENGTH: 4-5 mm. RANGE: throughout much of the United States and Canada.

Black and shining; elytra marked with two spots as pictured with red; the ventral segments red.

(b) 11218 The Asiatic Ladybird, *C. similas* Rossi, was introduced from China to help control the San Jose scale but did not satisfactorily establish itself. These two species are nearly identical.

*Axion plagiatum* (Oliv.) 11214, 6-7 mm., is marked like the preceding species but the red spots are much larger especially in the female.

**11a Upper surface pubescent.....................................12**

**11b Upper surface glabrous.......................................13**

**12a** Each elytron with seven black spots; thorax with 5 spots. Fig. 489.

Figure 489

**11229** *Epilachna borealis* Fabr. **Squash Beetle**

LENGTH: 7-10 mm. RANGE: Eastern third of United States.

Head, legs and upper surface yellow; markings black; under surface yellow to dark brown.

This genus has 4 known North American species. They are the "black sheep" of the Lady Beetle family as they are plant feeders while all the others are predacious on injurious pests. Both the adults and larvae of this species feed on cucurbits, especially squashes.

**12b** Thorax plain, each elytron with eight spots. Fig. 490.

Figure 490

**11231** *Epilachna varivestis* Muls. **Mexican Bean Beetle**

LENGTH: 6-9 mm. RANGE: originally Mexico but now covering much of the United States and Ontario.

Yellow to coppery brown, marked as pictured with black.

For many years this serious enemy of beans was found only in a few of our Western States. In 1920 it was found in Alabama from which point of infestation it has steadily spread. Both larvae and adults are leaf eaters. Another name is Bean Lady Beetle.

**13a** Antennae but slightly longer than the head; epipleura not reaching the tip of elytron......................................14

**13b** Antennae extending to or beyond the middle of thorax; epipleura entire. Fig. 491.

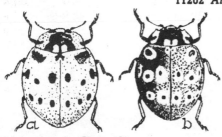

Figure 491

**11202** *Anatis quindecimpunctata* (Oliv.) **Fifteen-Spotted Lady Beetle**

LENGTH: 7-10 mm. RANGE: Eastern half U. S.

Head black and yellow; thorax and elytra yellowish to dark reddish-brown marked as pictured with black; the black spots almost obscure on the darker specimens.

In the variety *A. ocellata mali* (Say) 11202a (fig. 491b) each elytral spot is surrounded by a pale border. (Courtesy N. Y. State Museum)

**14a (a, b, c) Elytra plain red without any black marks. Fig. 492.**

11190 *Cycloneda munda* (Say) Red Lady Beetle
LENGTH: 4-5.5 mm. RANGE: United States and Canada.

Head black with two white spots in female and front margin white in male. Thorax black and white as pictured; elytra with varying intensities of reddish yellow sometimes very bright red.

*C. sanguinea* (L.) (11189) is highly similar and ranges throughout much of North America and South America.

Figure 492

**14b Each red elytron with one round black spot. Fig. 493.**

11193 *Adalia bipunctata* (L.) Two-Spotted Lady Beetle

LENGTH: 4-5 mm. RANGE: Europe and North America.

Head and thorax marked with black on a yellowish background; elytra yellowish red, with black spot as pictured; under parts black or reddish brown (U.S.D.A.).

This very common species hibernates in houses and is seen at the windows in early spring wanting out.

Figure 493

**14c Elytra red with nine black spots. Fig. 494.**

(a) 11184 *Coccinella novemnotata* Hbst.
LENGTH: 5.5-7 mm. RANGE: much of U. S.

Head and thorax black and pale yellowish; elytra yellowish-red marked with black as shown; legs and under surface black. (U.S.D.A.)

Both adults and larvae of this species, like many others of its family feed on plant lice. An adult has been known to eat 100 aphids per day.

(b) 11181 *C. trifasciata* L.
LENGTH: 4.5-5 mm. RANGE: Northern U. S. and Canada.

The black spots of the above are fused into bars for this species, as pictured.

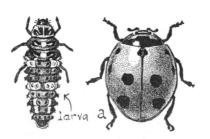

Figure 494

15a Claws divided into 2 sharp points, unequal in length; thorax with-
out a margin. . . . . . . . . . . . . . . . . . . . . . . . . . . . . . . . . . . . . . . . . . . . . . . . . . .16

15b Claws with a large quadrate basal tooth (a); thorax with a distinct
narrow margin at base. Fig. 495.
11158 *Ceratomegilla maculata* DeG. Spotted Lady Beetle

LENGTH: 5-7 mm. RANGE: most of the United
States and Canada.

Bright red or pink (not orange-red as in
many lady beetles) marked with black; undersurface black.

This very common species is destructive to
several important aphid pests. The adults congregate in rather large numbers for hibernation
and are thus found from late fall to early
spring.

Figure 495

The author has a tender feeling for this species, for it was with it
that he started his first insect collection when a child.

16a Legs wholly black; thorax with narrow white margin which does
not have a black dot. . . . . . . . . . . . . . . . . . . . . . . . . . . . . . . . . . . . . . . . . . .17

16b Tibiae and tarsi pale; each side of thorax with a wide white margin
and black dot. Fig. 496.
11162 *Hippodamia tredecim-punctata* (L.)
Thirteen-Spotted Lady Beetle

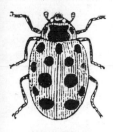

LENGTH: 4.5-5.5 mm. RANGE: widely distributed
throughout North America.

Head black at base, elytra yellowish-red with
black, markings which are variable in size in different specimens; femora and under surface of body
black. (After Riley)

Figure 496

Chapin, in his revision of the genus (1946) indicates that this species as such does not occur in North America but that ours is the subspecies *tribialis* (Say) which had formerly been considered a synonym
of *tredecim-punctata*.

**17a Black disk of thorax deeply indented at front and back with white. Fig. 497.**

11163 *Hippodamia parenthesis* (Say) Parenthesis Lady Beetle

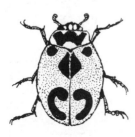

Figure 497

LENGTH: 4-5 mm. RANGE: most of the United States.

Elytra yellowish-red marked as pictured with black; legs and undersurface black.

We have known novice gardners to carefully pick the lady beetles from some aphid infested plant, supposing them to be the parents of the plant lice. If they had looked a bit closer they could have seen the lady beetles ravenously devouring the aphids and would not have made this costly mistake. It's a smart man who can correctly separate all his friends and enemies.

Asa Fitch, back in 1861, named twelve new species all from New York (maybe all from one garden). All twelve of these minor variants were presently made synonyms of the above species. Thus fame is sometimes short-lived with beetles as well as with politicians.

**17b Black disk of thorax marked with two converging yellowish-white dashes. Fig. 498.**     11173 *Hippodamia convergens* Guer. Convergent Lady Beetle; a, adult; b, pupa; c, larva.

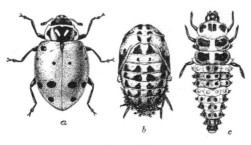

a

b

c

Figure 498

LENGTH: 6-7 mm. RANGE: throughout the United States and Canada.

Elytra from light to darker yellowish red marked with six or less black spots on each elytron. Legs and undersurface are wholly black.

*Hippodamia quindecim-maculata* Muls. (11172) is distinguished by the much larger spots and the front one along the suture somewhat double. The species *glacialis* (Fab.) (11171) lacks the three front spots or sometimes retains the humeral one.

The genus *Hippodamia* is a highly important one from the economic standpoint. It numbers less than 20 species but almost every one plays an important role.

HOW TO KNOW THE BEETLES

## OTHER LADY BEETLES

The Coccinellidae is another family, many species of which can be determined fairly accurately by the markings on the upper surface. A number of these as shown by Charles W. Leng and others, are reproduced here. Fig. 499.

Leng's catalog numbers appear over the drawings and opposite the names. The figures and letters following the names indicate the average size and color of the species. The main or ground color is indicated by capital letters. (B, black; N, brown; O, orange; R, red; W, white and Y, yellow.) Lower case letters following the capitals show the color of the markings. Thus No. 11028 as seen below is black with reddish-yellow markings and measures about 2 mm.; while No. 11150 has brown marking on a yellowish-white background and is about 2.5 mm. in length.

| 10880 | *Hyperaspis proba* (Say) | 3 B y-r |
| 10954 | *Hyperaspidius vittigera* (Lec.) | 2 N yw |
| 11028 | *Scymnus collaris* Melsh. | 2 B ry |
| 11094 | *Scymnus ornatus* Lec. | 2 B oy |
| 11097 | *Scymnus amabilis* Lec. | 2 B y |
| 11112 | *Scymnus myrimidon* Muls. | 2 B y |
| 11147 | *Coccidula lepida* Lec. | 3 YR b |
| 11150 | *Psyllobora viginta-maculata* (Say) | 2.5 YW n |
| 11150a | var. *parvinotata* Csy. | 2 YW n |
| 11150c | var. *renifer* Csy. | 1.6 YW n |
| 11150d | var. *taedata* Lec. | 2.5 YW n |
| 11154 | *Anisosticta strigata* Thunb. | 3 B y |
| 11155 | *Naemia seriata* (Melsh.) | 6 RY b |
| 11156 | *Macronaemia episcopalis* (Kby.) | 4 Y b |
| 11158a | *Ceratomegilla maculata floridana* (Leng) | 5 R b |
| 11159 | *Ceratomegilla vittigera* (Mann.) | 5 R b |
| 11165 | *Hippodamia sinuata* Muls. | 5 R b |
| 11165a | var. *spuria* Lec. | 5 OR b |
| 11168 | *Hippodamia americana* Cr. | 5 R b |
| 11169 | *Hippodamia dispar* Csy. | 4.5 R b *(now s. |11170) |

*Chapin—'46, has given subspecies rank to these, as indicated.

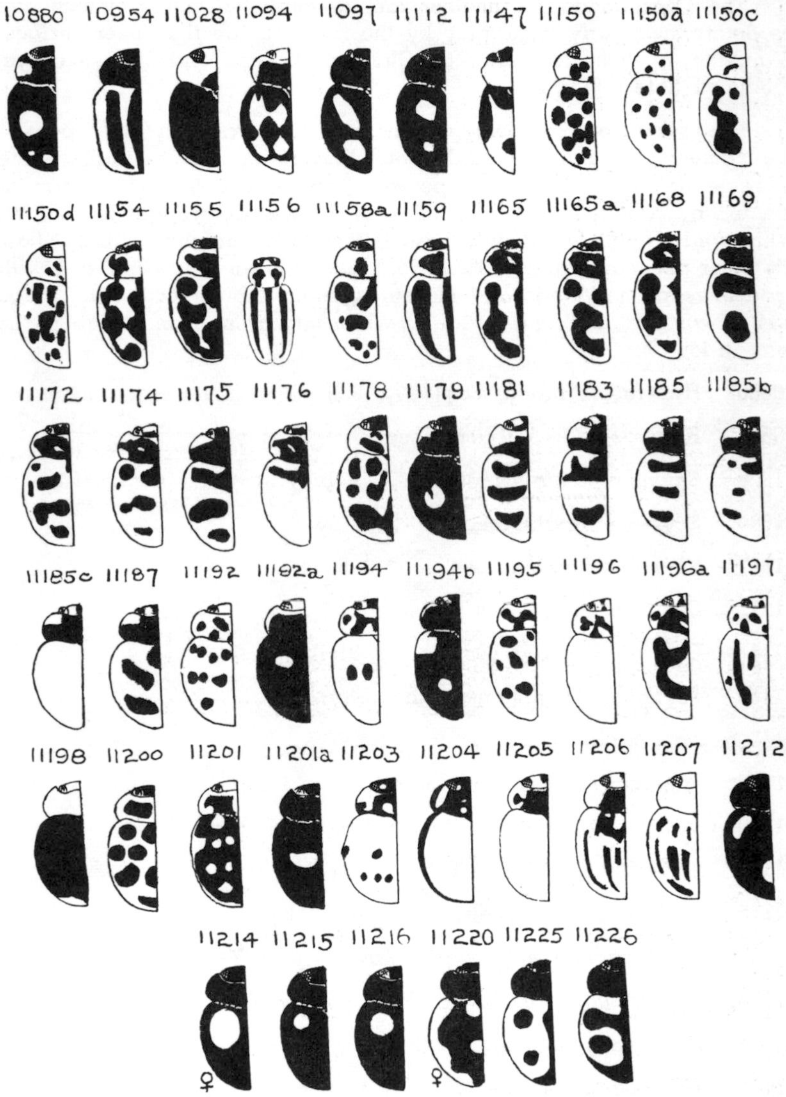

Figure 499

11172   *Hippodamia quindecim-maculata* Muls.      6 OR b
11174   *Hippodamia lecontei* Muls.      6 R b   *(now s. 11171)
11175   *Hippodamia quinquesignata* (Kby.)      6 R b
11176   *Hippodamia extensa* Muls.      5 R b   *(now s. 11171)
11178   *Neoharmonia venusta* (Melsh.)      6 Y b
11179   *Neoharmonia notulata* (Muls.)      5 B y
11181   *Coccinella trifasciata* L.      5 R b
11183   *Coccinella tricuspis* Kby.      4 R b
11185   *Coccinella transversoguttata* Fald.      7 O b
11185b   var. *nugatoria* Muls.      7 O b
11185c   (21863) *Coccinella californica* Mann.      6 R b
11187   *Coccinella monticola* Muls.      6 R b
11192   *Olla abdominalis* (Say)      5 NY b
11192a   var. *plagiata* Csy.      5 B r-w
11194   *Adalia frigida* (Schn.)      4.5 R b
11194b   var. *humeralis* (Say)      5 B r
11195   *Adalia annectans* Cr.      4.5 RY b
11196   *Cleis picta* (Rand.)      5 Y-ish b
11196a   var. *minor* Csy.      4 YW b
11197   *Cleis hudsonica* Csy.      4 YW b
11198   *Agrabia cyanoptera* (Muls.)      5 Blue
11200   *Anisocalvia duodecim-maculata* (Gebl.)      5 Y b
11201   *Anisocalvia quatuordecimguttata* (L.)      5 B yw
11201a   var. *similis* (Rand.)      5 B r
11203   *Anatis rathvoni* Lec.      8 R b
11204   *Anatis rathvoni s. lecontei* Csy.      10 NR b
11205   *Neomysia pullata* (Say)      7 YN b
11206   *Neomysia subvittata* (Muls.)      6 YN b
11207   *Neomysia horni* (Cr.)      7 YN b
11212   *Axion tripustulatum* (DeG.)      6.5 B r
11214   *Axion plagiatum* (Oliv.)      6.5 B r
11215   *Chilocorus tumidus* Leng      5 B r
11216   *Chilocorus cacti* L.      5 B r
11220   *Exochomus marginipennis* Lec.      3 B yn
11225   *Exochomus septentrionis* Weise      4 Y b
11226   *Exochomus davisi* Leng      5 Y b

*Chapin—'46, has given subspecies rank to these, as indicated.

# Family 86 ALLECULIDAE
## The Comb-clawed Bark Beetles

These are for the most part medium-sized plain brownish beetles, which may be found on leaves and flowers or under bark. The comb-cut tarsal claws are characteristic. The larvae, like those of the next family, resemble wireworms.

1a Tarsi with lobes on under side; thorax rounded in front. Fig. 500.

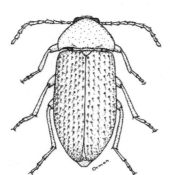

Figure 500

11251 *Hymenorus pilosus* (Melsh.)

LENGTH: 7-8 mm. RANGE: Central and Eastern States.

Shining. Dark reddish-brown to piceous; antennae, tibiae and tarsi lighter. Eyes separated by more than their own width.

*Lobopoda punctulata* (Melsh.) (11236), distinguished from the above genus by the head resting upon the prosternum and coxae, is dark chestnut with scattered fine yellowish pubescence. It has a wide range and measures 9-10 mm.

A good 50 species are known for this genus, most of them belonging to the Southwest.

1b Without lobes on under side of tarsi; apical segment of maxillary palpi broadly triangular...........................................2

2a Third segment of the long filiform antennae distinctly shorter than fourth; mandibles sharp pointed at tip. Fig. 501.

11355 *Androchirus erythropus* (Kby.)

Figure 501

LENGTH: 9-10 mm. RANGE: Eastern half of United States and Canada.

Dull. Grayish black; legs and antennae pale reddish-yellow. Third segment of antennae twice as long as second; eyes small and rather widely separated. (After Blatchley)

*A. femoralis* (Oliv.) (11356) ranging through the Southeast, is considerably darker in color.

2b Third segment of antennae wholly (or rarely, nearly) equal to the fourth............................................................3

3a Form elongate, sides somewhat parallel; antennae short and heavy; front tarsi not as long as tibiae. Fig. 502.

11327 *Mycetochara foveata* Lec.

Figure 502

LENGTH: 5-6 mm.   RANGE: Central States.

Shining   Dark reddish-brown; antennae and legs reddish-yellow; humerus of each elytron with a pale reddish spot as pictured. (After Blatchley)

*M. binotata* (Say) (11333), somewhat larger and ranging through the Central and Eastern States; has a large red spot about one-third way back on the elytra. It is a shining black.

3b Form more oval, with sides rounded; antennae slender. Fig. 503.

11311 *Isomira quadristriata* Couper

Figure 503

LENGTH: 5-6.5 mm. RANGE: Eastern half United States. and Canada.

Dark reddish-brown to piceous; the head and thorax nearly black; antennae and tibiae paler.

*I. sericea* (Say) (11307), with somewhat the same range and a bit smaller; is uniformly pale brownish-yellow and heavily covered with short pubescence. Its fourth segment of the maxillary palpi is long and slender instead of heavy as with most of the other members of the genus.

## Family 87   TENEBRIONIDAE
### The Darkling Beetles

These beetles are usually black or brown though occasionally more brightly marked.   Some are very small; others are medium sized or large.   The family is a large one.   Most of our American species are western in their range.

1a Ventral segments wholly corneous (stiff and heavily chitinized)....2

1b Hind margins of third and fourth ventral segments corneous.....9

2a Middle coxae with trochantins.................................3

2b No trochantins on middle coxae................................6

3a Labrum prominent; the mentum either small or somewhat notched..4

3b Labrum scarcely visible......................................5

4a Elytra wrapping well around the body; basal segments of front tarsi long; femora with bristly hairs. Fig. 504.

12019 *Megasattus erosus* (Horn)

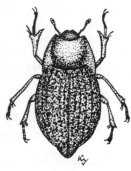

Figure 504

LENGTH: 17-19 mm.  RANGE: Southwestern states.

Moderately shining.  Black; elytra with coarse erosions and elevated smooth areas, but without definite ridges.

*Megasattus costatus* (Horn) (12020), having much the same range, size and color of the preceding is convex, and rather dull.  The elytra is subcostate with the intervening spaces closely punctured.

Discodemus reticulatus (Say) (12012) 12-15 mm. in length, is common in Arizona and New Mexico and may be found in some of the adjoining states.  Similar to *M. erosus*, it differs in having the epipleura and the elytral fold nearly smooth instead of roughly sculptured.

4b Elytra leaving much of the sides of the body exposed; basal joints of front tarsi shorter; eyes transversely reniform. Fig. 505.

12088 *Coniontis viatica* Esch.

Figure 505

LENGTH: 13-15 mm.  RANGE: California.

Smooth, shining.  Black; elongate, thorax wider than the base of elytra; legs wholly black, the under surface of front tibia being covered with spines.  Lives along the ocean shore.

*C. robusta* Horn (12064), more obtuse than the above and having heavier legs is variably punctured although sometimes wholly smooth.  Its size and range is similar to that of *viatica*.

**5a Mentum covering all the mouth parts without an attaching stalk. Fig. 506.**

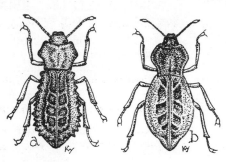

Figure 506

**(a) 11720 *Astrotus contortus* (Lec.)**

LENGTH: 10-12 mm. RANGE: Texas.

Dark brown with scattered scale-like hairs usually covered with a coating of gray matter. (Redrawn from Horn)

**(b) 11721 Astrotus regularis Horn**

LENGTH: 10-12 mm. RANGE: Texas.

Color and covering substantially the same as *contortus*. (Redrawn from Horn)

*Pactostoma anastomosis* (Say) (11724) 12-15 mm. in length and known from Kansas, Colorado and Arizona has the coxal cavities nearly rounded, the antennae slender with the segments longer than broad and the apex of the prosternum deflexed. The genus was formerly *Ologlyptus*.

**5b Mentum smaller, plainly stalked. Fig. 507.**

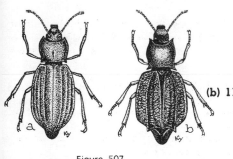

Figure 507

**(a) 11860 *Trichiasida semilaevis* (Horn)**

LENGTH: 18-23 mm. RANGE: southwestern states.

Dull black. Under surface with scattered coarse punctures. A stripe between suture and first costa. (Redrawn from Horn)

**(b) 11752 *Pelecyphorus aegrotus* Lec.**

LENGTH: 20-23 mm. RANGE: middle and southwestern states.

Black. Thorax with sides sinuate and base notched. (Redrawn from Horn)

**6a Mentum unusually large, covering both the ligula and the maxilla..7**

211

**6b Ligula and maxilla not covered by mentum. Fig. 508.**

**(a) 11671 *Phellopsis obcordata* (Kby.)**

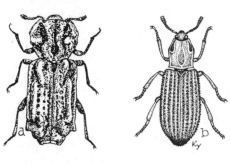

Figure 508

LENGTH: 11-14 mm. RANGE: Eastern United States.

Dull and somewhat flattened. Dark brown with rust-red effects. Thorax roughened and elevated as are also parts of the elytra. Feeds on fungi. (Courtesy N. Y. State Museum)

Closely related on our west coast *Phloeodes pustulosus* Lec. (11658) and *P. diabolicus* Lec. (11655) are known as Ironclad Beetles because of their very hard shell. The latter is wholly black while the former is grayish-black with whitish and black markings. Both are much roughened and measure 15-25 mm. They are found in California.

**(b) 11673 *Usechus lacerta* Mots.**

LENGTH: 5 mm. RANGE: Southwestern United States.

Differs from (a) in the eyes having large facets instead of small fine ones. The coxae are widely separated. (Redrawn from Horn)

**7a Front tibiae with but one terminal spur; mandibles with distinct external groove. Fig. 509.    11357 *Cnemodinus testaceous* Horn**

Figure 509

LENGTH: 7-8 mm. RANGE: Southwestern United States.

Yellowish-brown, pubescent with scattered yellow hairs. Scutellum triangular, longer than wide. (Redrawn from Horn)

*Metapoloba pruinosa* (Horn) (11575) 12 mm. long, is shining, rufopiceous, with the thorax broader than long. The body is winged as in the above but differs from it in having two spurs on the front tibiae.

**7b Two terminal spurs on front tibiae; mandibles not grooved on outer surface. . . . . . . . . . . . . . . . . . . . . . . . . . . . . . . . . . . . . . . . . . . . . . . . . . .8**

**8a Hind coxae small and widely separated; eyes with fine facets; legs long and slender. Fig. 510.**      **11634 *Craniotus pubescens* Lec.**

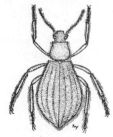

Figure 510

LENGTH: 11-13 mm. RANGE: Southwestern states.

Black. Antennae with 11 segments but appearing as 10 because of the very small conical first segment. (Redrawn from Horn)

*Bothrotes arundinis* (Lec.) 11551 ranging in the Central and Eastern States, has its thorax as wide as elytra. It measures 15-18 mm.

**8b Hind coxae not widely separated; scutellum well developed; antennae filiform. Fig. 511.**      **11514 *Trimytis pruinosa* Lec.**

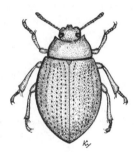

Figure 511

LENGTH: 5-7 mm. RANGE: Western States.

Shining. Black; thorax below with scattered coarse punctures. (Redrawn from Horn)

*Metoponium bicolor* Horn (11412) known from California and Arizona, (6-7 mm.) is black except head and thorax which are rusty-brown.

**9a Front wholly corneous.** . . . . . . . . . . . . . . . . . . . . . . . . . . . . . . . . . . . . . . . . . .**10**

**9b Front with a coriaceous margin or band between it and the labrum, metasternum very short. No inner wings. Fig. 512.**

         **12485 *Meracantha contracta* (Beauv.)**

Figure 512

LENGTH: 11-13 mm. RANGE: United States and Canada.

Very convex, robust. Black with greenish bronze sheen; antennae and legs piceous; elytral striae but feebly impressed with intervals thickly and finely punctured.

This very interesting beetle found under bark does not seem much like others of its family. There is but this one species of the genus, although it has been renamed several times to make 4 or 5 synonyms.

**10a Tarsi compressed; first joint very short.........................11**

**10b Tarsi not compressed, first joint not especially short...........12**

**11a Sides of head in front of eyes prominent; antennae 10 jointed. Fig. 513.**  12295 *Bolitotherus cornutus* (Panz.)

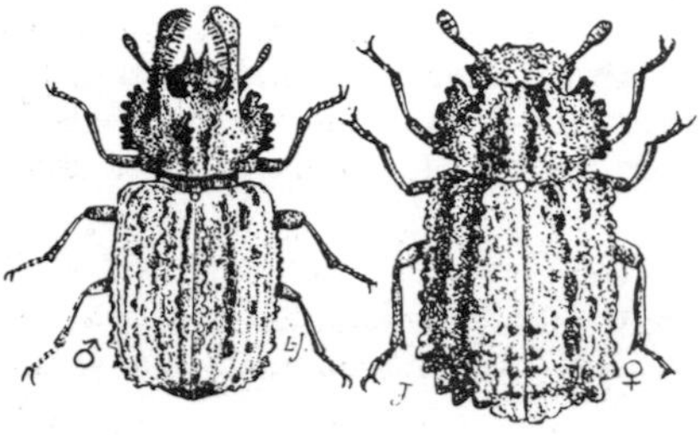

LENGTH: 10-12 mm.  RANGE: Eastern half United States.

Black or brownish, much roughened. The male (a) with two horns as shown. They live in old fungi, on old logs and when disturbed lie motionless so that they are very difficult to distinguish from pieces of the wood and fungi. (Courtesy N. Y. State Museum)

Figure 513

**11b Sides of head in front of eyes not prominent; antennae pectinate. Fig. 514.**  12301 *Rhipidandrus flabellicornis* (Sturm.)

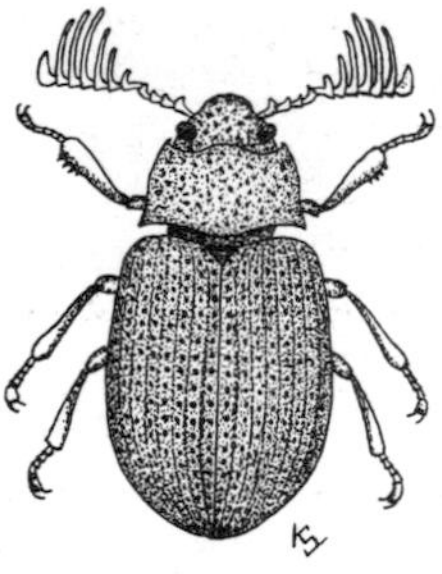

LENGTH: 2-3 mm.  RANGE: widely distributed.

Convex. Black, legs and antennae reddish-brown. Eyes large, convex, coarsely granulate. Antennae pectinate beginning at fifth joint. ((Redrawn from Horn)

*Eledona agaricola* (Hbst.), (12304) a dull brown species measuring 3-4 mm. ranges through Europe and North America. It is distinguished from the above by having emarginate eyes.

Figure 514

**12a Eyes usually rounded, more prominent than sides of front.......13**

**12b Eyes somewhat transverse, notched in front and less prominent than sides of front...........................................17**

**13a First segment of hind tarsi longer than second.................14**

214

**13b First segment of hind tarsi not longer than second. Fig. 515.**

12305 *Diaperis maculata* Oliv.

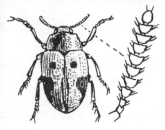

LENGTH: 6-7 mm. RANGE: general.

Convex. Black. Head and elytra marked with orange-red as pictured; legs wholly black. Commonly found living gregariously under bark and in fungi. (After Riley)

Out in the southwest *D. rufipes* Horn (12306), about the same size as the above but with pale orange markings on the legs and 2 cross bands and an apical spot orange on each elytron takes over.

Figure 515

**14a First joint of hind tarsi longer than 2nd and 3rd together........15**

**14b First joint of hind tarsi longer than the second only. Fig. 516.**

12309 *Hoplocephala bicornis* (Fab.)

LENGTH: 3-4 mm. RANGE: North America.

Upper surface metallic bluish-green; prothorax occasionally brownish; under parts piceous. Males with 2 short horns on clypeus and 2 longer ones on vertex. Females without horns. Very common on old fungi.

*Hoplocephala viridipennis* (Fab.), (12308) rather generally distributed and about the same size as the preceding differs from it in having the head, thorax and under surface orange-red.

THROCK
Figure 516

**15a Last joint of maxillary palpi elongate, triangular. Fig. 517.**

12332 *Alphitophagus bifasciatus* (Say)

LENGTH: 2-2.5 mm. RANGE: Europe and North America.

Reddish-brown to blackish; antennae and legs paler; elytra marked with dull yellow. Under bark and in fungi.

*Pentaphyllus pallidus* Lec. (12333) is much the same size and shape but is uniformly colored a pale reddish brown, without spots or striae.

Figure 517

**15b Last joint of maxillary palpi broadly triangular................16**

**16α Head with horns if male, or tubercules if female on concave front. Fig. 518.**                               **12314 *Platydema excavatum* (Say)**

THROCK

Figure 518

LENGTH: 4.5-5.5 mm. RANGE: much of the United States and Central America.

Convex. Shining. Black; antennae and legs reddish-brown or blackish. Common.

*P. erythrocerum* C. & B. (12316) somewhat smaller and ranging in our southeast differs in being a dull reddish brown.

**16b Head without horns or tubercles. Fig. 519.**

**(a) 12321 *Platydema ellipticum* (Fab.)**

LENGTH: 5.5-7 mm. RANGE: Eastern half of United States.

Dull black with irregular reddish spot near base of each elytron.

**(b) 12328 *Platydema subcostatum* C. & B.**

LENGTH: 5.5-6.5 mm. RANGE: Eastern half United States.

Shining. Black. Antennae reddish-brown; legs piceous. Common under bark and in fungi.

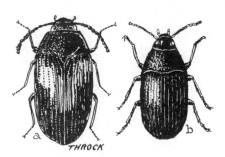

THROCK

Figure 519

*P. ruficorne* Sturm (12318) measuring 4-6 mm. and likely ranging through much of the eastern third of the United States, is dull black with a purplish tinge; the legs and under surface are brownish yellow; antennae pale reddish-yellow. The elytra have fine striae.

**17α Front coxae rounded; middle coxae with trochantin; third segment of antenna usually longer than 4th.** . . . . . . . . . . . . . . . . . . . . . . . . . .20

**17b Front coxae somewhat transverse; no trochantin on middle coxae; 3rd segment of antennae short.** . . . . . . . . . . . . . . . . . . . . . . . . . . . . . .18

18a Last 2 or 3 segments of antennae abruptly broadened. Fig. 520.
    (a) 12345 *Tribolium confusum* Duv. Confused Flour Beetle

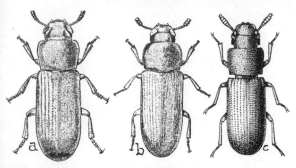

Figure 520

LENGTH: 4.5-5 mm. RANGE: Cosmopolitan.

Depressed. Reddish-brown. A very common pest of stored food products. Is distinguished from the Red Flour Beetle *T. castaneum* (Hbst.) (Fig. b.) (12343) which is also a universal food pest, by its gradually broadening antennae in contrast to the third abruptly widening segments at apex in the latter.

(c) 12341 *Latheticus oryzae* Wat.

LENGTH: 3 m. RANGE: cosmopolitan.

Pale yellow; antennae enlarging uniformly from base to beyond middle. A pest in cereal products and mills. (U.S.D.A.)

18b Antennae widening gradually from base to apex (see also 12341 above) ...................................................... 19

19a Scutellum scarcely wider than long; eyes but slightly emarginate; transverse. Fig. 521.     12338 *Gnathocerus maxillosus* (Fab.)

Figure 521

LENGTH: 3-4 mm. RANGE: cosmopolitan.

Reddish-brown. First segment of hind tarsus not longer than second and third. This introduced species thrives best in the Southern States. (U.S.D.A.)

The Broad-horned Flour Beetle *G. cornutus* (Fab.) (12336) is an introduced cosmopolitan pest of cereal products. It is shining brown, slender and 3-4 mm. long. Its name comes from the broad horns on the mandibles of the male.

19b Scutellum plainly wider than long; eyes rounded, not divided. Fig. 522.                    12349 *Palorus ratzeburgi* Wissm.

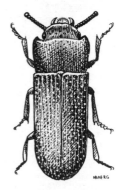

LENGTH: 3-3.5 mm.  RANGE: Europe and North America.

Shining. Reddish-brown. Thorax convex; nearly square.  Popularly known as the Small-eyed Flour Beetle.

The Depressed Flour Beetle *P. subdepressus* (Woll.) is a somewhat similar economic species.

Figure 522

20a Fourth segment of maxillary palpus, elongate, oval, acuminate. Head, thorax and legs clothed with yellowish scales. Fig. 523.
                    12271 *Alaudes singularis* Horn

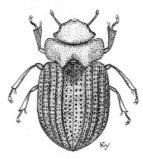

LENGTH: 1.5-2 mm.  RANGE: Southwestern United States.

Brownish moderately shining.  Head, thorax and legs clothed with yellow scales. This insect lives with ants and is blind. (Redrawn from Horn)

Figure 523

*Uloma impressa* Melsh. (12353) 11-12 mm. in length, common under bark, ranges through the eastern part of the United States.  It is shining, chestnut-brown with reddish-brown legs.

*U. imberbis* Lec. (12354) 8-9 mm. differs from *impressa* in having the end of the antennae obliquely pointed instead of rounded.  The colors and range are similar to the above.

20b Without scales as in 20a; fourth segment of maxillary palpi triangular. . . . . . . . . . . . . . . . . . . . . . . . . . . . . . . . . . . . . . . . . . . . . . . . . . . .21

218

**21a Front very short and broadly dilated on the sides.  Western species.  Fig. 524.**                    **12258 *Conibius gagates* Horn**

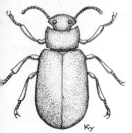

LENGTH: 6-7 mm.  RANGE: Southwest.

Rather dull.  Black.  Head, thorax and elytra densely set with fine punctures.  Under parts black, shining with whitish bloom when recently emerged.  (Redrawn from Horn)

Figure 524

In the genus *Blapstinus*, the antennal segments 4-8 are longer than broad instead of just the opposite, as in *Conibius*.  Some 50 species are known.

*B. dilatus* Lec. (12214) 9-10 mm. is abundant under logs in Arizona and California.  It is black or dark brown; the thorax is feebly convex and is strongly sinuate at its base.  It has a thin cover of brownish hairs.

*B. pulverulentus* Mann. (12234) 5-6 mm. is abundant throughout California.  It is shining black.  The thorax is less sinuate at its base than in *dilatatus*.

**21b Not as in 21a.............................................................22**

**22a Tarsi with a dense coating of fine silken hairs beneath.  Fig. 525.**
                                        **12389 *Merinus laevis* (Oliv.)**

LENGTH: 18-26 mm.  RANGE: Europe and United States.

Feebly shining.  Black.  Femora strongly club-shaped; epipleura not reaching tip of elytra.

A very common and widely scattered species, *Alobates pennsylvanica* (DeG.) (12407) resembles the former but the femora are more slender and the epipleura reaches to tip of elytra.  It measures 20-23 mm.  Hibernates gregariously under bark.  Associated with it but much less common *A. barbata* (Knoch) (12408) may be readily distinguished by a tuft of long yellowish hair on the mentum.

Figure 525

**22b Tarsi with scattered coarse pubescence or spines beneath.......23**

**23a** Elongate sub-depressed, cosmopolitan beetles; elytra not extending over most of the sides of the body. Fig. 526.

(a) 12413 *Tenebrio obscurus* Fab. The Dark Mealworm

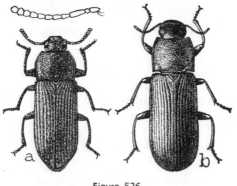

LENGTH: 14-17 mm.
RANGE: cosmopolitan.

Dull. Blackish on dark reddish-brown. Intervals granulate.

**(b) 12414 *Tenebrio molitor* L. The Yellow Mealworm**

LENGTH: 13-16 mm.
RANGE: cosmopolitan.

Shining. Blackish. Intervals convex densely punctured.

Figure 526

Both of these species have been introduced from Europe. Their larvae, known as meal worms, resemble wireworms. They are abundant in the grain debris at mills and storage places.

**23b** Elytra extended to cover much of the sides of the body; segments at apex of antennae broader.................................**24**

**24a** Epipleura very narrow not reaching the humeral angle. Fig. 527.

12008 *Embaphion muricatum* Say

LENGTH: 15-18 mm. RANGE: Western half of United States.

Shining. Black, occasionally brownish. The sides of the thorax and abdomen extend into thin lateral plates which are inclined at an angle and often tinted bluish. The wing covers are attached to the back. The larvae along with those of the following genus are known as false wireworms. (Courtesy Kansas State Bd. Agr.)

Figure 527

**24b** Epipleura broader at the base and reaching the humeral angles..**25**

**25a Front tarsi of both sexes wholly spinous beneath; elytra flattened.**
**Fig. 528.** **(a) 11953 *Eleodes suturalis* (Say)**
LENGTH: 23-26 mm. RANGE: the Midwest.

Shining. Black; often with a broad dull red stripe at middle of back; thorax flat. Flightless since wing covers cannot be raised. (U.S.D.A.)

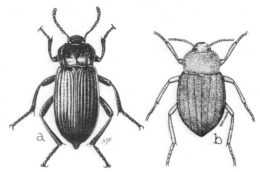

Figure 528

**(b) 11933 *E. tricostata* (Say)**
LENGTH: 16-20 mm. RANGE: Mexico to Canada in western half of continent.

Black with tinge of ash gray. Elytra with heavy ridges giving it its name. (Courtesy Kansas State Board of Agr.)

This genus is a large one and contains many of the beetles most frequently seen in the West.

**25b Anterior tarsi of males with first two or three segments only, pubescent beneath (not spinous). Fig. 529.**
**(a) 11949½ *Eleodes opaca* (Say)**
LENGTH: 11-14 mm. RANGE: West of the Missouri river.

Dull. Black, somewhat grayed with very fine white pubescence. Each elytron with 5 ridges. The larvae is known as the Plains False Wireworm and is a serious pest of wheat. (Courtesy K.S.B.A.)

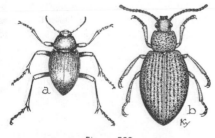

Figure 529

**(b) 11944 *Eleodes granosa* Lec.**

LENGTH: 16-19 mm. RANGE: California and Nevada.

Black. Elytra covered with rows of elevated rounded tubercles, not hairy. This genus is a large one with more than 75 recorded species, practically all of them western. (Redrawn from Horn)

A very large species (30-35 mm.) is *E. gigantea* Mann. (11993) from our West Coast. Its upper surface is smooth and shiny.

# Family 90 MELANDRYIDAE*
## The Melandryid Bark Beetles

These beetles live under bark or in fungi and vary considerably in size. Black or brown is their usual color. They are often covered with a heavy coat of pubescence.

1a Tarsal claws undivided......................................2

1b Tarsal claws with an appendage at base. Fig. 530.
12589 *Osphya varians* (Lec.)

Figure 530

LENGTH: 5-8 mm. RANGE: general.

Blackish. With scattered fine gray prostrate hairs. Thorax reddish-yellow marked with black as pictured, the marks often fused into one or variable.

*Mycterus scaber* Hald. (12594) measuring 4.5 mm., black with yellow legs and antennae, ranges through the Eastern half of the United States.

2a Next to last segment of tarsi simple............................3

2b Next to last segment of tarsi excavate and notched, somewhat lobed beneath. Fig. 531. 12552 *Melandrya striata* Say

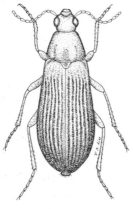

Figure 531

LENGTH: 8-15 mm. RANGE: Eastern half United States.

Shining. Black. Antennae reddish-brown, pubescence fine and scattered. Often common under bark.

*Dircaea quadrimaculata* (Say) (12570), ranging rather widely and measuring 7-11 mm., may be recognized by the two irregular yellowish spots on the reddish-brown to blackish elytra.

*A later name for this family is SERROPALPIDAE.

**3a The last 3 or 4 joints of antennae abruptly thickening into a club.**
**Fig. 532.**                    **12525 *Pisenus humeralis* (Kby.)**

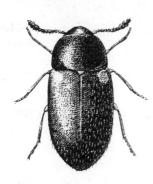

Figure 532

LENGTH: 3-4 mm. RANGE: Central and Eastern United States.

Convex. Shining. Blackish with scattered fine short yellowish hairs; legs and antennae dark reddish-brown. Elytra marked with a reddish spot on each humeri as shown. Often common on fungi.

*Abstrulia tesselata* (Melsh.) (12521), with a length of 3.5 mm. and ranging from New York to Virginia westward, differs from the above in having four segments in the antennal club instead of but three. It is pisceous with dull yellow legs and antenna.

*Tetratoma truncorum* Lec. (12519) 4.5-6 mm. in length and known from Iowa eastward, is elongate-oval and strongly convex. The elytra are steel blue; head and antennae black; thorax, legs and under surface reddish-yellow. The thorax is wider than long with its sides much rounded and its hind angles obtuse. It is told from the above species by its larger size and the margins of the thorax not turning upward as in the other two.

**3b Antennae thickening gradually or filiform.................4**

**4a Front coxal cavities with opening at side. Fig. 533.**
                    **12527 *Penthe obliquata* (Fab.)**

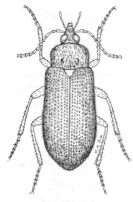

Figure 533

LENGTH: 11-14 mm. RANGE: Eastern half United States.

Somewhat flattened. Velvety black throughout except scutellum which is densely covered with long yellow-orange hairs.

*P. pimelia* (Fab.) (12528) about the same size and range is almost identical with the above except that the scutellum is black (lacking the orange hairs). Both species hibernate under bark gregariously.

223

**4b Front coxal cavity without a fissure at side. Fig. 534.**

12531 *Eustrophinus bicolor* (Fab.)

THROCA

Figure 534

LENGTH: 5-6 mm.  RANGE: United States.

Convex.  Shining.  Black, sparsely pubescent; abdomen and legs reddish-brown; last segment of antennae reddish-yellow.

*Holostrophus bifasciatus* (Say) (12537), ranging through the eastern half of our country and measuring 4-6 mm., has blackish elytra marked with two yellowish bands.

*Hallomenus scapularis* (Melsh.) (12540) 4.5-5 mm. in length, lives in fleshy fungi and is widely distributed.  It is piceous to dark reddish-brown, with antennae, legs and base of elytra dull brownish-yellow. The thorax is one-half wider than long, with deep impressions on each side near the base.

# Family 91   PTINIDAE
## The Spider Beetles

Some 500 or more species are known.  They are dull colored and feed on organic matter and often cause serious damage to food stores.

**1a Erect hairs on elytra shorter; areas as shown marked with pale scales. Fig. 535.**

12613 *Ptinus fur* L. White-Marked Spider Beetle

Figure 535

LENGTH: 2.5-3.5 mm.  RANGE: cosmopolitan.

Male, pale brown to reddish-yellow; female, darker brown.  This beetle is sometimes a serious pest of stored grain products and museum specimens.

Two other similar species of the Hairy Spider Beetle *P. villiger* (Reit) (12610) and the Storehouse Beetle, *Gibbium psylloides* (Czemp.) (12600) shining brown above and measuring 3 mm. or less, are in each case economic and widely distributed.

1b Erect hairs of elytra longer; no markings on elytra, except on humeral area of female. Fig. 536.

      **12612 Ptinus hirtellus Sturm**    Brown Spider Beetle

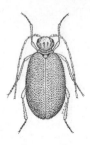

Figure 536

LENGTH: 2.7-3.5 mm. RANGE: widely distributed.

Pale brown to darker. Head, back of antennae smooth. An introduced species.

*Sphaericus gibboides* (Boield.) (12602) is a tiny species (1.8-2.2 mm.), brown, clothed with pale brown and yellow scales. It is distributed world wide and lives in all kinds of food products.

*Mezium americanum* Lap. (12601) 2.5-3 mm. long, dull yellow with shining black elytra, feeds upon dry animal substances and is cosmopolitan. The thorax is sub-cylindrical with a blunt tubercle at each side.

## Family 92 ANOBIIDAE
### The Drug-store and Death-watch Beetles

These are small dull-colored beetles which bore in wood or other organic substances. The mating call in some cases is made by bumping the head against the wall of the wooden burrow, giving rise to strange tales of haunted houses, etc. More than 1000 species are known.

1a Thorax not margined at sides; front of head not margined. Fig. 537.
      **12639 Eucrada humeralis (Melsh.)**

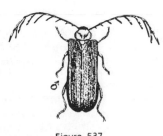

Figure 537

LENGTH: 4-6 mm. RANGE: Eastern half of United States and Canada.

Dull. Black, marked on thorax and elytra as pictured with reddish-yellow; elytra with coarse punctures in rows. (After Blatchley)

*Ernobius cupressi* VanD. (12651), 5-6 mm. long, shining brown with yellow pubescence, breeds in the cones and dead wood of the Monterey cypress in California.

1b Thorax margined at sides and front of head with margin at apex...2

**2a Antennae of male fan-shaped; outer margin of front tibia forming an apical tooth with margin above it finely dentate. Fig. 538.**
12864 *Ptilinus ruficornis* Say

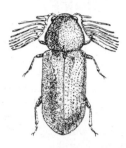

LENGTH: 3-5 mm. RANGE:Eastern United States and Canada.

Cylindrical. Dull. Black; antennae and legs reddish-yellow. Often common on dead branches of oak and maple in which the larvae live. (Courtesy N. Y. State Museum)

*P. pruinosus* Csy. (12868) is also black and dull. It measures from 3 to 3.5 mm. and is known from Indiana and Ontario. It differs from *ruficornis* in that the margin of the thorax is poorly defined.

Figure 538

**2b Not as in 2a..................................................3**

**3a Head when at rest received on the under surface of the thorax which is excavated for it. Fig. 539.**
12689 *Sitodrepa panicea* (L.)

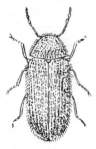

LENGTH: 2.5-3.5 mm. RANGE: cosmopolitan.

Fairly robust. Reddish-brown with yellowish pubescence. Elytra finely striate, the striae punctured. This "drug store beetle" has some amazing tastes in the field of drugs as well as food products.

*Xeranobium desertum* Fall (12680) 7-8 mm. long, brown with gray hairs, breeds in the stems of greasewood in the Southwest.

Figure 539

*Trichodesma gibbosa* (Say) (12695) measuring 4.5-6.5 mm. and known from Iowa, Florida, Canada, etc., is oblong, robust and densely covered with grayish-white hairs. The thorax is a bit narrower than the elytra, its disk elevated and bearing many fine erect hairs. At the crest of the thorax is a divided tuft of brown and brownish-yellow hairs with two smaller tufts in front of it. The front coxae are widely separated.

**3b Head very strongly reflexed and retracted; the mandibles often reaching the metasternum.....................................4**

**4a** 2nd and 3rd legs received at rest in special cavities on ventral side; antennae usually received between front coxae. Fig. 540.

12824 *Catorama confusum* Fall

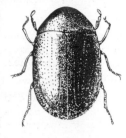

LENGTH: 2-3 mm. RANGE: general.

Convex. Dark piceous brown, pubescent, coarse punctures on sides of elytra and thorax.

*Dorcatoma dresdensis* Hbst. (12839) about the same size and cosmopolitan in range is shining black with gray pubescence. The segments of the antennal club are notched on their front edge.

Figure 540

**4b** Without grooves to receive 2nd and 3rd legs; grooves for antennae on head. Fig. 541.

12742 *Lasioderma serricorne* (Fab.) Cigarette Beetle

LENGTH: 2-3 mm. RANGE: cosmopolitan.

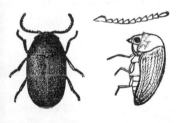

Convex. Dull. Reddish - brown or brownish-yellow. Front angles of thorax acute. This beetle feeds not only on tobacco but also on such tasty foods as ginger, cayenne pepper, figs and other hot stuff. (U.S.D.A.)

*Vrilletta decorata* VanD. (12724), 5-6 mm., black with yellow markings on the elytra, breeds in the dead wood of live oak in the Southwest.

Figure 541

*Petalium bistriatum* (Say) (12754) 1.7-2 mm. in length, is fairly common and widely distributed from Texas north and east. It is black or dark reddish-brown, with antennae and legs usually lighter. It differs from the above species in having the front coxae expanded at the apex into horizontal plates.

## Family 93   BOSTRICHIDAE
### The Powder-post Beetles

Many of these are so tiny that their larvae make "pinholes" in lumber; a few species are large with a maximum length of about two inches. Reddish-brown to black are the usual colors.

**1a** Head not covered by the prothorax; front coxae separated by a lobe. Fig. 542.                                                                      12924 *Polycaon stouti* (Lec.)

Figure 542

LENGTH: 11-21 mm.   RANGE: Western States.

Wholly black; punctures on head and thorax coarse, on elytra fine.   It breeds in the dead wood of many western trees and occasionally invades living wood.

*P. confertus* Lec. (12927) 7-15 mm. in length, elongated, cylindrical, black with brown elytra, damages many fruit trees and other plants in California and Oregon.

The Spotted Limb Borer, *Psoa maculata* (Lec.) 6-8 mm. is another destructive California species.   It is bronze-colored with a covering of gray hairs.   The elytra, blackish or bluish-green, bear several reddish, yellow or white spots.

**1b** Head covered by prothorax.....................................2

**2a** First and second segments of antennae longer than the middle ones. Fig. 543.                                                                12877 *Xylobiops basillare* (Say)

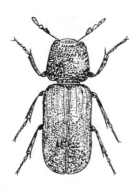

Figure 543

LENGTH: 5-6 mm.   RANGE: United States and Canada.

Cylindrical.   Black, marked with dull reddish-yellow as pictured; antennae with 10 segments.

The "Lead Cable Borer" *Scobicia declivis* (Lec.) (12874) is an interesting near relative, known from the West.   This cylindrical black or dark brown beetle (5-6 mm.) feeds on dry wood of several species as a steady diet, but tops off on lead telephone cables to the consternation of the linemen, who have dubbed it the "Short Circuit Beetle."

**2b** First and second antennal segments shorter than the middle ones; front without margin. Fig. 544.

12888 *Amphicerus hamatus* (Fab.)

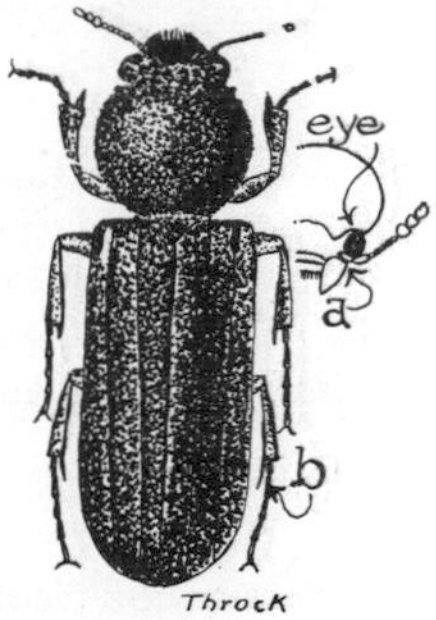

LENGTH: 6-9 mm. RANGE: East of the Rockies.

Cylindrical. Brownish-black, with scattered recumbent pubescence. Its official common name is "Apple Twig Borer."

The "big boy" of the family is *Dinapate wrighti* Horn (12923) which measures 30-52 mm., dark brown to black, and bores in palms in Southern California.

*Bostrichus bicornis* (Web.) (12902) 7-12 mm. in length, ranges from Iowa to Florida and Connecticut. It is dull, piceous and ornamented with irregular patches of yellow scales. Each elytron has two longitudinal ridges which distinguish it from *Lichenophanes armiger* (Lec.) (12898) which has but one short ridge on each elytron and is somewhat smaller.

Throck

Figure 544

# Family 94   LYCTIDAE
## The Lyctid Powder-post Beetles

Less than 100 species of tiny but highly destructive woodborers belong to this family. They range in color from yellow to brown, reddish and black.

**1a (a. b. c)** Thorax longer than wide. Fig. 545.

12938 *Lyctus opaculus* Lec.

LENGTH: 3-5 mm. RANGE: Eastern half United States.

Dark reddish-brown or blackish, with scattered yellow hairs, head and thorax usually darker than elytra. Feeds in dead oak and other wood. (After Blatchley)

*L. brunneus* (Steph.) (12937) is an Oriental species introduced in bamboo goods. The head and thorax are black and the other parts brown. (4-5 mm.)

Figure 545

1b **Thorax as wide as long. Fig. 546.**

**12940 *Lyctus planicollis* Lec. Southern Lyctus Beetle**

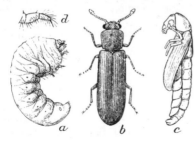

Figure 546

LENGTH: 4.5-5.5 mm. RANGE: general.

Subdepressed. Black, elytra with fine punctures in rows. (U.S. D.A.)

a, larva and leg (d); b, adult; c, pupa.

*L. parallelopipedus* (Melsh.) (12934) may be distinguished from *planicollis* by the front angles of the thorax being not rounded. The elytra are only a bit wider than the thorax, but about three times as long. It has a coat of fine yellowish hairs over dull reddish-brown. It measures 3.5-4 mm. and is known from Iowa and to the east and southeast.

1c **With single row of large punctures on elytra. Fig. 547.**

**12943 *Lyctus linearis* (Goeze.)**

Figure 547

LENGTH: 2.5-3.5 mm. RANGE: cosmopolitan.

Subdepressed. Reddish-brown. Introduced from Europe. (Courtesy N. Y. State Museum)

The Western Lyctus, *L. cavicollis* Lec., (12939) rusty-brown, slender and measuring 2.5 to 3 mm. bores in hickory, oak, orange and eucalyptus on the West Coast area.

# Family 96 CISIDAE
## The Minute Tree-fungus Beetles

These black or brownish, somewhat-elongate beetles seldom measure over 3 mm. They live under bark and in bracket fungi.

1a Clypeus with 2 triangular teeth; thorax of male with a lobe in front. Fig. 548.                    12958 *Cis cornuta* Blatch.

LENGTH: 2-2.5 mm.   RANGE: Eastern United States.

Robust.   Dark reddish-brown, clothed with erect yellowish hairs; the legs and antennae paler.   (After Blatchley)

*Ennearthron* is another important genus being characterized by antennae of nine segments instead of 10 as in *Cis*. *E. thoracicorne* Ziegl. (13018) which ranges widely throughout the United States and Canada is but 1.5 mm. long.   It is dark reddish brown and highly polished.

Figure 548

1b Clypeus without teeth; third segment of antennae longer than fourth. Fig. 549.                    12972 *Cis fuscipes* Mellie

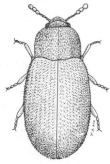

LENGTH: 2.5-3 mm.   RANGE: Eastern half of United States.

Convex.   Black to dark reddish-brown; antennae and legs paler.   Common beneath bark and in fungi.

The members of the genus *Ceracis* have only 8 antennal segments.   *C. sallei* Mell. (13030), dull reddish-yellow with elytra blackish at base and ranging widely, is but 1.3 mm. in length.

Figure 549

## SCARABAEOIDEA

1a Plates composing antennal club flattened and capable of close apposition.   Fig. 550......2

flattened plates

Figure 550

1b Plates of antennal club not capable of close apposition, usually but slightly flattened. Fig. 551.
..............................................3

Figure 551

Antennae are really quite remarkable organs. Their function is sensory; receptors for the senses of at least touch, hearing and smell often have their principal location on the antennae. When a beetle is seen opening and closing the antennal plates, he is both "sticking up his ears" and "sniffing the air."

2a Abdomen with five visible ventral segments; epimera of the mesathorax not reaching the coxae (a). Elytra usually covered with tubercules. (The Skin Beetles) Fig. 552. Family 98, TROGIDAE.
.................................................. page 246

Figure 552

They are shaped like many of the Scarabaeids but have the elytra roughened with tubercles. The color is a blackish gray but they are often so incrusted with foreign matter that they must be cleaned to be sure of the color.

2b Abdomen with six visible ventral segments, or if only five, then the epimera of the metathorax reaching the coxae. (The Scarabaeids or Dung Beetles) Fig. 553. Family 97, SCARABAEIDAE..page 233

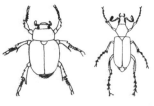

Figure 553

The species of this large family are highly variable in size and coloring yet the beginner soon comes to recognize members of the family at sight. The antennae and other key characters need to be checked when in doubt.

3a Antennae not elbowed. Mentum deeply notched, the ligula, filling the notch. Fig. 554. Family 100, PASSALIDAE.

14064 *Popilius disjunctus* (Ill.)

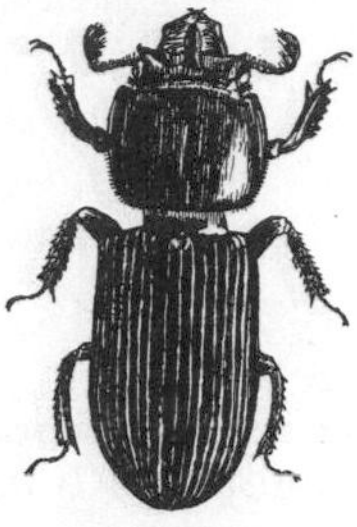

LENGTH: 30-36 mm. RANGE: Eastern half United States.

Somewhat flattened, shining. Black, head with short bent horn. Elytral striae deep and finely punctured.

This is known as the "Horned Passalus" or the "Bess-beetle." Both adults and larvae are often very abundant in decaying logs. The light brown adults sometimes found, have of course but recently emerged and have not had time to turn black. A revision of the family in 1935 changed the well known name of *Passalus cornutus* Fab. to the above.

Figure 554

3b Antennae nearly always geniculate (elbowed); mentum entire. (The Stag Beetles). Fig. 555. Family 99, LUCANIDAE.........page 247

Only about 30 species are known for our whole region, many others, fine big fellows live in the tropics. The large head and very large mandibles are characteristic of the more outstanding species.

Figure 555

# Family 97  SCARABAEIDAE
## The Lamellicorn Beetles

Here is a great group of some 30,000 species of small to very large beetles. Some systematists would prefer to make it into several families, but only the Trogidae is being separated here. *Megasoma actaeon* Linn. from South America, is likely the largest and heaviest beetle known. The Atlas Beetle *Chalcosoma atlas* (L.), found in Asia, is an attractive, bulky beetle measuring 4 inches or more. This family has produced a good number of extra large, heavy species, the largest of which are found in tropical areas.

1a Spiracles placed in a line on membrane at side of abdomen; last 3 segments of club gray tomentose; dung beetles...................2

1b Club of antennae glabrous; not more than 1 or 2 spiracles on membrane, not living on dung.....................................11

233

2a Hind tibiae with 2 spurs at apex; pygidium usually covered; coxae
   touching. . . . . . . . . . . . . . . . . . . . . . . . . . . . . . . . . . . . . . . . . . . . . . . . . . . . . . . .7

2b Hind tibiae with but one apical spur; pygidium exposed; hind coxae
   usually separated. . . . . . . . . . . . . . . . . . . . . . . . . . . . . . . . . . . . . . . . . . . . . . . .3

3a Middle and hind tibiae much widened at tip; males often with horn
   on head or thorax. . . . . . . . . . . . . . . . . . . . . . . . . . . . . . . . . . . . . . . . . . . . . . .4

3b Middle and hind tibiae slender, curved; no horn on head or thorax.
   Fig. 556.                                    13048 *Canthon laevis* (Drury)

LENGTH: 11-19 mm.  RANGE: United States.

   Usually, dull black with coppery tinge; (in south and west becoming deep blue or bright green). The ball which it rolls receives an egg and contains enough dung to mature a grub. It is presently buried for protection while the grub hatches and matures.

Figure 556

4a Labial palpi 3 jointed. . . . . . . . . . . . . . . . . . . . . . . . . . . . . . . . . . . . . . . . . . .5

4b Labial palpi 2 jointed; not over 9 mm., scutellum not visible.  Fig. 557.
                                               13080 *Onthophagus hecate* Panz.

LENGTH: 6-9 mm.  RANGE: United States and Canada.

   Dull.  Black with scattered grayish hairs; thorax of male with scoop like horn, variable; much smaller on female.  Common in carrion and dung.  (After Forbes)

   *O. cribricollis* Horn (13087), rather widely scattered from Indiana to Texas, is a deep metallic purple and much smaller (3.5 mm.).  Both sexes display the same convex thorax, without a horn or other protuberance.

Figure 557

5a Large beetles; 10 mm. or more; front coxae short. . . . . . . . . . . . . . . . .6

**5b Front coxae transverse; not over 8 mm. Fig. 558.**

13057 *Ateuchus histeroides* (Web.)

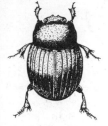

LENGTH: 6-7 mm. RANGE: Eastern half of United States.

Convex. Bronzed-black above; under parts chestnut-brown. Clypeus notched, usually with 2 teeth. Elytral striae fine. Often common in dung. (After Blatchley)

The genus name was formerly *Choeridium*, Chapin in '46 made the change to the above generic name.

Figure 558

**6a Metallic green; no tarsi on front legs of male. Fig. 559.**

13072 *Phanaeus vindex* MacL.

LENGTH: 14-23 mm. RANGE: from Rockies eastward.

Robust; flattened above. Head bronzed; thorax coppery; elytra bluish-green or green. Clypeus of male with long curved horn; with a tubercle in female. Showy flattened disk on thorax of male. This is a much decorated beetle that seldom fails to attract attention.

Figure 559

**6b Black; front legs with tarsi. Fig. 560.**

13059 *Pinotus carolinus* (L.)

LENGTH: 20 - 30 mm. RANGE: widely distributed.

Robust. Shining. Black. Elytra each with seven shallow striae. Street light attracts many insects. This species is often among them. (After Riley)

Figure 560

This is our most bulky member of the family and is found in many parts of our area. Some tropical Scarabaeids rival small mammals in size.

**7a Antennae of eleven segments.....................................10**

235

**7b** Only 9 segments in antennae.................................... 8

**8a** Outer terminal angle of hind tibiae obtuse...................... 9

**8b** Outer terminal angle of hind tibiae elongated into a spine; color black. Fig. 561.                13233 *Ataenius cognatus* (Lec.)

LENGTH: 4-5 mm.  RANGE: general.

Convex.  Shining.  Piceous-black; legs and narrow front margin of thorax reddish-brown; clypeus with several fine wrinkles.  Common in dung and fungi and at lights.

*Psammodius interruptus* Say (13244) is a central and western species (3-4 mm.).  Thorax black with head and elytra brown and under parts reddish-brown.  This genus is distinguished from the preceding by its triangular tarsal segments instead of cylindrical ones.

Figure 561

**9a** Head with 3 small tubercles on vertex, hind tibia fringed at apex, with short equal spinules.  Fig. 562.

(a) 13119 *Aphodius fimetarius* (L.)

LENGTH: 6-8.5 mm.
RANGE: Europe and North America.

C o n v e x.  Shining. Black; elytra brick red; thorax reddish-yellow near front angles. Very common in half-dry cow dung.

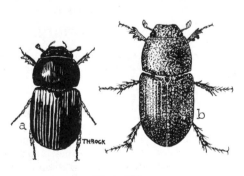

Figure 562

(b) 13131 *A. granarius* (L.)

LENGTH: 4-6 mm.
RANGE: cosmopolitan.

C o n v e x.  Shining. Piceous; legs reddish-brown, antennae paler. Common in dung and fungi.

236

**9b Spinules on apical edge of hind tibiae unequal, head ordinarily without tubercles. Fig. 563.**

13184 *Aphodius distinctus* (Mull.)

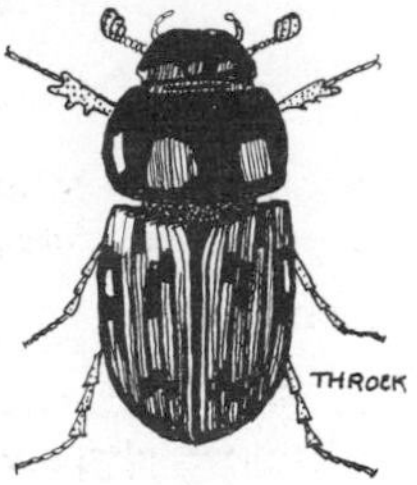

Figure 563

LENGTH: 4.5-5.5 mm. RANGE: Europe and North America.

Convex. Head and thorax piceous; elytra dull yellow marked with black as pictured. Very common.

More than a hundred species of this genus have been named. *A. femoralis* Say (13201) is a widely distributed and very common native species (4.5-6.5 mm.). Head and thorax are black, the latter with yellowish margins; the elytra are brownish with paler margins; legs and antennae reddish-brown.

**10a Antennal club large, round, and convex on both sides; eyes entirely divided. Fig. 564.**

13288 *Bolbocerosoma farctum* (Fab.)

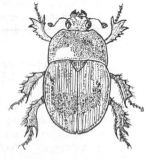

Figure 564

LENGTH: 8-12 mm. RANGE: East of Rockies.

Robust. Convex. Yellowish-red with variable black markings on whole upper surface. An interesting and attractive beetle, not very common.

With eyes but partly divided, *Eucanthus lazarus* (Fab.) (13289) a shining, chestnut-brown species, 6-11 mm., is rather widely scattered but is more common. It is occasionally fairly abundant at lights.

**10b Antennae with smaller club, composed of leaf-like plates. Fig. 565.**

13299 *Geotrupes splendidus* (Fab.)

LENGTH: 12-17 mm. RANGE: Eastern half of United States.

Convex, robust. Brilliant metallic purple, green or bronze. Common under manure but sometimes on carrion.

*G. blackburni* (Fab.) (13293) (13-16 mm.) is black with sheen of bronze; its first hind tarsal joint equals the next three. *G. opacus* Hald. (13296) is dull black, sometimes with purplish tinge, (12-15 mm.).

Figure 565

11a Mandibles plainly visible from above, bent, leaf-like; front coxae transverse............................................................21

11b Mandibles scarcely visible from above, not leaf-like............12

12a Claws of equal length or no spur on hind tibiae...............14

12b Claws, especially of hind leg almost always unequal in length; 2 apical spurs on hind tibiae....................................13

13a Elytra with membranous border; hind tibiae longer than the femur. Fig. 566.

(a) 13754 *Popillia japonica* Newm. Japanese Beetle

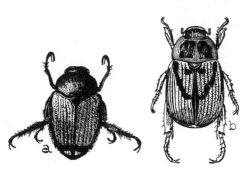

Figure 566

LENGTH: 7-13 mm.

RANGE: Asia and steadily spreading in United States.

Robust. Head and thorax shining greenish-bronze; elytra tan or brownish with green margins; abdomen metallic green with white spots along sides and two white spots on pygidium. This pest was introduced into our country in 1916. The adults eat the leaves and fruit of many plants while the grubs feed on the roots.

(b) 19986 *Anomala orientalis* Waterh. Oriental Beetle

LENGTH: 6-9 mm. RANGE: Eastern United States.

Yellowish brown with black markings as pictured; highly variable, the upper surface being sometimes almost wholly black.

238

13b Elytra without a membranous border. Fig. 567.

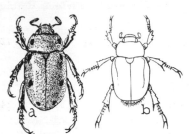

(a) 13755 *Pelidnota punctata* (L.)

LENGTH: 20-25 mm. RANGE: North America.

Convex, rather dull brownish-yellow with black markings. Under parts blackish or greenish-bronze. The adults feed on grape leaves while the grubs feed on the roots of various trees.

(b) 13769 *Cotalpa lanigera* (L.)

Figure 567

LENGTH: 20-26 mm. RANGE: Eastern half of United States and Canada.

Robust. Head, thorax and scutellum greenish or yellow with a strong metallic sheen; elytra yellowish, less metallic; under parts dark, densely clothed with long wooly hairs. Feeds on willow. Popularly known as the "Goldsmith Beetle." Occasional sport forms show areas of dark green or chestnut. A western form *C. tau* Wick. (13773) was so named by Wickham from the brown "T" formed by a sutural stripe, topped by a stripe across the thorax. Saylor in his revision ('40) has reduced it to a synonym.

14a Clypeus notched at sides in front of eyes, exposing base of antennae.................................................................24

14b Clypeus not as in 14a......................................15

15a Head with an erect horn between the eyes; mentum nearly semicircular. Fig. 567½.

13302 *Pleocoma fimbriata* Lec. Fimbriate June Beetle

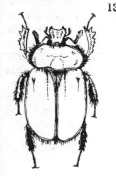

LENGTH: 18-28 mm. RANGE: California.

Females; robust, shining, brown; heavily clothed on under side with long fine hairs. Males; considerably smaller than females and black.

Several other species of this genus are found in California and adjoining states.

Figure 567½

15b Mentum large, nearly square..............................16

16a Only one spur at most on middle and hind tibia; hind tarsae with but one claw; body scaly. Fig. 568.

13695 *Hoplia trivialis* Harold

LENGTH: 6-7 mm. RANGE: Central and Eastern United States.

Dull black; upper surface covered with hair-like scales; pygidium and abdomen covered with silvery scales.

The Grape-vine Hoplia of the west coast, *H. callipyge* Lec. (13689) is destructive to many other plants as well as grape. It measures around 7 mm. and is mottled brown.

Figure 568

16b Two spurs on both middle and hind tibiae; tarsi with 2 claws.....17

17a Brownish, (sometimes iridescent) heavy, robust beetles.........18

17b Dull yellow or metallic green or bronzed elongated beetles.......20

18a With five ventral segments; with punctured striae or elytra rather evenly punctured. Fig. 569.      13455 *Diplotaxis harperi* Blanch.

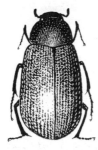

LENGTH: 8-10 mm. RANGE: Eastern half of United States.

Convex, shining. Reddish-brown to blackish; elytra each with three indistinct ridges each of which bears scattered punctures with a row of punctures on each side.

*D. tenebrosa* Fall (13395) (7.5-10 mm.) ranges throughout the West. It is black, and damages young fruit trees.

Figure 569

18b With six ventral segments....................................19

**19a Not over 10 mm. with small regular grooves on disk. Fig. 570.**
**13356 *Serica evidens* Blatch.**

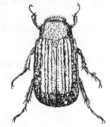

LENGTH: 8-10 mm.  RANGE: Central States.

Brown, feebly shining; under parts reddish-brown.

*S. anthracina* Lec. (13369), 7.5 mm., dark brown to black defoliates fruit trees from British Columbia to California.

Figure 570

Some 23 species in all are known for this genus, of which *S. sericae* (Ill.) (13364) is one or the most common and widely distributed. It is piceous or purplish-brown with a marked iridescence. Several species have a notch at each side of the clypeus; this and a few others do not. It is 8-10 mm. long.

**19b 11.5 mm. or larger; without striae or grooves. Fig. 571.**
**(a) 13515 *Phyllophaga fervida* (Fab.)**

LENGTH: 17-23 mm.  RANGE: general.

Robust, shining.  Dark reddish-brown to blackish.  This is one of the more abundant of our over 100 species of May beetles, the larvae of which are the well known "white grubs" (c).

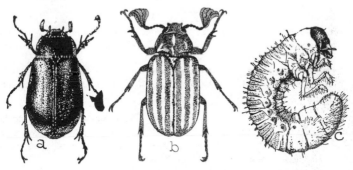

Figure 571

**(b) 13610 *Polyphylla crinata* Lec.**

LENGTH: 22-28 mm.  RANGE: Pacific Coast States.

Robust, brown, striped with silver scales as pictured.  This is one of a number of "Lined June Beetles" belonging for the most part to the West or South-west.

241

**20a Elytra covered with hairs, not scaly. Fig. 572**

13649 *Dichelonyx elongata* (Fab.)

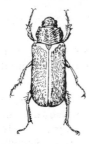

LENGTH: 8-10 mm. RANGE: Eastern half United States and Canada.

Head and thorax dark reddish-brown or blackish; elytra dull brownish-yellow often with greenish, bronze or purplish sheen.

Crotch's Green Pine Chafer *D. fulgida* Lec. (13657), a slender reddish-black beetle measuring about 9 mm. has bright metallic green elytra. It feeds on pine leaves in the mountains from Montana and British Columbia to California.

Figure 572

**20b Elytra densely covered with elongate yellowish scales. Fig. 573.**

13685 *Macrodactylus subspinosus* (Fab.) Rose Chafer

LENGTH: 8-10 mm. RANGE: United States.

Dull brownish-yellow or reddish-brown thickly clothed with yellow scales. Under parts darker. (U.S.D.A.)

The Western Rose Chafer, *M. uniformis* Horn (13687), about 10 mm. long and yellowish brown, resembles *subspinosus* in structure and habits.

Figure 573

**21a Head or thorax, or both, with either a horn or tubercle.........22**

**21b Without horn or tubercles as above. Fig. 574.**

13803 *Cyclocephala borealis* Arrow

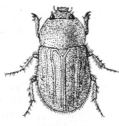

LENGTH: 11-14 mm. RANGE: United States. Convex. Pale yellow to dull brown clothed with scattered fine hairs. This "Desert June Beetle" ranges throughout the United States. Its grub is foe to the roots of grasses and cereals. The adults feed on pigweed. Being active at night it is often abundant at lights. (After Forbes)

Figure 574

**22a Greenish-gray with black spots; front tarsi of males elongated. Fig. 575.**
13908 *Dynastes tityus* (L.)

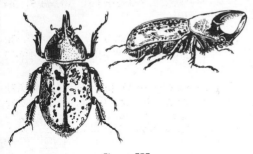

Figure 575

LENGTH: male 45-60 mm., female 40-48 mm.

RANGE: South, Central and Southeast United States.

Heavy. Usually gray with variable black or brown markings; rarely wholly chestnut brown. Male with horns as pictured; female with small tubercules only on head. (After Riley)

This genus has the distinction of including one of the world's largest known beetle *D. hercules* (L.). It lives in the West Indies and northern South America. The males may measure 6 inches or more. It is shaped much like *tityus*. The female is dull brownish or blackish and roughened with coarse punctures and a small tubercle on the head. The male is shining black; its elytra are spotted with black and dull green. A fringe of rust-red hairs ornament the long upper horn on its ventral side.

**22b Dark reddish-brown or blackish; males with front tarsi not elongated.** ...................................................................23

**23a Vertex with long horn (male) or tubercle (female); hind tibiae with blunt rounded teeth at tip. Fig. 576.**

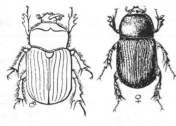

Figure 576

13902 *Xyloryctes jamaicensis* (Drury) LENGTH: 25-30 mm. RANGE: general.

Robust. Reddish or blackish-brown; under parts paler and covered thickly with red-brown hairs. Commonly known as "Rhinoceros beetle" but several other species also bear that name. (After Glover)

A very interesting mahogany-brown species, *Strategus antaeus* (Drury) (13896), inhabits our southern states. The male in addition to a prominent horn on its head has two other large horns, one at each side of the thorax. It is called the "Ox-beetle."

**23b Hind tibiae with hairs at apex but no teeth; head with a transverse ridge. Fig. 577.** (a) 13843 *Ligyrus gibbosus* (DeG.) Carrot Beetle

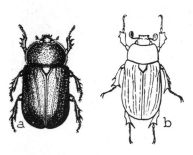

LENGTH: 11-16 mm. RANGE: general.

Robust. Reddish-brown, paler beneath. Punctures on elytra coarser than on thorax. This beetle becomes very abundant at times and may be taken in large quantities in light traps. (Courtesy Kans. St. Bd. Agr.)

(b) 13834 *L. relictus* (Say)

LENGTH: 18-23 mm. RANGE: Eastern half United States.

Figure 577

Robust. Shining. Brownish-black; transverse carina of head broken at middle. (After Knobel)

**24a Epimera of mesothorax not visable from above; sides of elytra not sinuate behind the shoulders.................................27**

**24b Epimera of mesothorax visable from above; sides of elytra sinuate back of shoulder............................................25**

**25a Thorax lobed to cover the scutellum. Fig. 578.**
13931 *Cotinis nitida* (L.) Green June Beetle

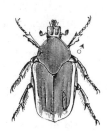

LENGTH: 20-23 mm. RANGE: Eastern and Southern States.

Robust. Dull velvety green marked with yellowish-brown as shown; under parts with metallic green and reddish-yellow. The larvae which feed on grass roots are peculiar in crawling on their back. Some other members of the genus are shining metallic green. (After Riley)

Figure 578

The Green Peach Beetle *C. texana* Csy. (13924), green to coppery and violet and somewhat larger than *nitida*, is abundant from Texas to Arizona on ripe fruit.

**25b Thorax not covering the scutellum...........................26**

26a Color wholly black; mentum cup-shaped; clypeus broad. Fig. 579.
13974 *Cremastocheilus castaneae* Knoch.

LENGTH: 9-10 mm. RANGE: from Colorado eastward.

Black, slightly shining. Elytra somewhat flattened with shallow impressions. Pygidium very coarsely punctate. The members of this genus of nearly 50 species seem to be associated with ants (perhaps even enslaved by them). (After Wheeler)

Figure 579

26b Color never wholly black; clypeus narrow; mentum normal. Fig. 580.          13940 *Euphoria inda* (L.) Bumble Flower Beetle

LENGTH: 13-16 mm. Range: general.

Heavy. Head and thorax dark, somewhat bronzed; elytra brownish-yellow with black spots. The whole insect densely hairy. It gets its name because of the buzzing noise it makes as it flies near the ground. The adults feed on fruit.

Figure 580

27a Hind coxae touching; thorax not grooved.....................28

27b Hind coxae separated; thorax with deep groove at middle. Fig. 581.          14030 *Valgus seticollis* (Beauv.)

LENGTH: 6-7.5 mm. RANGE: Eastern half United States.

Blackish-brown. Thorax coarsely punctate with large teeth on margins; elytra and pygidium granulate. Found on flowers during the Spring. (After Blatchley)

Figure 581

**28a Body very hairy; not over 13 mm. Fig. 582.**

14016 *Trichiotinus piger* (Fab.)

Figure 582

LENGTH: 9-11 mm. RANGE: Eastern half United States.

Robust. Head and thorax dark with greenish sheen and usually covered with erect yellowish hairs; elytra reddish-brown to piceous, marked with white; under parts bronzed, clothed with long white silken hairs. (U.S.D.A.)

Common on flowers of wild roses and many other plants. It is an interesting beetle which seems somewhat like a bee.

**28b Body almost wholly without hairs. Fig. 583.**

14012 *Osmoderma eremicola* Knoch.

Figure 583

LENGTH: 25-30 mm. RANGE: Eastern half United States.

Robust, flattened above, shining. Dark mahogany-brown to blackish; head deeply excavated between the eyes. Thorax with deep median line on basal half.

*O. scabra* (Beauv.) (14010) is similar in color and range but is smaller. 18-25 mm.

Both of these are found in rotting logs.

# Family 98   TROGIDAE
## The Skin Beetles

This family of about 150 cosmopolitan species (less than 30 in the United States) has been taken from within the Scarabaeidae which accounts for the catalog numbers being as they are. They are dull blackish gray with roughened thorax and elytra. They are carrion and dung feeders and often require cleaning before one can tell much about them.

Some systematists would now abandon the family and return them to the Scarabaeidae. Since there is no over-all umpire in the nomenclature game, changes like this are continually occurring, thus making even more difficult the always hard job of being consistent.

1a Elytra with very distinct rows of tubercles, covered with fine hairs.
Fig. 584.                                    13329 *Trox monachus* Hbst.

Figure 584

LENGTH: 13-16 mm.  RANGE: much of United States.

Dark brownish.  Elytra each with five rows of rounded or oval tubercles, tomentose at tip. Scutellum spear shaped.

The Trox beetles are so different in appearance from any other beetles as to be readily recognized.

1b Tubercles on elytra less distinct and without hairs.  Fig. 585.
                                             13331 *Trox suberosus* Fab.

Figure 585

LENGTH: 12-17 mm.  RANGE: United States and Canada.

Dull grayish-brown; elytra with blackish mottling.  Tubercles small with tiny tufts of hairs between them.

*T. terrestris* Say (13341) and *T. foveicollis* Harold (13340) are smaller species measuring only 5-6 mm.  Both have the scutellum oval.  The latter has erect brownish hairs on the tubercles while with *terrestris* the hairs are pale yellowish and scale-like.

## Family 99  LUCANIDAE
### The Stag Beetles

This family of usually large mahogany or black beetles are often characterized by great mandibles.  The larvae live in decaying wood. They are widely distributed and number nearly a thousand species, with but a few in our region.

1a Elytra smooth; front tibia with large teeth on outer side.........2

1b Elytra with striae and punctures.............................3

2a Mandibles with one tooth on inner side; femora light brown. Fig.
586.                                      14034 *Pseudolucanus capreolus* (L.)

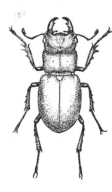

Figure 586

LENGTH: 22-35 mm.   RANGE: Eastern half of
United States.

Reddish-brown.   Mandibles of male twice as
long as those of female.   The larvae live in wood.
The adults are known as "Pinching bugs."

*P. placidus* (Say) (14036) 19-32 mm., is nearly
black.   Both sexes have more than one tooth on
inside of mandible.

*P. mazama* (Lec.) (14040) breeds in cottonwood
from Utah to Arizona and New Mexico.   It is
brown with black femora and measures 24-32
mm.

2b Female with black legs; male with mandibles as long as abdomen.
Fig. 587.                                      14037 *Lucanus elaphus* Fab.

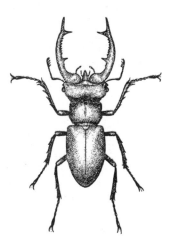

Figure 587

LENGTH: male including mandibles 45-
60 mm., female 30-35 mm.   RANGE:
Southeastern United States.

Shining.   Dark chestnut brown.   Legs
and antennae nearly black.

Closely related are some tropical species which attain extraordinary size.
Likely largest of all is an East Indies
species *Odontolabis alces* Fab.   This
bulky beetle may be fully 4 inches or
more in length.   India and Java present
the Giraffe Stag Beetle, *Cladognathus
giraffa* (Fab.); it is reddish-brown and
black.   Chile's "giant" *Chaisognathus
granti* Steph. is colored metallic dark
green with an iridescence of red.   Both
of these last two species have great
branched mandibles as long as the rest
of the body, giving them an over-all
length of about 4 inches.

These "pinch beetles" never fail to
attract attention even from chickens, cats
and dogs.

248

3a  Eyes notched.  Fig. 588.          14039 *Dorcus parallelus* Say

LENGTH: 15-26 mm.  RANGE: Eastern half United States.

Nearly black.  Males with head about as broad as thorax.  Elytra with deep striae and punctures.  It is known as the "antelope beetle."

The Rugose Stag Beetle, *Sinodendron rugosum* Mann. (14063) breeds in rotting oak, alder, laurel and willow from British Columbia to California.  It measures up to 18 mm., is shining black and has a short horn (more prominent on the male) on the head.

Figure 588

3b Eyes not notched.  Fig. 589      14041 *Platycerus virescens* (Fab.)

LENGTH: 10-12 mm.  RANGE: Northeastern half United States.

Black to dark reddish-brown, sometimes with metallic sheen.  Male with much larger mandibles than female.  Striae with scattered punctures but prominent.

The Oak Stag Beetle, *Platyceroides agassii* Lec. (14047), black and 10 mm. in length, breeds in some of the oaks of California while *P. latus* (Fall) (14053) a heavy-set, nearly-black species, 9-11 mm. is found within dead incense cedar in the same state.

Figure 589

## Family 101  CERAMBYCIDAE
## The Long-horned Woodborers

Here is a great family of some 20,000 widely scattered species.  The beetles usually possess long-to-very-long antennae.  They vary much in size and color, some tropical species attaining a length of several inches.  Brilliant metallic and pigmented colors are common.

1a Pronotum with a margin; labrum attached at sides.............3

1b Pronotum without a margin; labrum free........................2

2a Front tibiae with a groove, palpi pointed at tip.................37

2b Front tibiae without a groove; palpi not pointed at tip.........6

3a Antennae reaching beyond the thorax; segments not all alike.....4

**3b Antennae not reaching beyond thorax; segments similar. Fig. 590.**
**14067 *Parandra brunnea* (Fab.)**

Figure 590

LENGTH: 9-18 mm. RANGE: United States.

Somewhat flattened, shining. Mahogany brown or reddish, the mandibles darker. Elytra margined, not striate.

This beetle which bores in soft maple and other trees does not look much like a long-horned woodborer. The few members of this genus were formerly put in a separate family (Spondylidae), since the fourth joint of the tarsi is distinct and the antenna much shorter than with the other Cerambycids.

**4a Eyes surrounding the base of antennae on under side. Fig. 591.**
**14097a *Tragosoma depsarium harrisi* Lec.**

Figure 591

LENGTH: 30-34 mm. RANGE: United States and Canada.

Elongate, heavy, shining. Brown; antennae slender; elytra with raised lines and punctures. A variety of *depsarium* which is native to Europe and Asia. The eggs are said to be laid in pine stumps. (Courtesy N. Y. State Museum)

**4b Base of antennae not surrounded beneath by eyes; margin of pronotum with 3 teeth..........................................5**

**5a Form rather slender; antennae with 11 segments. Fig. 592.**
**14081 *Orthosoma brunneum* (Forst.)**

Figure 592

LENGTH: 22-40 mm. RANGE: general.

Shining. Chestnut brown; head deeply indented between the antennae. Elytra each with three raised lines, surface with closely placed fine punctures.

Bores in pine and possibly some of our broad leaves.

**5b Form broader; antennal segments more than 11. Fig. 593.**

14084 *Prionus laticollis* (Drury)

LENGTH: 22-48 mm. RANGE: Eastern half United States and Canada.

Shining. Blackish. Antennae of male longer than body. Its common name is "Broad-necked Root Borer."

"California Prionus," *P. californicus* Mots. (14086), 40-60 mm. long, shining dark reddish brown is a native of our west coast. Its thorax has a much narrower margin than in the preceding.

Figure 593

"Tile-horned Prionus," *P. imbricornis* (L.) (14089), 20-47 mm. and ranging from Kansas, north eastward, is readily told by the 16-20 overlapping segments in its antennae. It is dark reddish-brown.

**6a Base of antennae at least partly surrounded by the eyes; front coxae not conical...................................................24**

**6b Base of antennae not surrounded by the eyes...................7**

**7a Front coxae conical...........................................13**

**7b Front coxae transverse, not conical............................8**

**8a Ligula membranous, eyes finely granulate......................9**

**8b Ligula of chitin, base of pronotum not notched..................12**

**9a Elytra with narrow raised white lines; femora club-shaped; deep median groove in thorax. Fig. 594.**

14608 *Physocnemum brevilineum* (Say)

LENGTH: 12-16 mm. RANGE: Eastern United States and Canada.

Black. Elytra with bluish tinge, and raised whitish lines as shown. Bores in elm. (Courtesy N. Y. State Museum)

*Ropalopus sanguinicollis* (Horn) (14612), a related species, lacks the raised white lines on the elytra of the above. The thorax is very short and is colored red, while the remainder of the beetle is black. It measures 15-19 mm. and ranges from Canada to Pennsylvania and Ohio.

Figure 594

**9b Elytra without distinctly elevated whitish lines..................10**

**10a Labial palpi much shorter than the maxillary palpi; thorax rounded. .......................................................11**

**10b Palpi about equal; mesosternum obtusely triangular. Fig. 595.**

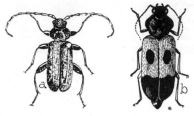

Figure 595

**(a) 14620 Callidium antennatum Newn.**

LENGTH: 13-14 mm. RANGE. United States.

Blackish-blue. Thorax and elytra thickly punctate, the punctures on the elytra being coarse. Feeds in pine. (Courtesy N. Y. State Museum)

**(b) 14614 Semanotus lignea (Fab.)**

LENGTH: 7-12 mm. RANGE: United States.

Black. Elytra with yellow or reddish markings. The front coxae are separated in contrast to those of the former which touch.

Several other species of *Callidium* may be mentioned. *C. violaceum* L. (14622) 10-13 mm. has blue elytra and thorax but is distinguished from *antennatum* by deeper punctures on the thorax. It seems to range widely in Europe and America. *C. californicum* Csy. (14624) also closely resembles *antennatum* but is smaller with shorter antennae. It bores in junipers in California and Oregon.

Fisher in 1920 named three other species of western range. *C. juniperi* Fisher (20097) 10 mm. is dark greenish-blue and known from New Mexico. *C. pseudotsuga* Fisher (20095) 10-13 mm. and dull black is known in California and Oregon. *C. sequarium* Fisher (20096) 11-12 mm. and wholly black, is found in dead sequoia limbs in California. (The higher catalog numbers indicate later naming, and record in the first supplement.)

**11a Length 5-9 mm. Fig. 596.**

Figure 596

**(a) 14646 Phymatodes varius Fab.**

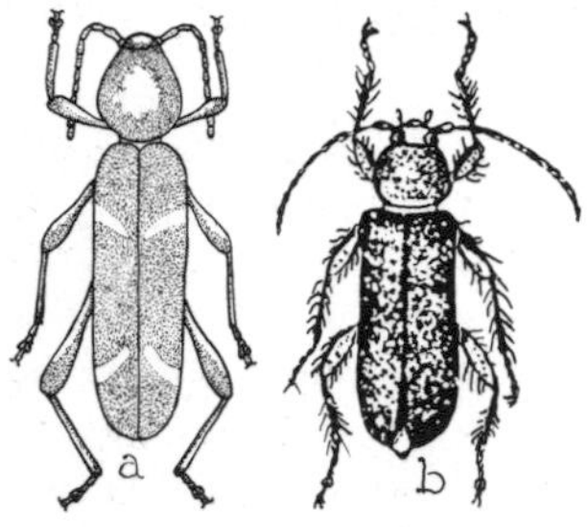

LENGTH: 6-9 mm. RANGE: United States.

Black, with prostrate pubescence. Elytra marked with white as shown and often reddish-brown at base.

**(b) 14630 P. amoenus (Say)**

LENGTH: 5-8 mm. RANGE: from Kansas east and in Canada.

Reddish-yellow; elytra shining blue. The larvae bore in grape stems. (After Packard)

**11b Length over 9 mm. Fig. 597.**

**(a) 14640 *Phymatodes dimidiatus* (Kby.)**

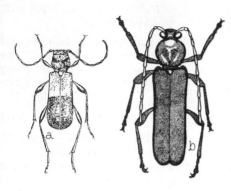

Figure 597

LENGTH: 9-13 mm. RANGE: United States, Canada and Alaska.

Head, thorax and back part of wings black. Basal half of wings, and the legs brownish. Feeds on spruce. (Courtesy N. Y. State Museum)

**(b) 14634a *P. testaceus variabilis* (L.)**

LENGTH: 12-13 mm. RANGE: Europe and North America.

Head blackish; thorax reddish-yellow, the center often darker. Elytra yellow, sometimes with blue at middle. Femora yellow or blue. Oak is its food plant.

*P. blandus* Lec. (14632) is orange-yellow with metallic blue or purple elytra. It feeds on wild grade in California and measures 5-6 mm.

*P. obscurus* Lec. (14638) 10-12 mm. is reddish-brown with violet elytra and feeds on some of the California oaks.

**12a Eyes divided; seemingly four. Fig. 598.**

**14124 *Tetropium cinnamopterum* Kby.**

Figure 598

LENGTH: 12-14 mm. RANGE: United States, Canada and Alaska.

Slaty or sooty brown; under surface and often sides of elytra reddish-brown. Two slightly raised lines on each elytron. Feeds on pine. (Courtesy N. Y. State Museum)

Two other members of the genus, *T. abietis* Fall (14123) 13-17 mm., brown, and *T. velutinum* Lec. (14128) 9-19 mm., blackish or brown, damage conifers. The latter ranges from Montana and British Columbia to Northern California, while *abietis* lives in the mountains of California.

253

12b Eyes not wholly divided though frequently deeply notched. Fig. 599.                                                        14107 *Asemum moestum* Hald.

LENGTH: 12-15 mm.  RANGE: general.

Blackish-brown; elytra with two prominent ridges. It seems to feed on pine and spruce. (Courtesy N. Y. State Museum)

The genus *Criocephalus* is closely related. The eyes are larger, not hairy, and more coarsely granulate.

Figure 599

*C. asperatus* Lec. (14135) ranging throughout the West is a slender almost black beetle measuring 20-27 mm.

13a Mandibles with a fringe on inner margin....................14

13b Mandibles normal; without a fringe........................23

14a Prosternum with a broad impression crossing its middle; pronotum with spines or tubercules on the side; hind tarsus with first segment pubescent beneath....................................15

14b Prosternum convex, with an impressed place at anterior end; neither spines or tubercules on pronotum....................19

15a Closed cell in anal region of wing...........................16

15b Wing not as in 15a.........................................18

16a Antenna slender and nearly uniform in diameter...............17

16b Antennal segments 5-11, much heavier than the preceding ones. Elytra with prominent ridges.  Fig. 600.

14298 *Rhagium lineatum* Oliv.

LENGTH: 13-18 mm.  RANGE: general.

Robust.  Black with markings of gray and reddish-brown pubescence as pictured.  Each elytron with three elevated lines; intervals with scattered coarse punctures.  The large white larvae burrow within the bark and sapwood of several species of pines. (After Marx.)

Figure 600

**17a Eyes prominent, large, coarsely granulate. Fig. 601.**

**14311 Centrodera decolorata (Har.)**

Figure 601

LENGTH: 25-28 mm.  RANGE: Eastern half United States and Canada.

Reddish-brown with scattered pubescence. Elytra truncate at tip.  Bores in beech and maple.  (Courtesy N. Y. State Museum)

C. sublineata Lec. (14315) with a length of 14 mm. and dark piceous, ranges from Pennsylvania to North Carolina, while Evodinus monticola Rand. (14349) is black with dull yellow elytra which bear black tips and four black spots near the suture.  It measures 9 mm. and ranges out of Canada to Wisconsin and North Carolina.

**17b Eyes finely granulated, large, with notch in margin. Fig. 602.**

**14415 Anthophylax attenuatus (Hald.)**

Figure 602

LENGTH: 15-17 mm.  RANGE: Northeastern United States.

Elytra olive, mottled with grayish pubescence; head and thorax black with scattered golden hairs.  Thorax with depressed line at middle.  Lives in beech.

A. malachiticus Hald. (14416) measuring 13 mm. is metallic blue to coppery and ranges around the Lake Superior region and into Canada.

**18a Upper surface polished, shining; but slight if any pubescence. Fig. 603.**

**14411 Gaurotes cyanipennis (Say)**

Figure 603

LENGTH: 9-10 mm. RANGE: Eastern United States and Canada.

Head, thorax and under surface black; elytra bluish-green; antennae and legs pale brownish-yellow.  (Courtesy N. Y. State Museum)

Feeding on pines on our West Coast and throughout northern United States and Canada as well as in Eurasia, Anoplodera sexmaculata (L.) (14424), 12 mm., is black with yellow elytra, each of which have three black areas.

255

**18b Upper surface heavily punctate and covered with a thick pubescent coat. Fig. 604.**      14407 *Acmaeops bivittatus* (Say)

Figure 604

LENGTH: 6-9 mm. RANGE: Eastern half United States.

Dull. Pale brownish-yellow; thorax and elytra marked in black as shown. Highly variable, being sometimes almost without markings. (After Wickham)

*A. pratensis* (Laich.) (14396) has its front and mouth much prolonged. It is wholly black except that the elytra are sometimes entirely or in part fuscous or dull yellow. It is 6-8 mm. long and is widely distributed.

**19a Last segment of labial palpi short and wide; usually truncate at end.** ....................................................20

**19b Last segment of labial palpi slender; body very slender. Fig. 605.**      14556 *Ophistomis luteicornis* (Fab.)

Figure 605

LENGTH: 9-13 mm. RANGE: Eastern United States and Canada.

Reddish-yellow with markings of black as pictured. The very narrow form of this genus attracts special attention. (After Blatchley)

Others of similar range are *O. famelica* (Newn.) (14553), 12-14 mm. with antennae black instead of reddish-yellow and elytra with spots on sides, *O. acuminata* (Oliv.) (14554), 8-10 mm. with head and thorax black; elytra yellow bordered with blackish, and *O. bicolor* (Swed.) (14560), 12-14 mm., reddish-yellow, with elytra wholly black.

**20a Apical antennal segments with definite pore-bearing spaces. Fig. 606.**      (a) 14540 *Typocerus zebra* (Oliv.)

Figure 606

LENGTH: 15-17 mm. RANGE: Eastern United States.

Upper surface black and golden yellow; under surface with dense golden pubescence; legs yellowish-red. (Courtesy N. Y. State Museum)

**(b) 14543 *T. velutina* (Oliv.)**
LENGTH: 10-14 mm. RANGE: Eastern United States.

Head, thorax and antennae black; elytra yellow, marked with reddish-brown as pictured; each puncture bearing a prostrate yellow hair.

20b Antennae without pore-bearing areas........................21

21a Hind angles of prothorax elongated.........................22

21b Hind angles of prothorax not lengthened. Fig. 607.
14441 *Brachyleptura vagans* (Oliv.)

LENGTH: 9-12 mm. RANGE: Eastern United States and Canada.

Black, usually with yellowish or reddish margin on elytra; sometimes with elytra wholly black or entirely yellow. (Courtesy N. Y. State Museum)

B. *rubrica* (Say) (14438), 10-16 mm., has reddish elytra and abdomen in male. The abdomen of female is black as is also all the remainder of the beetle.

Figure 607

22a Thorax with sides much rounded. Fig. 608.
14508 *Strophiona nitens* (Forst.)

LENGTH: 10-13 mm. RANGE: Eastern half United States and Canada.

Black, marked with golden yellow pubescence; antennae dark reddish-brown and legs pale reddish-yellow. (After Blatchley)

In the West, S. *laeta* (Lec.) (14510), 10-13 mm. golden yellow with three fairly wide black bands crossing the elytra, is abundant, breeding in oaks.

Figure 608

22b Thorax with sides not much rounded in front of middle. Fig. 609.
14482 *Strangalia subhamata* (Rand.)

LENGTH: 12-14 mm. RANGE: Eastern half United States and Canada.

Female reddish-yellow, marked with black as pictured. Male with black head and thorax; elytra with yellow stripe. (Courtesy N. Y. State Museum)

S. *soror* (Lec.) (14480) 12-18 mm., black and pale brownish-yellow, ranges in the Southwest.

Figure 609

257

23a Elytra with more than apical half blue. Fig. 610.

14574 *Desmocerus palliatus* (Forst.)

Figure 610

LENGTH: 17-23 mm. RANGE: Eastern United States and Canada.

Robust. Dark metallic blue. Elytra marked as pictured with golden yellow. This is a small genus of very attractive beetles. The other four species are western in range. All feed on elderberry, the larvae boring in the living stems. The adults congregate on the flowers.

Two species closely related to the above, yet appearing quite different, are of interest. In both the elytra are very short and do not cover the wings. *Necydalis mellitus* Say (14580) 13-21 mm. and found from Indiana eastward, is black and dull yellow with the tiny elytra reddish-brown or brownish-yellow.

*Ulochaetes leoninus* Lec. (14579) 20-26 mm. known from British Columbia to California is black and yellow; the long, densely placed yellow hairs on the thorax give it the appearance of a bumblebee.

23b Elytra wholly golden orange or as pictured. Fig. 611.

14575 *Desmocerus auripennis* Chev.

Figure 611

LENGTH: 23-28 mm. RANGE: California, Nevada.

Black with bluish sheen. Elytra of male wholly golden orange; female with mid-dorsal variable greenish or bluish mark.

*D. californicus* Horn (14577), has the elytra margined orange in both sexes, while *D. piperi* Webb (14578), 15-20 mm., is black with orange elytra in the male and blue-green with orange margins in the female. British Columbia to Oregon and Idaho.

24a Stridulating plate on mesonotum large, never divided, though occasionally absent; second segment of antennae small..........25

**24b** Stridulating plate on mesonotum divided by a smooth excavation; eyes nearly cut in two; second segment of antennae long. Fig. 612.

14772 *Atimia confusa* (Say)

Figure 612

LENGTH: 7-9 mm. RANGE: Eastern half United States and Canada.

Subdepressed, dull. Black, marked as shown with fairly long yellowish pubescence. Elytra truncate at tips, with many fine punctures among scattered large ones. Bores in Red Cedar. (After Blatchley)

**25a** Front coxal cavities open behind...........................26

**25b** Front coxal cavities closed behind; eyes finely granulated. Fig. 613.

(a) 14584 *Molorchus bimaculatus* (Say)

LENGTH: 5-7 mm. RANGE: Eastern half United States.

Dull black, with scattered grayish hairs. Elytra short blackish with dull yellow spot at center; legs and antennae reddish-brown. On flowers of Hawthorn. (After Wickham)

(b) 14586 *Callimoxys fuscipennis* (Lec.)

LENGTH: 8-10 mm. RANGE: general.

Figure 613

Dull black. Thorax of male red with black margins. Hind legs yellow, with tips of segments black. (After Blatchley)

**26a** Eyes finely granulated....................................27

**26b** Eyes coarsely granulated..................................33

**27a** Scutellum broadly triangular or rounded behind...............28

**27b Scutellum acutely triangular. Fig. 614.**

14857 *Batyleoma suturale* (Say)

Figure 614

LENGTH: 6-8 mm. RANGE: general.

Dark red; antennae, legs and sometimes elytral suture black or darkened; clothed with scattered long gray hairs. Elytra with tips rounded, punctures scattered and coarse.

Many of the long-horns gather on flowers to feed and meet their mates. This simplifies collecting. This one in common with several other species, has found the flowers of New Jersey Tea and of Dogwood much to its liking.

**28a Middle coxal cavities open behind...........................29**

**28b Middle coxal cavities closed behind. Fig. 615.**

14745 *Euderces picipes* (Fab.)

Figure 615

LENGTH: 5-8 mm. RANGE: Eastern half United States and Canada.

Shining. Black or dark reddish-brown; clothed with scattered grayish hairs. Marked on elytra as pictured with raised ivory-like bars. Legs and antennae reddish-brown. (Courtesy N. Y. State Museum)

Another species, *E. reichei* Lec. (14748), 4-5 mm., is much like the preceding but smaller and more slender, and has the elytral bars transverse. Its range extends from Indiana to Texas.

*Purpuricensus humeralis* (Fab.) (14795) 14-18 mm. in length, is fairly common in our Central and Eastern States and Canada. It is robust, dull velvety black with a large triangular scarlet spot on the humerous of each elytron. The thorax has a small spine on each side. It is a beetle any collector will prize. The larvae develop in oak and hickory; the adults are found on mid-summer roadside flowers.

**29a Head small; front short; process of first ventral segment between the hind coxae rounded.....................................30**

**29b Head large; front long; process behind the hind coxae acute. Fig.
616.** (a) **14679** *Xylotrechus colonus* (Fab.) Rustic Borer.

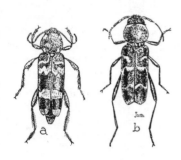

LENGTH: 8-16 mm. RANGE: Eastern
half United States.

Thorax without apical and basal
margins of paler hairs. Black or
brown; pubescence yellowish or white
marking the upper surface as pictured.

(b) **14691** *X. undulatus* (Say)
LENGTH: 11-21 mm. RANGE: general.

Thorax with apical and basal margins of light pubescence. Black or
dark brown. Elytra marked with
yellow or white pubescence as pictured. (Courtesy N. Y. State Museum)

Figure 616

A western species of general range, *X. nauticus* (Mann.) (14694)
8-15 mm. is grayish-brown to blackish with three irregular transverse
white lines crossing the elytra. English walnut and peach trees as well
as other trees are victims of the larvae.

**30a Antennal segments 3-6 without definite spines on outer side of
apex.** ........................................................**31**

**30b Antennal segments 3-6 with definite spines on outer side at apex.
Fig. 617.** **14660** *Megacyllene antennata* (White)

LENGTH: 12-30 mm. RANGE: Southwest.

Brown, with markings of gray scales as shown.
Larvae a grub to 40 mm. long bores in mesquite. It
is known as the Round-headed Mesquite Borer.

This was the only species of the genus but Hopping's revision in 1937 changed the several species
of *Cyllene* (some of which follow) to this genus.

Figure 617

**31a Thorax transversely excavated at sides near the base; prosternum
perpendicular at tip**........................................**32**

**31b Prosternum sloping downward at tip; thorax not excavated at sides. Fig. 618.**              (a) 14673 *Glycobius speciosus* (Say) Sugar-maple Borer.

LENGTH: 23-25 mm.  RANGE: Northern United States and Canada.

Black with markings of dense yellow pubescence as shown; antenna compressed.

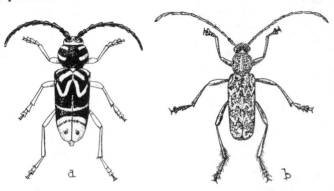

Figure 618

(b) 14672 *Arhopalus fulminans* (Fab.)

LENGTH: 12-18 mm.  RANGE: Connecticut to Indiana.

Black; head, thorax and elytra marked as pictured with grayish pubescence; antenna filiform.  The larvae live in oak, chestnut and butternut.

Differing from *Arhopalus* in its larger size and the thorax being wholly black, *Calloides nobilis* (Harris) (14674) 20-23 mm. is dull black and covered with a short dense pubescence.  Each elytron has a round yellow spot at its base.

**32a Basal third of elytra with three narrow yellow bands, the last W shaped.  Fig. 619.**

14671 *Megacyllene robiniae* (Forst.) Locust Borer

Figure 619

LENGTH: 14-20 mm.  RANGE: general.

Velvety black with markings of golden yellow. It is a handsome beetle.  The adults are common on the flowers of goldenrod in the fall.  *M. caryae* (Gahan) (14670), the Painted Hickory Borer, is found in the spring on hickory logs and wood.  The second segment of its hind tarsus is glabrous at its middle where as *robiniae* is densely pubescent. The two species are difficult to tell apart.  In fact several other species of the genus have essentially the same markings.  (U.S.D.A.)

**32b** Basal third of elytra not as above; often wholly yellow, though highly variable. Fig. 620.          14666 *Megacyllene decora* (Oliv.)

Figure 620

LENGTH: 14-20 mm.  RANGE: general.

Golden yellow with variable markings of velvety black.  Under parts yellow.  Found on goldenrod flowers in Fall.  Seven aberrant forms are recognized by Hopping '37.  Any sizable collection of this species is likely to show several patterns varying in greater or less degree from the one here pictured.

**33a** Not more than one yellow cross-band on body...............34
**33b** Body with six yellow cross-bands.  Fig. 621.

14153 *Dryobius sexfasciatus* (Say)

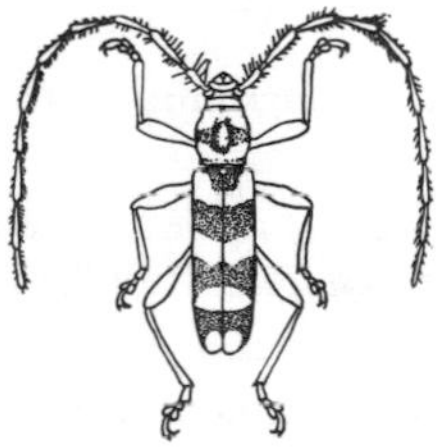

LENGTH: 19-27 mm.  RANGE: Central and Southern States.

Shining, black.  Marked as shown with cross bands of bright yellow pubescence.  Black spaces on elytra smooth but with scattered fine punctures . (After Smith)

Figure 621

A related species, Oeme gracilis Lec. (14149) is deep brown and measures 12 mm.  The thorax is oval with its narrowest part at the base.  It is found in California; the grubs feed in dead coast live oak.

**34a** Scutellum rounded behind....................................35
**34b** Thorax with spine on each side; scutellum triangular, acute.  Fig. 622.          14181 *Chion cinctus* (Drury) Banded Hickory Borer.

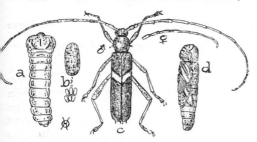

Figure 622

LENGTH: 16-32 mm. RANGE: general.

Blackish - brown, w i t h scattered grayish pubescence.  Elytra usually marked with yellow as shown.  It seems to prefer hickory for the larvae.  (a, larva; b, eggs; c, adult; d, pupa.) (After Osborn)

*Stromatium pubescens* Hald. (14179) measuring 15 mm. is known to occur in Pennsylvania.  It is pale yellowish brown.

**35a Antenna not bearing spines. Fig. 623.**

14190 *Eburia quadrigeminata* (Say)

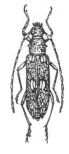

Figure 623

LENGTH: 14-24 mm.  RANGE: Eastern half North America.

Pale brownish-yellow marked as shown with ivory-like white spots on elytra.  The larvae bore in honey locust, oak, etc. and seem to live unusually long,—forty years or more.  We have had several of these "patri-archal" grubs brought in and have reared them to adult stage.

**35b Antennae with some segments bearing sharp spines at outer apical end.** ...................................................**36**

**36a Spines long.  Fig. 624.**     14220 *Elaphidion mucronatum* (Say)

Figure 624

LENGTH: 15-20 mm.  RANGE: Eastern half United States.

Dull reddish-brown, marked as shown with yellowish-gray pubescence.  Thorax with median elevated ridge and two lateral elevated spots smooth.  Elytra with scattered coarse punctures and two spines at tip of each.  Bores in oak and other trees.  (U.S.D.A.)

**36b Spines short.  Fig. 625.**

14211 *Hypermallus villosus* (Fab.) Twig Pruner

Figure 625

LENGTH: 11-18 mm.  RANGE: general.

Dark brown, mottled with grayish-yellow pubescence; legs and antennae reddish-brown.  Elytra each with two short spines at tip.

This beetle lays its eggs near the tip of a branch of several species of trees, then girdles the twig at a lower level so that it dies and breaks off.  The larvae mature in the dead branches on the ground.  It's a clever act, but hard on the trees.

37a Elytra with an oval protuberance near the scutellum. Fig. 626.
    14894 *Psenocerus supernotatus* (Say) Currant Tip Borer

LENGTH: 3-6 mm. RANGE: general.

Blackish or dark reddish-brown; bands of white pubescence on elytra as shown. (After Wickham)

Casey has named two varieties, (a) *tristis* and (b) *funebris,* the first from North Carolina and the other from Pennsylvania.

Its larvae live in the tips of grape, currant, gooseberry, etc.

Figure 626

37b Elytra without protuberance at base........................38

38a Scape of antennae with elevated spot (cicatrix) at apex........39

38b Scape of antennae without cicatrix at apex...................41

39a Legs long; front pair of legs and the antennae longer in male. Fig.
    627.        14895 *Monochamus titillator (Fab.) Southern Pine Sawyer*

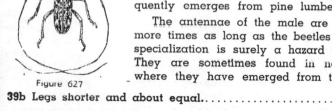

LENGTH: 20-32 mm. RANGE: United States and Canada.

Brown. Elytra mottled irregularly with gray and white pubescence. Lives in pine and frequently emerges from pine lumber. (U.S.D.A.)

The antennae of the male are often two or more times as long as the beetles body. Such specialization is surely a hazard to its owner. They are sometimes found in new buildings where they have emerged from the lumber.

Figure 627

39b Legs shorter and about equal...............................40

40a Color black and white. Fig. 628.
    14925 *Plectrodera scalator* (Fab.) Cottonwood Borer

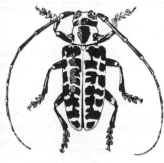

LENGTH: 25-35 mm. RANGE: general.

Robust, shining. Black and white as pictured. A very attractive beetle which breeds in quaking aspen and other poplars. (After LeConte)

They are not very abundant but their large size and unusual pattern make them prize specimens in a collection.

Figure 628

**40b** Color brown and gray; thorax with lateral spines. Fig. 629.

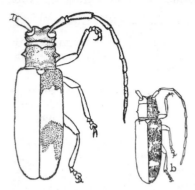

Figure 629

(a) 14918 *Goes pulchra* (Hald.)

LENGTH: 22-25 mm. RANGE: Eastern half United States.

Brownish with clay-yellow pubescence marking upper surface as pictured.

**(b) 14922 *G. debilis* Lec.**

LENGTH: 11-15 mm. RANGE: Eastern half United States.

Brown. Head, thorax and apical third of elytra clothed with reddish-yellow pubescence. Pubescence on basal half of elytra gray. Lives on hickory and oak.

**41a** Color black. Fig. 630.

Figure 630

14910 *Dorcaschema nigrum* (Say)

LENGTH: 8-10 mm. RANGE: Eastern United States and Canada to Texas.

Head with narrow raised line. Thorax and elytra granulate, the latter with scattered, deep, fine punctures. Breeds in hickory. (Courtesy N. Y. State Museum)

*D. wildii Uhler* (14908) differs from *nigrum* in having a cylindrical thorax and in being brown with a covering of grayish pubescence. The elytra have numerous small round bare spots and a large irregular one behind the middle. It measures 15 to 22 mm., breeds in mulberry and osage-orange, and is found from Kentucky to Massachusetts.

**41b** Not as in 41a............................................42

**42a** Front coxal cavities rounded, middle cavities closed (or nearly so). ...............................................43

**42b** Front coxal cavities angulate; middle cavities open behind......47

**43a** Basal joint of antennae club-shaped; thorax with lateral spine at middle and a dorsal tubercle. Fig. 631.

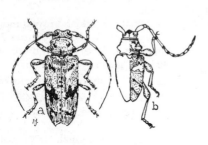

Figure 631

(a) 14932 *Aegoschema modesta* Gyll.

LENGTH: 10-13 mm. RANGE: United States and Canada.

Dark brown, marked with prostrate yellowish-gray pubescence.

(b) 14931 *Psapharochrus quadrigibbus* (Say)

LENGTH: 10-13 mm. RANGE: Eastern half United States.

Dark brown, marked with yellow-brown prostrate pubescence. White markings on elytra as shown. Two elevations on each elytron near base. Antennae with white rings.

**43b** Lateral spines on thorax behind middle; basal joint of antennae cylindrical. . . . . . . . . . . . . . . . . . . . . . . . . . . . . . . . . . . . . . . . . . . . . . . . . . . . . . .**44**

**44a** Females with elongated ovipositor. Fig. 632.

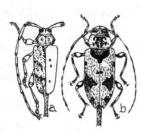

Figure 632

(a) 15021 *Acanthocinus fasciatus* (DeG.)

LENGTH: 8-14 mm. RANGE: Eastern half United States and Canada.

Thorax and elytra gray with black dots and blotches. Antennae and legs with rings. (After Smith)

(b) 15023 *A. triangulifera* (Hald.)

LENGTH: 13-15 mm. RANGE: Southern States.

Brown marked with pubescence of clay-yellow. (U.S.D.A.)

An outstanding species r a n g i n g through the west *A. spectabilis* (Lec.) (15031), 19-23 mm., has antennae several times as long as the body. Gray, with back elytral band and many small black dots.

**44b** Females without elongated ovipositor. . . . . . . . . . . . . . . . . . . . . . . . .**45**

**45a Mesosternum broad, thorax with small lateral tubercles a bit behind the middle. Fig. 633.**

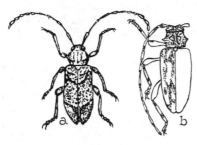

Figure 633

**(a) 14943 *Leptostylus tuberculatus* (Frol.)**
LENGTH: 7-10 mm. RANGE: Eastern half United States and Canada.

Robust. Blackish-brown, marked as shown with short prostrate grayish hairs. Five blunt tubercles on disk of thorax. Common.

**(b) 14961 *Astylopsis guttata* (Say)**
LENGTH: 7-10 mm. RANGE: Eastern half United States and Canada.

Robust. Brownish with pattern as shown of grayish pubescence. Tibiae and antennae annulate. (After Smith)

*A. macula* Say (14960) 4-9 mm. brownish, thorax with a broad whitish stripe on sides banded by a narrow blackish stripe. Each elytron with a wide irregular white spot behind the middle and six lines of small black dots. Known from Iowa to Virginia and Canada.

*Lepturges querci* Fitch (15001) 3.5-6 mm. differs from the above in lacking the ridge on the side. The head and thorax are dark brown; elytra pale purplish-brown marked with a wide irregular crossband covering a good part of the apical half but leaving the tip mostly light, and with 3 or 4 dark spots on the humeral half. Antennae more than twice as long as the body. It ranges from Iowa eastward and northward.

**45b Mesosternum triangular or narrow; thorax angulate or with sharp spine behind the middle.....................................46**

**46a Antennae with fringe of hairs on under side; elytra with a prominent ridge on the side. Fig. 634.**

**15005 *Hyperplatys maculata* Hald.**

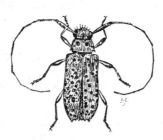

Figure 634

LENGTH: 4-6 mm. RANGE: general.

Reddish-brown, a dense coat of grayish pubescence and black spots form the pattern. (Courtesy N. Y. State Museum)

*H. aspersa* (Say) (15016) is similar in size, but has longer antennae and heavier pubescence.

**46b Antennae without fringe of hairs. Fig. 635.**

14985 *Leiopus alpha* (Say)

Figure 635

LENGTH: 5-7 mm. RANGE: general.
Dull reddish-brown. Marked with black spots and with grayish pubescence. (Courtesy N. Y. State Museum)

*L. variegatus* (Hald.) (14968), 8-12 mm., differs from the preceding in having the front flat instead of convex. It is purplish-brown mottled with black and clothed with a short pubescence. The antennae and tibiae are ringed with gray. It ranges from Alaska and Canada to Kansas and Indiana.

**47a Tarsal claws divided or bearing an appendage**................52

**47b Tarsal claws not as in 47a**.................................48

**48a Thorax with a spine or tubercle; small flattened species. Fig. 636.**

15056 *Pogonocherus mixtus* Hald.

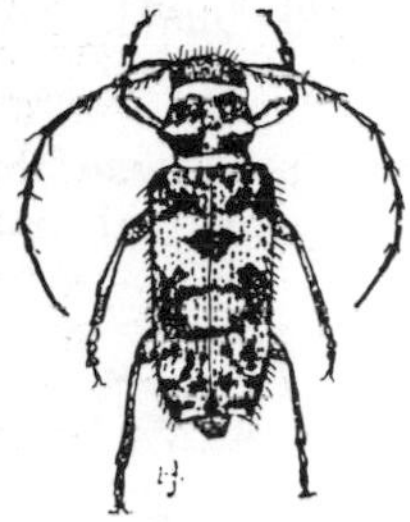

Figure 636

LENGTH: 4-7 mm. RANGE: United States and Canada.

Head and thorax piceous; elytra blackish marked as shown with dull brownish-yellow. Elytra with scattered erect black hairs and band of white pubescence. Lives on pine, pear, willow, etc.

*P. penicellatus* Lec. (15049), 6 mm., is piceous with the elytra back of the base covered with gray pubescence. It ranges widely through Canada and the United States.

**48b Thorax without spines or tubercules; larger**...................49

**49a Antennae with colored rings (annulate). Fig. 637.**

15109 *Saperda obliqua* Say Alder Borer

Figure 637

LENGTH: 21-26 mm. RANGE: Eastern half United States and Canada.

Yellowish-brown, marked with oblique darker bands. Elytra with spine at tip. (After Smith)

We picture and key several members of this genus as it is of high economic importance and widely distributed, as well as their being very attractive beetles.

**49b Antennae of one color, not ringed.........................50**

**50a Elytra with spine at suture on rounded tip. Fig. 638.**

15113 *Saperda calcarata* Say    Poplar Borer

LENGTH: 21-30 mm.    RANGE: general.

Reddish-brown, with dense prostrate yellow and gray pubescence. Lines and other markings orange-yellow and many small black dots. (After Smith)

Three species that are western in their range are S. *horni* Joutel (15111), 16-20 mm., shining black with a coat of dense light yellowish gray pubescence and breeding in willow; S. *populnea* (L.) (15122), 12 mm., gray with yellow markings and feeding on poplar; and S. *concolor* Lec. (15123), 6-20 mm., black, clothed with fine gray pubescence and breeding in willow and poplar.

Figure 638

**50b Elytra without spine at suture.................................51**

**51a Elytra with stripes. Fig. 639.    (a) 15112 *Saperda candida* Fab.**
LENGTH: 15-20 mm.    RANGE: general.

Brownish with silvery white pubescent stripes. Its larvae the "Round-head Apple Tree Borer" is destructive to apple trees and their near relatives.

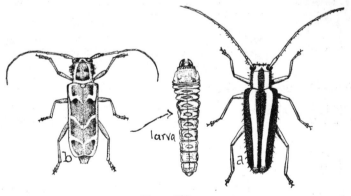

larva

Figure 639

**(b) 15114 *S. tridentata* Oliv.    Elm Borer**
LENGTH: 9-14 mm.    RANGE: general.

Brownish-black, ornamented with gray and orange pubescence, the latter forming the stripes as pictured.

51b Elytra with spots or solid color. Fig. 640.

(a) 15115 *Saperda cretata* Newn. Spotted Appletree Borer

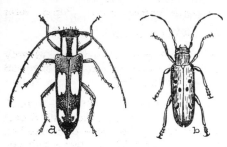

LENGTH: 12-20 mm. RANGE: general.

Cinnamon b r o w n with white spots as pictured. Breeds in *Craetegus*.

(b) 15117 *S. vestita* Say
Linden Borer
LENGTH: 12-21 mm. RANGE: Eastern half United States.

Dark reddish-brown, densely covered with prostrate o l i v e - yellow pubescence. Marked with black as shown.

Figure 640

52a Eyes completely divided into two widely separated parts; red with black spots. Fig. 641.

15170 *Tetraopes tetrophthalmus* (Forst.) Red Milkweed Beetle

LENGTH: 9-14 mm. RANGE: Eastern half United States and Canada.

Black. Head, thorax and elytra red, marked with black dots as shown. Antennae not ringed, it and scutellum black.

The members of this genus of which there are about 25 species feed on milkweed.

*T. femoratus* Lec. (15182), 10-15 mm., ranges throughout our country. Its antennae have a white ring on each segment.

Figure 641

52b Eyes not wholly divided, though deeply notched................53

53a Body above uniform gray; claws with small tooth or slightly cleft. Fig. 642.                    15126 *Mecas inornata* (Say)

LENGTH: 8-15 mm. RANGE: Central and Western States.

Black, thickly clothed with uniform gray pubescence; legs black.

*M. pergrata* (Say) (15129), 8-10 mm., differs from the former by having reddish femora. It is black with a heavy coating of gray and whitish hairs. The thorax has four black spots, and the antennae are ringed. It seems to be rare but to range widely.

Figure 642

**53b Not uniformly gray. Fig. 643.**

15138 *Oberea tripunctata* (Swed.) Dogwood Twig Borer

Figure 643

LENGTH: 8-16 mm. RANGE: United States and Canada.

Usually the under parts largely yellow with black markings; rarely wholly black. Upper surface yellow, marked with black as shown, though variable.

The "Cottonwood Twig Borer," of the West Coast, O. *quadricallosa* Lec. (15133) 11-14 mm., is orange with dull grayish and black markings.

## Family 102   CHRYSOMELIDAE
### The Leaf Beetles

Almost one-tenth of the known beetles belong to this great family. Any general collection of insects is practically certain to contain leaf beetles. Their size is never very large; some are so tiny as to be almost microscopic. What they lack in size many species more than make up for in their beauty of pattern and brilliant colors. No wonder they are favorites with many collectors.

1a **Head standing out with visible neck-like part back of eyes; thorax without margins, much narrower than elytra; mandibles simple...2**

1b **Thorax usually about as broad as elytra; several teeth on mandibles; head visible only to eyes...............................5**

2a **Form elongate; thorax very narrow; claws simple; first ventral segment about half the length of entire abdomen. Fig. 644.**

15202 *Donacia piscatrix* Lac.

LENGTH: 6.5-10 mm. RANGE: general.

Figure 644

Convex, shining. Bronze with varying sheen of green, coppery or brownish-yellow. Legs and antennae reddish-yellow. (After Blatchley)

D. *emarginata* Kby. (15216), 5-7 mm., is dark metallic blue with heavy pubescence beneath. It ranges throughout much of North America.

A large member of the genus is D. *pubicollis* Suffr. (15195), measuring 10-12 mm. It is distinguished by the heavy pubescence on both head and thorax. The members of this genus range widely but feed quite largely on waterlilies.

**2b First ventral abdominal segment not longer than the next two segments.** .................................................................3

**3a Claws simple; thorax narrow; punctures on elytra in rows.**........4

**3b Claws cleft or toothed; punctures on elytra scattered. Fig. 645.**

(a) 15219a *Orsodacne atra childreni* Kby.

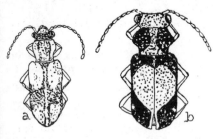

LENGTH: 4-7 mm. RANGE: United States and Canada.

Elytra dark brown marked with yellow. Six or more varieties are recognized varying much in color and markings. (After Wickham)

Figure 645

(b) 15233 *Zeugophora varians* Cr.

LENGTH: 3-4 mm. RANGE: general.

Black marked with yellowish. Legs and antennae dull reddish-yellow. Found on leaves of poplar trees. The front coxae touch in this genus but are separated in the preceding. (After Wickham)

Z. *scutellaris* Suffr. (15229) 3.5-4 mm. with wide distribution in both hemispheres, has head, thorax and legs yellow, with the abdomen and elytra shining black. The short, rather heavy antennae segments 1-3 yellow, the others piceous.

**4a Thorax constricted near its middle. Fig. 646.**

15253 *Lema trilineata* (Oliv.) Three-lined Potato Beetle

LENGTH: 6-7 mm. RANGE: general.

Reddish-yellow marked with black. Years ago this was regarded as a serious pest of potatoes. Ordinarily they are not now sufficiently abundant to even attract attention. Many of our worst insect pests, as with the weeds, are introduced species.

Figure 646

**4b** Thorax not constricted. Fig. 647.

(a) 15234 *Crioceris asparagi* (L.) Asparagus Beetle

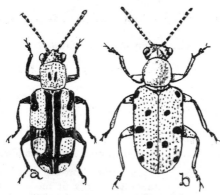

LENGTH: 7-8 mm. RANGE: Europe and United States.

Bluish-green; thorax red marked with green; elytra red with yellow markings. A handsome beetle; quite squirrel like in dodging around the asparagus stems when you try to catch it. (U.S.D.A.)

(b) 15235 *Crioceris duodecim-punctata* (L.)

Spotted Asparagus Beetle

LENGTH: 7-9 mm. RANGE: Europe and part of the United States.

Figure 647

Brownish-red with black spots as shown. These two beetles do heavy damage to asparagus. (U.S.D.A.)

**5a** More or less broadly expanded margins on thorax and elytra; head often not visible from above..................................63

**5b** Head usually visible from above; thorax and elytra without widely expanded margins.............................................6

**6a** Mouth turned down; front inflexed; usually wider behind and wedge-shaped. ...................................................61

**6b** Mouth directed ahead; front normal............................7

**7a** Last dorsal segment of abdomen (pygidium) exposed beyond elytra and sloping downward (a). Fig. 648.....................10

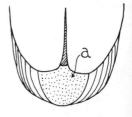

Figure 648

**7b** Last dorsal segment not exposed, middle ventral segment not narrow. ...................................................8

274

**8a** Antennae placed close together on the front; front coxae conical.
................................................................34

**8b** Antennae widely separated at base (usually greater distance than
length of first joint)..........................................9

**9a** Front coxae transverse; third tarsal segment usually not divided...24

**9b** Third tarsal segment with two lobes; front coxae rounded.......15

**10a** Surface of body much roughened above.  Fig. 649.
                          15297 *Arthrochlamys gibbosa* (Fab.)

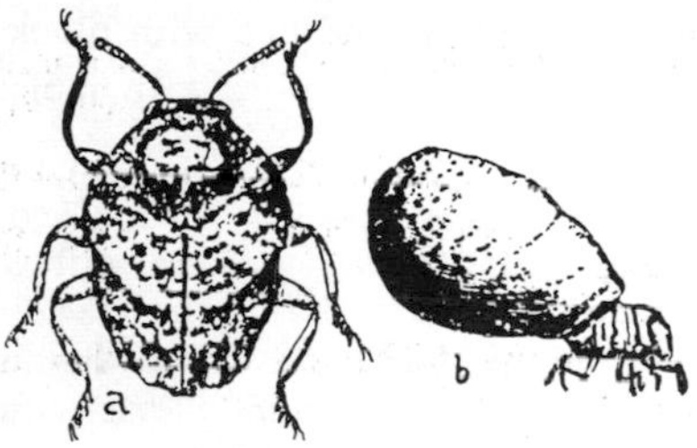

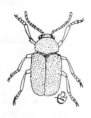

LENGTH: 4 mm.  RANGE: Eastern half United States.

Brownish, bronzed often with
purplish sheen, 12-15 tubercles on
each elytron.  The larvae carry
a case for protection (b).  (After
Marlatt)

Figure 649

**10b** Upper surface without tubercles............................11

**11a** Antenna serrate, short; front coxae touching.  Fig. 650.
                          15267 *Coscinoptera dominicana* (Fab.)

LENGTH: 4-7 mm.  RANGE: general.

Black, with ash gray pubescence on both upper
and lower surface, very dense below.  (After Riley)

*Babia quadriguttata* (Oliv.) (15282) measuring
3.5-4 mm. and ranging throughout the United States,
is convex, shining, and black with two reddish-yellow spots on each elytron.  It is often common on
milkweed.

Figure 650

**11b** Front coxae separated by prosternum antennae usually long and
slender. ................................................12

275

12a Thorax margined at base; front femora heavier than hind ones. Fig. 651.

(a) 15432 *Pachybrachys tridens* (Melsh.)

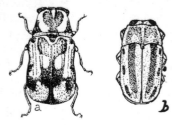

Figure 651

LENGTH: 2-3 mm. RANGE: Eastern half United States.

Robust. Yellow with black markings; the pattern is highly variable. Under surface black, legs and antennae yellow. Feeds on hickory and elm as well as some roadside weeds. (After Blatchley)

(b) 15440 *P. bivittatus* (Say)

LENGTH: 3.5-6 mm. RANGE: general.

Robust. Yellow, marked with black. Legs and under parts mostly reddish. It is found on grasses in moist places. (After Wickham)

The genus is a large one with some 200 named species. *P. melanostictus* Suffr. (15392) 3 mm. mottled black and yellow, feeds on willow in the states of the Rockies and westward. *P. varicolor* Suffr. (15428) 4.25 mm. yellow with mixed black markings feeds on white fir in Colorado and southward. *P. donneri* Cr. (15323) 3-4.5 mm. black with yellow markings, feeds on willows in the Pacific Coast states.

12b Thorax without a basal margin; front femora not heavier.......13

13a With tooth on front edge of thoracic flank. Fig. 652.

(21351) *Bassareus clathratus* (Melsh.)

Figure 652

LENGTH: 4-5 mm. RANGE: Eastern half United States.

Robust. Dull red marked as shown with pale yellow. Antenna and legs reddish at base becoming blackish at apex.

*B. lituratus* (Fab.) (15536) 3-4.5 mm. has a black head, thorax reddish yellow with three black spots and elytra each with three yellow stripes; the one on the fifth interval being short and at the base only.

13b Without tooth as in 13a.....................................14

**14a Elytra black. Fig. 653.**

    **(a) 15479a** *Cryptocephalus notatus quadrimaculatus* **Say**

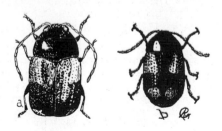

Figure 653

LENGTH: 4-5 mm. RANGE: Eastern half of United States.

Robust, shining. Black with red markings. Base of antennae pale. (Courtesy N. Y. State Museum)

    **(b) 15480** *C. quadruplex* **Newn.**

LENGTH: 2.5-3 mm. RANGE: Eastern United States.

Shining. Black marked with red. Base of antennae yellow.

Both of these species feed on several species of plants. (After Riley)

**14b Elytra not black. Fig. 654.**

    **15495** *Cryptocephalus venustus* **Fab.**

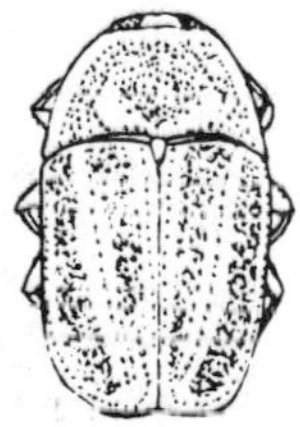

LENGTH: 4.5-5.5 mm. RANGE: Eastern half United States.

Robust. Head and thorax reddish-brown. Elytra yellow with black or brown stripes as pictured; the pattern and coloring are quite variable. (After Wickham)

This beetle may often be found in abundance on the flowers of Fleabane in meadows.

Figure 654

**15a Under part of front margin of thorax curved to form a lobe behind the eye**..................................................20

**15b Under part of front margin of thorax straight**....................16

**16a Thorax margined on the sides**..............................17

**16b Thorax without distinct side margins**.......................19

17a Middle and hind tibiae with notch near apex; distinct grooves above the eyes. Fig. 655.          15595 *Metachroma marginalis* Cr.

LENGTH: 6-8 mm.   RANGE: Eastern half United States.

Light brown; head and thorax darker than elytra. Found on hard pine.   (U.S.D.A.)

*M. parallelum* Horn (15592), 5-6 mm., and ranging widely is shining black with legs, base of antennae and sometimes the elytral suture yellow.

Figure 655

17b No grooves on head above the eyes..........................18

18a Thorax with regular and entire side margins; third joint of antennae longer than second. Fig. 656.

15549 *Nodonota puncticollis* (Say)

LENGTH: 3.5-4.5 mm.   RANGE: United States.

Convex, moderately shining.   Bronzed, greenish or bluish; antenna and sometimes the leg reddish-yellow.

A similar species, *N. tristis* (Oliv.) (15545), 3-4 mm., is bronze, greenish blue or metallic blue, is widely distributed and is more oval in form than *puncticollis*.

Figure 656

18b Side margins of thorax in waves or irregular. Fig. 657.

15555 *Colaspis brunnea* (Fab.)

LENGTH: 4.5-6 mm.   RANGE: United States.

Convex.   Dull brownish or reddish-yellow; legs pale.   Elytra with faint ridges and irregular rows of deep punctures between.   (U.S.D.A.)

It feeds on grapes, beans, strawberries and many other plants.

Figure 657

**19a Body bronzed or metallic above; groove above eye. Fig. 658.**

**15567 *Graphops pubescens* (Melsh.)**

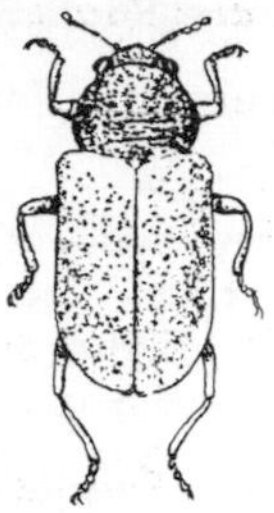

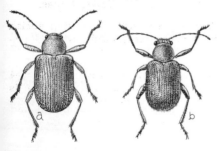

LENGTH: 3.5-4 mm. RANGE: Eastern half United States and Canada.

Cuperous bronzed with scant grayish pubescence. Fine punctures on elytra. (After Blatchley)

During the summer it seems to feed on evening-primrose; it hibernates as an adult during the winter.

Figure 658

*G. curtipennis* (Melsh.) (15568) 2-2.5 mm. in length, is heavier set than the above. It is coppery-brown with scattered short gray hairs and is known from Iowa, New York, Florida and Texas.

**19b Body not metallic above. Fig. 659.**

**(a) 15577 *Fidia viticida* Walsh Grape Rootworm**

LENGTH: 6-7 mm. RANGE: Eastern half United States.

Dull reddish-brown with coat of yellowish-gray pubescence. Legs and antennae paler. Feeds on leaves of grapes; the larvae on the roots. (U.S.D.A.)

**(b) 15578 *F. longipes* (Melsh.)**

Figure 659

LENGTH: 5-6.5 mm. RANGE: Eastern United States.

Brownish or smoky with prostrate coat of gray hairs. Also feeds on grape. (U.S.D.A.)

*Xanthonia decemnotata* (Say) (15573), 3 mm. dull yellow to brownish-red, with 8 to 10 blackish spots on elytra is common Texas to Canada.

**20a Upper surface without pubescence or scales..................23**

**20b Upper surface covered with scales or pubescence............21**

**21a Plain margins at sides of thorax............................22**

**21b Thorax without distinct side margins; elytra brown or black. Fig. 660.** 15604 *Adoxus obscurus (L.)* **Western Grape Rootworm**

LENGTH: 5-6 mm. RANGE: Eurasia, North America.

Elytra brown or brownish-yellow with scattered prostrate yellowish hairs. Head, thorax and under surface brown to black. Elytra with irregular rows of fine punctures. (U.S.D.A.)

This species has several named varieties. The beetles eat characteristic holes in the leaves of grapes while the larvae feed on the roots of these plants.

Figure 660

**22a Margin of thorax toothed; front tibia with teeth near apex on inner side. Fig. 661.** 15608 *Myochrous denticollis* **(Say) Southern Corn-leaf Beetle**

LENGTH: 5-7 mm. RANGE: general.

Convex. Brown, bronzed; antennae dull red at base. Thorax with three teeth at side and coated with grayish yellow scales.

The Long Leaf Beetle, *M. longulus* Lec. (15609) similar in size and color ranges through the Southwest and does damage to cotton, muskmellon and grape buds.

Figure 661

**22b Tibiae and thoracic margins without teeth. Fig. 662.** 15615 *Glytoscelis liebecki* **Blatch.**

LENGTH: 7-9 mm. RANGE: East Central States.

Convex, shining. Reddish-brown with sheen of bronze. Both upper and lower surface with thick coat of prostrate gray hair-like scales. Elytra with fine, scattered punctures. (After Blatchley)

The Gray Leaf Beetle, *G. albida* Lec. (15617), 6-7 mm., is metallic bronzed and covered with fine gray scales. It ranges from British Columbia to California and damages the buds and leaves of fruit trees.

Figure 662

**23a Elytral punctures in distinct rows; outer edge of middle and hind tibiae notched near apex. Fig. 663.**

15626 *Paria canella* (Fab.)

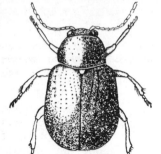

Figure 663

LENGTH: 3-4 mm. RANGE: United States and Canada.

Convex, usually shining and smooth. Horn described 14 varieties with elytra wholly black, spotted or entirely pale. (After Forbes)

Such highly variable forms give the systematist of hair splitting mind, a foretouch of Paradise. No two specimens are exactly alike so he can make himself "author" of as many varieties or species as he may wish. And the field of Entomology is likely little the worse but surely none the better for it.

**23b Punctures on elytra scattered irregularly; tibiae entire. Fig. 664.**

15627 *Chrysochus auratus* (Fab.)

Figure 664

LENGTH: 8-11 mm. RANGE: Eastern half United States and Canada.

Convex, shining. Brilliant green with brassy or coppery sheen. Under parts and antennae bluish-black. A very attractive beetle sometimes exceedingly common on dogbane and milkweed.

In the West it is replaced with *C. cobaltinus* Lec. (15628) somewhat shorter and stouter, and darker colored, a metallic dark blue or greenish.

**24a Tibia without teeth, slim claws with two prongs or a tooth. Fig. 665.**

15715 *Phytodecta americana* Schffr.

Figure 665

LENGTH: 6-8 mm. RANGE: Eurasia and United States.

Convex. Shining. Pale yellowish-brown marked as pictured with black. This "Poplar leaf beetle" feeds on both willow and poplar. (Courtesy N. Y. State Museum)

The willow family has many insect pests; another willow-feeding species, *Phyllodecta vitellinae* (L.) (15718), 4-5 mm., is shining purple, and was introduced from Europe.

24b Claws simple.................................................25

25a Third joint of tarsi notched or bilobed........................32

25b Third joint of tarsi uncut or but feebly notched (bilobed in *Praso-curis*). ...................................................26

26a No margin at base of thorax; body elongate, striped. Fig. 666.
15635 *Prasocuris phellandrii* (L.)

LENGTH: 5-6 mm. RANGE: Europe and United States.

Blackish with bronze sheen marked with dull yellow as shown. Fine punctures on elytra set closely in rows. (After Blatchley)

A similar but considerably smaller species *P. vittata* Oliv. (15636), 3.5-4.5 mm., is greenish-black with markings of reddish-yellow. The two elytral stripes unite at the base and the thorax is but little wider than long.

Figure 666

26b Margin at base of thorax; stout; convex......................27

27a Last joint of palpi cut square, shorter than preceding.........28

27b Last joint of palpi no shorter than the preceding one..........29

28a Mesosternum enlarged into a tubercle between the middle coxae. Fig. 667. 15639 *Labidomera clivicollis* (Kby.)

LENGTH: 8-12 mm. RANGE: North America.

Robust, convex. Dark bluish-black; elytra reddish-yellow with markings of black as shown. Often common on milkweeds.

An attractive beetle. (After Knobel)

Figure 667

**28b Mesosternum on same level with the prosternum. Fig. 668.**
**(a) 15648 *Leptinotarsa decimlineata* (Say) Colorado Potato Beetle**

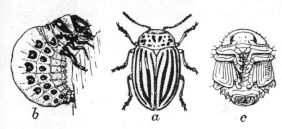

Figure 668

LENGTH: 5-11 mm.

RANGE: United States and Canada.

Robust convex. Dull yellow, marked as shown with black. This beetle was likely the first insect to be con-trolled with an arsenical spray. (U.S.D.A.)

*L. juncta* (Germ.) (15650) False Potato Beetle with a length of 10-12 mm. and ranging through the Southern States, closely resembles the above. The elytra have single instead of double rows of punctures and the outer face of the femora has a black dot.

**29a Claws diverging; joint simple**..................................30

**29b Claws united at base, parallel; joint with tooth beneath. Fig. 669.**
**15655 *Zygrogramma suturalis* (Fab.)**

LENGTH: 5.5-6.5 mm.  RANGE: Colorado to East.

Convex, shining. Brown, with metallic sheen; elytra yellow marked with brown as pictured.

There are several other similar species of the genus most of them occuring in the West.

Figure 669

**30a Elytra with brown and yellow stripes. Fig. 670.**
**15668 *Calligrapha praecelsis* Rog.**

LENGTH: 7-8 mm.  RANGE: Central United States.

Convex. Dark reddish-brown, bronzed, marked as shown with yellowish . (After Rogers)

*C. similis* Rogers (15665), 5-7 mm., a rather common species with much the same range, has its thorax wholly brown.

Figure 670

283

30b Elytra with various spots................................31

31a Thorax wholly dark green.  Fig. 671.

(a) 15671 *Calligrapha scalaris* (Lec.)  Elm Calligrapha

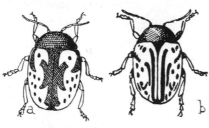

LENGTH: 8-10 mm.  RANGE: Eastern half United States.

Robust, convex, shining.  Dark metallic green; elytra creamy-white marked with green as pictured.  Live in basswood.  (After Knobel)

(b) 15674 *C. philadelphica* (L.)

LENGTH: 8-9 mm.  RANGE: Eastern half United States.

Figure 671

Robust, convex, shining.  Dark olive metallic green.  E l y t r a creamy-white marked with dark green as shown.  There are several other species closely similar to this one.  (After Knobel)

31b Thorax partly pale.  Fig. 672.

15676a *Calligrapha multipunctata bigsbyana* (Kby.)

LENGTH: 6.5-8.5 mm., RANGE: United States and Canada.

Robust, convex.  Brown to greenish, somewhat bronzed.  Upper surface pale, marked as shown with brown or dark green.  (Courtesy N. Y. State Museum)

It differs from *C. multipunctata* (Say) (15676) in having the pronotum pale with reddish-brown spots at center; the many elytral spots

Figure 672

are black instead of greenish.

32a Sides of thorax unthickened.  Fig. 673.

15701 *Gastrophysa polygoni* L.

LENGTH: 4-5 mm.  RANGE: Europe, United States.

Head, elytra and under surface metallic green or bluish.  Thorax, legs, base of antennae and tip of abdomen reddish.  Tarsi and part of antennae black.

*G. cyanea Melsh.* (15703), popularly known as the Green Dock Beetle, is found from coast to coast.  It is a brilliant metallic green, measures 4-5 mm. and is

Figure 673

known to damage rhubarb.

32b Sides of thorax thickened.....................................33

33a (a, b, c) Elytra reddish with black spots. Fig. 674.

15708 *Lina lapponica* (L.)

Figure 674

LENGTH: 6-9 mm. RANGE: Eurasia and United States.

Black. Upper surface reddish with black markings. Adults and larvae both feed on willow. Often mistaken by beginners for a lady beetle. Has several forms, three of which are pictured here.

33b Elytra greenish-yellow or dull reddish with elongate spots. Fig. 675.

15710 *Lina scripta* (Fab.)

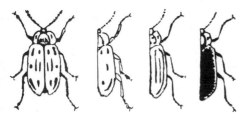

Figure 675

LENGTH: 7-10 mm. RANGE: general.

Colors as in key. Markings as pictured. Highly variable. Both adults and larvae feed on poplar and are often very abundant. The figure by Riley shows four variations in the pattern.

33c Elytra dull yellow, without spots. Fig. 676.

15709 *Lina tremulae* (Fab.)

Figure 676

LENGTH: 7-9 mm. RANGE: Eurasia, eastern United States.

Head and thorax green; elytra yellowish-brown. Introduced from Europe.

Defoliates poplars and willows. (Courtesy N. Y. State Museum)

This, like some other leaf beetles, could be mistaken for a lady beetle. The number of tarsi clears up any doubt.

285

34a Hind legs for leaping, with much thickened femora (a). (Flea Beetles) Fig. 677.
. . . . . . . . . . . . . . . . . . . . . . . . . . . . . . . . . . . . .42

Figure 677

34b Hind legs for walking; femora slender. . . . . . . . . . . . . . . . . . . . . . .35

35a Front coxal cavities closed behind. Fig. 678.
15854 *Cerotoma trifurcata* (Forst.) Bean Leaf Beetle

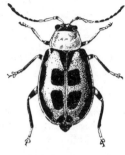

LENGTH: 3.5-5 mm. RANGE: Eastern half United States and Canada.

Convex. Under parts black. Upper surface dull yellow, occasionally reddish, marked as pictured with black. (U.S.D.A.)

This as well as several other species of leaf beetles are sometimes mistaken for lady beetles by beginners. A careful check of the tarsal segments will permit one to be certain about that.

Figure 678

35b Front coxal cavities open behind. . . . . . . . . . . . . . . . . . . . . . . . . .36

36a Claws with a broad appendage at base. Fig. 679.
15850 *Phyllecthrus gentilis* Lec.
LENGTH: 2.5-4 mm. RANGE: general.

Upper surface black with yellow markings. Thorax frequently wholly yellow; elytra sometimes wholly black. Antennae dark. Under parts yellow.

*P. dorsalis* (Oliv.) (15851), 6 mm., ranging from District of Columbia to Texas, differs from *gentilis* in having elytra but slightly if at all wider than the thorax and the antennae of the male with 11 segments instead of 10. The under parts are black.

Figure 679

*Luperodes cyanellus* Lec. (15824) 3.5-4.5 mm. differs from the above in having spurs on the tibiae and in the elytra being a solid dark blue instead of being marked in two colors; the antennae and legs are yellow. It is known in Iowa, Missouri and Pennsylvania. It feeds on wild roses.

**36b Claws without appendage at base**..........................37

**37a At least part of the tibiae with terminal spurs**.................41

**37b No terminal spurs on the tibiae**.............................38

**38a Antennae not reaching the middle of the body, third joint longer than fourth. Fig. 680.**   (a) 15755 *Monoxia puncticollis* (Say)

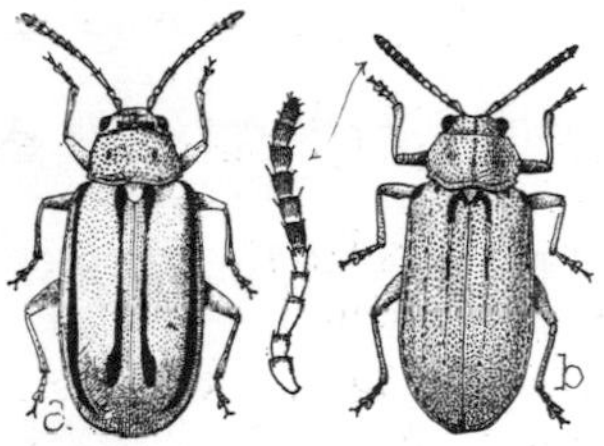

Figure 680

LENGTH: 7-9 mm. RANGE: United States.

Wholly pale yellow to dark brown; the elytral margins and suture sometimes marked with black. (U.S.D.A.)

(b) 15756 *M. consputa* (Lec.)

LENGTH: 3.5-4.5 mm. RANGE: Western half United States.

Wholly pale yellowish-brown often darker on dorsum. The adults injure the leaves of the sugar beet. It is known as the "Western Beet Leaf Beetle." (U.S.D.A.)

**38b Antennae extending beyond middle of the body, claws with two prongs.** ....................................................39

**39a Fourth segment of antennae longer than third. Fig. 681.**
15727 *Trirhabda canadensis* Kby.

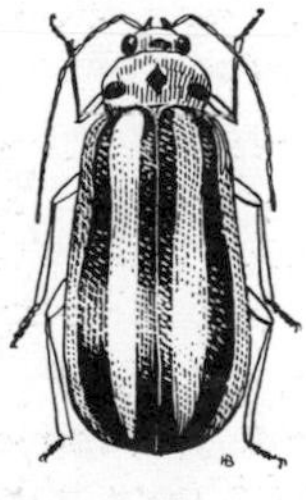

Figure 681

LENGTH: 7-10 mm. RANGE: United States.

Upper parts yellowish, marked as shown with black. Common name "Goldenrod Beetle."

*T. luteocincta* (Lec.) (15735) of similar size and ranging in the West is iridescent green to blue to deep purple. The larvae feed on wormwood.

**39b Fourth segment of antennae shorter than third.................40**

**40a Elytra with long black markings or narrow stripes. Fig. 682.**
**(a) 15750 *Galerucella notata* (Fab.)**

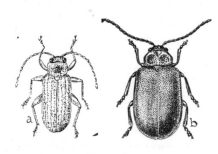

Figure 682

LENGTH: 3.5-5 mm. RANGE: United States and Canada.

Pale yellow with scattered prostrate pubescence. Elytra and thorax marked as shown in black.

**(b) 15746 *G. cavicollis* (Lec.)**
**Cherry Leaf Beetle**

LENGTH: 4.5-5.5 mm. RANGE: Eastern United States and Canada.

Bright red with eyes, antennae and tips of legs black. It ranges throughout our country and eats the leaves of peach and cherry.

*G. xanthomelaena* (Schrank) (15754). The Elm Leaf Beetle, 5 mm. yellow or orange with two black stripes and a spot on each elytron, reached this country from Europe around 1834 and has spread through many of our states. Both larvae and adults are serious pests in defoliating elm trees.

**40b No elongated black marks on elytra, subdepressed. Fig. 683.**
**(a) 15751 *Galerucella nymphaeae* (L.) Waterlily Leaf Beetle**

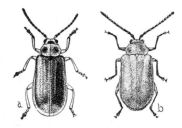

Figure 683

LENGTH: 4.5-6 mm. RANGE: Eurasia and North America.

Blackish-brown with fine pubescence. Thorax dull yellow with dark spots; legs pale. As the name indicates it feeds on waterlilies. (U.S.D.A.)

**(b) 15753 *G. decora* (Say)**
LENGTH: 4.5-5.5 mm. RANGE: United States and Canada.

Dull yellow to brown with yellowish pubescence. Antennae dark; legs pale. Lives on willows. (U.S.D.A.)

41a (a, b, c) Elytra with black stripes.  Fig. 684.

15782 *Diabrotica vittata* (Fab.)

Figure 684

LENGTH: 4.5-6 mm.  RANGE: Colorado east and Canada.

Upper surface yellow, marked as shown with black. This "Striped Cucumber Beetle" is a general pest. In the West it is replaced by *D. trivittata* (Mann.) (15783), about the same size, but having the thorax darker and only the basal half of the first antennal joint, and the base of the femora pale yellow.

41b Elytra with spots.  Fig. 685.

15769 *Diabrotica duodecimpunctata* (Fab.)
Spotted Cucumber Beetle

Figure 685

LENGTH: 6-7.5 mm.  RANGE: United States.

Pale greenish-yellow marked with black. Three basal joints of antennae and base of femora pale yellow. It is also known as the Southern Corn Rootworm.

West of the Rockies a somewhat smaller species *D. soror* Lec. (15770) is more common. The antennae, legs and body are entirely black.

41c Elytra with neither spots or stripes.  Fig. 686.

15774 *Diabrotica longicornis* (Say) Corn Rootworm

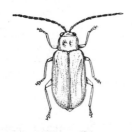

Figure 686

LENGTH: 5-6 mm.  RANGE: Central States.

Pale green or greenish-yellow. Antennae and sometimes the head and thorax with reddish-brown tinge. This "Northern Corn Rootworm" is often abundant feeding on corn silk, and on the flowers of golden-rod and sunflowers. Since the eggs are laid in corn fields rotation effectively controls the larvae.

42a Front coxal cavities open behind....................43

42b Front coxal cavities closed behind............................52

43a Last joint of hind tarsus hemisphere shaped; elytral punctures scattered. ................................................44

43b Last joint of hind tarsi not as in 43a; usually slender...........45

44a Antennae stouter, short; elytral margins not flattened. Fig. 687.
15868 *Oedionychis vians* (Ill.)

LENGTH: 4.5-7 mm. RANGE: West of Colorado.

Black, often with greenish or violet sheen. Thorax reddish-yellow with black spot which sometimes is an inverted W. Abdomen yellowish at margins and apex. (After Blatchley)

Figure 687

44b Antennae slender; reaching at least to middle of body. Fig. 688.
15887 *Oedionychis sexmaculata* (Ill.)

LENGTH: 3-4 mm. RANGE: Eastern half United States.

Brownish or reddish-yellow with markings as pictured with black. Antennae and legs dull yellow. Common. (After Blatchley)

Figure 688

### Others of the Genus *Oedionychis*

Horn has pictured the upper surface of a good number of the flea beetles belonging to this genus. We reproduce his drawings with the name of the beetles which in many cases should be sufficient for identification. Their color is for the most part pale yellow and brownish or blackish. The Leng catalog numbers associate picture and name. Fig. 689.

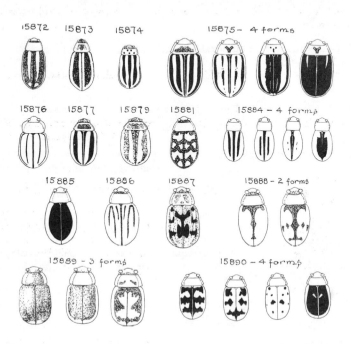

Figure 689

| Cat. No. | Name | Length | Range |
|---|---|---|---|
| 15872 | O. *interjectionis* Cr. | 6-6.5 mm | Texas, Mexico |
| 15873 | O. *fimbriata* (Forst.) | 5-7.5 mm | From Texas east |
| 15874 | O. *aemula* Horn | 4.5-5.5 mm | Arizona |
| 15875 | O. *peturista* (Fab.) 4 forms | 5.5-8.5 mm | From Texas east |
| 15876 | O. *tenuilineata* Horn | 6.5-7 mm | So. Arizona |
| 15877 | O. *miniata* (Fab.) | 5-6.5 mm | From Texas east |
| 15879 | O. *ulkei* Horn | 4.5-5 mm | Florida |
| 15881 | O. *jacobiana* Horn | 6.5 mm | So. Arizona |
| 15884 | O. *texana* Cr. 4 forms | 4-4.5 mm | Texas |
| 15885 | O. *thyamoides* Cr. | 4-4.5 mm | Eastern half U. S. |
| 15886 | O. *circumdata* Rand. | 3.5-5 mm | Texas and eastward |
| 15887 | O. *sexmaculata* (Ill.) | 3.5-4 mm | Eastern half U. S. |
| 15888 | O. *suturalis* (Fab.) 2 forms | 3.5-4 mm | Georgia, Florida |
| 15889 | O. *quercata* (Fab.) 3 forms | 3.5-4 mm | From Colo. eastward |
| 15890 | O. *scalaris* Melsh. 4 forms | 4.5-5 mm | Texas and eastward |

291

**45a** Thorax with a transverse impressed line across its base.......48

**45b** Thorax without a transverse impression as in 45a.............46

**46a** First segment of hind tarsi comparatively short and broad; claws with appendages...........................................47

**46b** First segment of hind tarsi long and slender; claws simple......49

**47a** Elytra striped black and yellow.  Fig. 690.

15901 *Disonycha glabrata* (Fab.)

Figure 690

LENGTH: 5-5.5 mm.  RANGE: general.

Highly shining.  Upper surface yellow marked with varying amounts of black.  Common.

*D. quinquevittata* (Say) (15896) r a n g i n g throughout much of the United States is larger 5-9 mm. and has four black dots on thorax.  It feeds on willow.  *D. pennsylvanica* (Ill.) (15895); is another wide ranging species 6.5-7.5 mm., striped black and white or pale yellow.

**47b** Elytra not striped.  Fig. 691.

Figure 691

(a) 15906 *Disonycha triangularis* (Say) LENGTH: 5-6.5 mm.  RANGE: general.

Black, the elytra with a bluish sheen.  Thorax yellow with three black dots as pictured.  Common on beets, spinach and related plants.

(b) 15907 *D. xanthomelaena* (Dalm.) Spinach Flea Beetle

LENGTH: 4.5-5.5 mm.  RANGE: general.

Marked like the preceding except that the thorax is plain yellow and the elytra somewhat greenish.  The legs are partly or wholly yellow, instead of entirely black.  It has much the same food tastes as its near relative.

**48a Usually not over 4 mm. long.  Fig. 692.**

15920 *Haltica ignitia* Ill.

Figure 692

LENGTH: 3-4 mm.  RANGE: United States.

Metallic green, brassy, bronzed or sometimes purplish.  It is sometimes known as the Strawberry Flea Beetle.

A pest of grapes in the Southwest, *H. torquata* Lec. (15934) 3-4 mm. is metallic blue or purple while the "Apple Flea Beetle" another western species, *H. foliaceae* Lec. (15946) is similar in color and size.

**48b Length over 4 mm.  Fig. 693.**

15917 *Haltica chalybea* Ill.

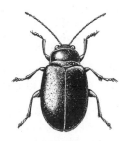

Figure 693

LENGTH: 4-5 mm.  RANGE: general.

Metallic blue.  Feeds on wild grape and poison ivy.

The "Alder Flea Beetle" *H. bimarginata* Say (15916) ranging throughout North America and measuring 5-6 mm., dark steel blue is readily distinguished by a longitudinal fold on the sides of the elytra.

**49a Elytra usually with yellow spots or stripe; hind tibiae not grooved on outer edge.....................................................50**

**49b Elytra without yellow spots or stripe; hind tibiae with a groove on the tip of outer edge.....................................................51**

**50a Elytra black and yellow.  Fig. 694.**

(a) 16074 *Phyllotreta bipustulata* (Fab.)

LENGTH: 2-2.5 mm.  RANGE: Europe and eastern half United States.
Robust.  Non-metallic black and marked as pictured with yellow.

(b) 16075 *P. armoraciae* (Koch.)
Horseradish Flea Beetle

LENGTH: 3-3.5 mm.  RANGE: Europe and eastern half United States.
Convex, shining.  Black marked as pictured with dull yellow.

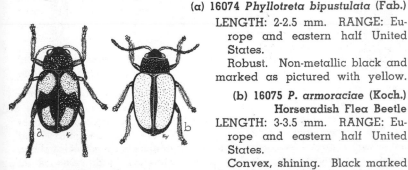

Figure 694

**50b Elytra of one color. Fig. 695A.**
**16080 *Phyllotreta pusilla* Horn   Western Black Flea Beetle**

Figure 695a

LENGTH: 1.5-2 mm.   RANGE: Western half United States.

Robust, shining.   Black or dark olive-green. Travels in swarms and causes heavy losses to mustard crops.

The Colorado Cabbage Flea Beetle *P. albionica* (Lec.) (16072) is a western pest of the mustard family as well as other plants.   It is wholly black with a faint brassy sheen and measures 1.5-2 mm.

### Others of the Genus *Phyllotreta*

The left elytron and the characteristic antenna of six other species of the Genus *Phyllotreta* as pictured by Horn are reproduced below (Fig. 695B).   The name, size and distribution is associated with the catalog number.   The ground color is black and the markings pale yellow in each case.

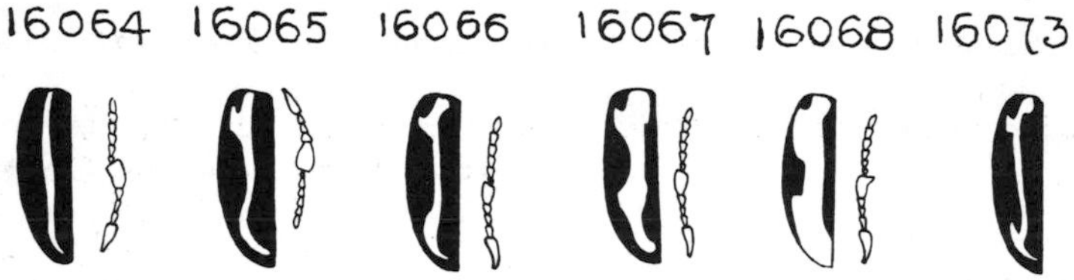

16064  16065   16066   16067  16068  16073

Figure 695 b

16064...*P. lepidula* (Lec.)............2-2.5 mm. .........Southwest
16065...*P. zimmermanni* (Cr.)........2.5 mm..........N. Eng.-Man.
16066...*P. vittata* (Fab.).............2 mm........Eastern half U. S.
         Striped Flea Beetle
16067...*P. oregonensis* (Cr.)..........2.5-3 mm...Oregon, Texas, Cal.
16068...*P. robusta* Lec...............2 mm............Mich., Man.
16073...*P. ramosa* (Cr.).............2 mm......Calif., Nev. N. Y.
         Western Striped Flea Beetle

51a Elytral punctures in regular rows.   Fig. 696.

16060 *Glyptina brunnea* Horn

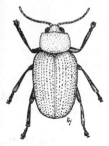

Figure 696

LENGTH: 1.8-2 mm.   RANGE: Eastern half United States.

Convex; shining.   Uniformly reddish-brown above, under parts brown; antennae and legs paler.

G. *cerina* (Lec.) (16062) a southwestern species is pale reddish-yellow with darker head and measures 2-2.5 mm.   It feeds on potatoes.

51b Elytral punctures scattered, not in rows; first joint of hind tarsi long. Fig. 697.                     16049 *Longitarsus melanurus* Melsh.

Figure 697

LENGTH: 2-2.5 mm.   RANGE: Eastern half United States and Canada.

Convex, shining.   Blackish or dark reddish-brown.   First and second legs dull yellow.   Elytral punctures deep, coarse and abundant.

52a (a, b. c) Antennae with 12 segments; claws divided.   Fig. 698.

15858 *Blepharida rhois* (Forst.)

Figure 698

LENGTH: 5-6.5 mm.   RANGE: general.

Robust, convex.   Upper surface dull yellow with irregular blotches of reddish-brown, head and thorax darker; under parts reddish-brown.   Feeds on sumach and known as "sumach flea beetle" or the "jumping sumach beetle."   It is the only member of its genus.

295

52b Antennae with only 10 segments; hind tarsi attached above the
    apex. Fig. 699.                    16090 *Psylliodes convexior* Lec.

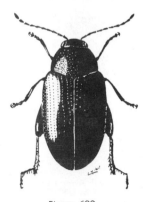

LENGTH: 2-2.5 mm.  RANGE: general.

Convex, shining.  Piceous with sheen of
bronze, antennae piceous, the first three joints
paler.  (After Hart)

The Hop Flea Beetle *P. punctulata* Melsh.
(16089) is similar in size, color and range.
The larvae feed on hop roots, while the adults
eat the leaves of many plants.  Its impressed
striae and more abundant elytral punctures
distinguish it from the preceding.

Figure 699

52c Antennae with 11 segments....................................53

53a Hind tibiae sinuate near apex; their outer margin with a tooth.
    Thorax not impressed at base...............................59

53b Neither tooth or sinuation on hind tibiae.....................54

54a Distinct impression across thorax near its base; punctures in rows
    on elytra. ................................................55

54b No impression across thorax in front of base; punctures scattered
    on elytra. ................................................58

55a Elytra with stiff hairs arranged in rows on the intervals........56

55b Elytra without hairs as in 55a.  Fig. 700.
                                    15969 *Derocrepis erythropus* Melsh.

LENGTH: 2.5-3 mm.  RANGE: general.

Elytra dark blue shining; head, thorax and
legs reddish-yellow; under surface blackish.
Feeds on black locust and other trees.  Introduced from Europe.  (After Howard)

*Crepidodera fulvicornis* (Fab.) (15968) is a
widely scattered species running into several
varieties.  It measures 2.5-3.5 mm., is colored
with metallic bronzes, blues or greens (including the thorax) and feeds on the leaves of
various trees.

Figure 700

56a Upper surface piceous.....................................57

**56b Upper surface not piceous; lighter. Fig. 701.**

15986 *Epitrix parvula* (Fab.)

Figure 701

LENGTH: 1.5-2 mm. RANGE: United States.

Dull. Reddish-yellow; elytra sometimes with darkened band across middle. Antennae and legs pale reddish-yellow. Under surface brown. It is known as the Tobacco Flea Beetle, but feeds on many plants, such as tomato, potato, eggplant, ground-cherry, almond, squash, orange, etc. It eats many tiny holes in the leaves and is often very destructive.

**57a Thorax with light punctures, scattered. Fig. 702.**

(a) 15982 *Epitrix cucumeris* Har.
LENGTH: 1.5-2 mm. RANGE: United States.

Shining. Black, legs and antennae reddish, elytral striae rather shallow. This Potato Flea Beetle feeds on practically all members of the nightshade family as well as some other plants. It is a serious pest. (U.S.D.A.)

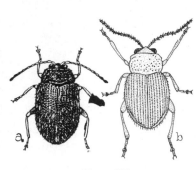

Figure 702

(b) 15983 *E. brevis* Sz.
LENGTH: 1.5 mm. RANGE: Eastern half of United States.

Shining. Piceous. Antennae and legs pale reddish-brown; hind femora piceous.

**57b Punctures on thorax heavy and crowded. Fig. 703.**

15979 *Epitrix fuscula* Cr.
LENGTH: 2 mm. RANGE: Eastern half of United States.

Robust, convex, feebly shining. Piceous. Antennae and legs except femora reddish yellow. Elytral intervals with seta bearing punctures. This is the flea beetle that works havoc with egg plants.

Figure 703

The genus *Epitrix* is not large but makes a serious menace to garden crops. They are so small as to often pass unnoticed. They eat small holes in the leaves and are difficult to control.

58a Elytra wholly dark.  Fig. 704.

(a) 16022 *Systena hudsonias* (Forst.)

LENGTH: 4-4.5 mm. RANGE: general.

Shining.  Black; segments 3-4-5 of antennae dull yellow, the others dark; legs black.  Elytra with crowded coarse punctures.

(b) 16023 *S. frontalis* (Fab.)

LENGTH: 3.5-4.5 mm. RANGE: general.

Head dull reddish-yellow, otherwise much like the preceding but less shining.

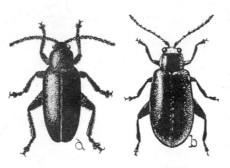

Figure 704

58b Elytra striped.  Fig. 705.

16028 *Systena taeniata* (Say)

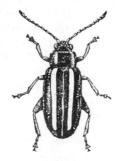

LENGTH: 3-4.5 mm.  RANGE: general.

Head and thorax usually reddish brown; elytra blackish to pale yellow with lighter stripes. This is a very common and serious pest of many garden plants.  It is highly variable in shades and marking.

Figure 705

59a Thorax with no marginal line at base; sides of thorax cut obliquely at front angles.  Fig. 706.            16016 *Chaetocnema confinus* Cr.

LENGTH: 1.5-1.8 mm.  RANGE: general.

Robust, oval.  Piceous, with tinge of bronze; legs and antennae reddish yellow; hind femora black; head without punctures but finely alutaceous. Thorax twice as wide as long.  A common pest of sweet potatoes and other garden plants where it eats channels along the veins.  (After Smith)

Figure 706

**59b Sides of thorax not cut as in 59a but curved from base to apex...60**

**60a Head without punctures. Fig. 707.**

16014 *Chaetocnema pulicaria* Melsh.

Figure 707

LENGTH: 1.5-1.8 mm. RANGE: general.

Convex, shining. Black with tinges of blue green or bronze; antennae with basal joints reddish yellow, the apical darker. It is common on corn and grasses.

The Desert Corn Flea Beetle, *C. ectypa* Horn (16012) about 1.5 mm. long is a western species living on wild grasses but becoming a pest of several cultivated crops. It is metallic bronze with black antennae which become reddish at the base.

**60b Head with punctures. Fig. 708.**

16001 *Chaetocnema denticulata* (Ill.)

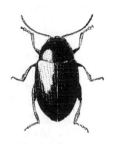

Figure 708

LENGTH: 2-2.5 mm. RANGE: United States.

Robust, sub-opaque. Piceous with bronze or brassy sheen. Antennae reddish-yellow at base, darker at apex. Tibiae and tarsi reddish-yellow. This Toothed Flea Beetle often damages corn, beets, sorghum and other grass crops.

*C. cribrifrons* Lec. (16002), 2.5 mm. and widely distributed, is quite similar to the above but differs in being shining and in having the punctures on the head coarse and well separated.

**61a Antennae with only eight segments. Fig. 709.**

16124 *Octotoma plicatula* (Fab.)

Figure 709

LENGTH: 4.5-5 mm. RANGE: Eastern half United States.

Depressed, dull. Piceous, with tinge of bronze. Antennae reddish brown, club darker. Thorax in front, scutellum and base of femora dull reddish-yellow. Elytra and thorax with a design of ridges as pictured. (After Chittenden)

This and the two genera which follow are made up of a few peculiar wedge-shaped beetles, very interesting in form and coloring but of little economic importance.

**61b Antennae with 11 segments**................................62

**62a Elytra with but three entire ridges. Fig. 710.**

**16113 *Chalepus dorsalis* Thunb.**

LENGTH: 6-6.5 mm. RANGE: Eastern half United States.

Shining bluish black with thorax and part of elytra, scarlet. A mid dorsal stripe on elytra black widening from base to apex. It seems to find its interest in leguminous plants. (After Chittenden)

*C. scapularis* (Oliv.) (16111) 5-7 mm., differs in having black elytra with red shoulders and the underparts wholly black. The thorax is red, but darkened at center. It ranges from Arizona eastward.

Figure 710

*C. bicolor* Oliv. (16109), 6 mm., is red beneath with thorax wholly red and elytra entirely black.

**62b Elytra with a partial fourth ridge inserted between the second and third at both apex and base. Fig. 711.**

**16116 *Baliosus ruber* (Web.)**

LENGTH: 6-6.5 mm. RANGE: general.

Much flattened. Reddish-yellow to rosy. Under parts reddish, legs yellow. Reported to live on maple, oak, basswood and locust trees. (After Chittenden)

*B. californicus* Horn (16115) belongs to the Southwest.

Figure 711

Still another closely related genus, *Stenispa*, has two fairly common species. The members of this genus possess eleven segments in the antennae, but the elytra lack the ridges displayed by these two other genera. *S. metallica* (Fab.) (16094) is wholly black with a slightly bronze tinge. It ranges throughout the eastern half of the United States and measures 5-6 mm.

*S. collaris* Baly (16095) is a bit larger (6-7 mm.) and differs in having its thorax red, and the other parts with a bluish tinge to the black. It seems to belong to our Southern States but has been reported also from Michigan.

**63a Head partly exposed; thorax not so much rounded in front. Fig. 712.**

**16139 *Chelymorpha cassidea* (Fab.)**

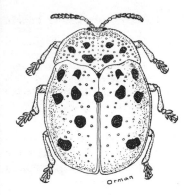

Figure 712

LENGTH: 9.5-11.5 mm. RANGE: general.

Convex. Brick-red marked with black. Underparts black. Beginners sometimes mistake it for a lady beetle. Four varieties have been named. It feeds on plants of the morning-glory family and is sometimes found on milkweed.

It is known popularly as the Argus Tortoise Beetle and is one of the largest of our leaf beetles and often very abundant.

**63b Head concealed beneath the margin of the rounded thorax......64**

**64a Length 9 mm. or more; margin thickened. Fig. 713.**

**16142 *Physonota unipunctata* (Say)**

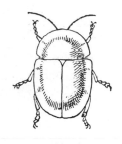

Figure 713

LENGTH: 9-11.5 mm. RANGE: general.

Convex. Pale greenish yellow; thorax with three black dots, the middle one oblong; underparts largely black. Sometimes very abundant on rosin weed and other plants. The larva are oddly shaped slimy creatures. (After Knobel)

In collections the specimens often fade to an unmarked straw color quite different from the living ones.

**64b Smaller; margins thin and flattened.........................65**

**65a Claws simple. ...............................................66**

**65b Claws with angular dilations at base........................67**

**66a Depressed. Fig. 714.**                    **16144 *Cassida nebulosa* L.**

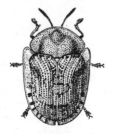

Figure 714

LENGTH: 6-7 mm.  RANGE: Europe and introduced.

Yellowish-gray to pale green with blackish markings. This "Beet Tortoise Beetle" is a serious pest in European beet fields but while, supposedly, having been introduced here it has not caused serious damage.  (U.S.D.A.)

**66b Convex, red.  Fig. 715.**          **16149 *Jonthonota nigripes* (Oliv.)**

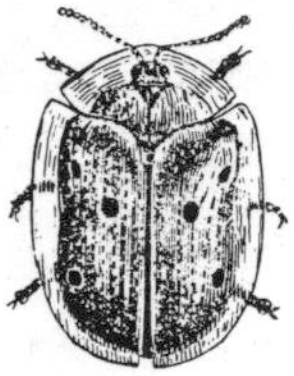

LENGTH: 6-7.5 mm.  RANGE: general.

Dull red; three indistinct black spots on each elytron. Legs and under surface black. Feeds on wild morning-glory and sweet potato vines.

Three varieties have been named (a) *atripes* Lec. and (b) *ellipsis* Lec. occur in Colorado and (c) *novemmaculata* (Mann.) has been described from California.

Figure 715

**67a Antennae when at rest, with basal segments in a groove with a sharp ridge at its side; third segment twice as long as second. Fig. 716.**          **16152 *Chirida guttata* (Oliv.)**

LENGTH: 5.5-6 mm.  RANGE: general.

Dull yellow; thorax usually with sizeable black spot enclosing two lighter ones; elytra black with yellow spots, and pale margins. Common on members of the morning-glory family.

Figure 716

**67b Third segment of antennae but little longer than second; no antennal groove.** ................................................ **68**

**68a Elytra roughened. Fig. 717.**        **16155** *Deloyala clavata* (Fab.)

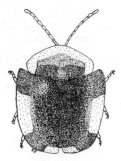

Figure 717

LENGTH: 7-7.5 mm.  RANGE: general.

Broadly oval.  Margins of thorax and elytra translucent with brown markings as pictured. Under surface pale yellow.  A large and very interesting species reminding one of a turtle even more than the other species of the family.  It is said to damage chili peppers in New Mexico and Arizona.

**68b Elytra smooth.  Fig. 718.**        **(a) 16156** *Metriona bivittata* (Say)

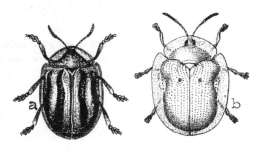

Figure 718

LENGTH: 4.5-6 mm. RANGE: general.

Thorax yellowish with center area brown; elytra dull yellow with black stripes as pictured. Common on sweet potato and wild morning-glory plants. (Courtesy Kans. St. Bd. Agr.)

**(b) 16157** *M. bicolor* (Fab.)

LENGTH: 5.5-6 mm. RANGE: Eastern half of United States.

This very brilliant brassy-gold-while-living beetle attracts much attention but proves a disappointment to collectors for it becomes a dull reddish-yellow when dead. Under parts black. It is often called "Gold Bug."  (U.S.D.A.)

## Family 103   BRUCHIDAE
### The Pea and Bean Weevils

Nearly 1000 species are known.  Practically all (with the exception of a few feeding on the seeds of palm trees) develop within the seeds of legumes.  Their size is necessarily usually small.  The colors are often dull though a few species are ornamented with red.  It might be guessed that "Mexican Jumping Beans" belong here but that insect involved is the caterpillar of a moth and the seed is not a "bean" after all but fruit of a member of the Spurge family.

1a Hind tibiae with two jointed spurs..............................2

1b Hind tibiae without jointed spurs; front coxae prominent........3

2a Claws simple; not over 3 mm. Fig. 719.

16254 *Zabrotes pectoralis* Sharp.

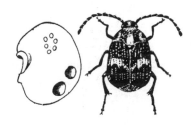

Figure 719

LENGTH: 1.5-2 mm. RANGE: Southwestern United States.

Pale to dark brown or black, marked as shown with white. It is known as the "Mexican Bean Weevil" and while originally a pest of the black and red Mexican beans it seems to thrive on beans of any variety and breeds continuously. The figure shows a bean with six eggs and two emergence holes. (U.S.D.A.)

Several other species are known for this genus, most of which are western in their range.

2b Claws not simple; over 6 mm. Fig. 720.

16246 *Spermophagus hoffmannseggi* Gyll.

Figure 720

LENGTH: 7-8 mm. RANGE: Eastern half United States.

Dull reddish-brown, thickly covered with prostrate yellowish pubescence; thorax darker. Elytra with tiny black spots in rows. The larvae inhabit the seeds of honeylocust and perhaps the black locust. These beetles are fairly common wherever these trees fruit abundantly.

*S. vitis* Schaeffer (16247), reddish brown with a coating of paler hairs, is known from Arizona. Its larvae are exceptional in breeding in the seeds of wild grape. It measures 4 mm.

**3a Thorax with lateral tooth at middle. Fig. 721.**

**(a) 16165 *Bruchus pisorum* (L.)**

LENGTH: 4.5-5 mm. RANGE: cosmopolitan.

Black, thickly covered with reddish-brown, yellowish and whitish hairs to form the pattern pictured. Pygidium with two black spots on gray background. This is the Pea Weevil. The eggs are laid on young pods and the larvae (c) develops only in growing peas. The adults spend the winter within the pea seed but do not lay any eggs in stored peas.

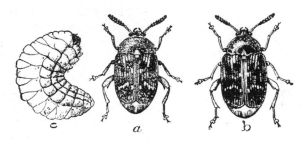

Figure 721

**(b) *Bruchus rufimanus* Boheman**

LENGTH: 3-4 mm. RANGE: cosmopolitan.

Black with pattern of white scales. It is single brooded and infests the so-called horse, Windsor or tick bean. Its popular name is "Broad Bean Weevil." (U.S.D.A.)

This genus is the largest one of the family. It has been repeatedly revised and split up. The name *Mylabris* has been preferred by some systematists. Since this is the type genus, the name used for it decides the family name. Accordingly the family name has vascillated from Bruchidae to Mylabridae and back again. Still other titles are sometimes offered for both genus and family.

Other species ranging in our Southwest are *B. limbatus* Horn (16187) 3 mm., dull gray with 8 brown stripes on each elytron; *B. pruinosus* Horn (16191) 2-3 mm., black covered with brown pubescence and with a gray spot on each elytron and on the thorax and *B. desertorum* Lec. (16198) 3-5 mm., in varying shades of reddish with whitish pubescence and sometimes brown markings breeds in the seeds of mesquite and related plants.

**3b Thorax without lateral tooth.....................................4**

4a Hind femur with a tooth on both the inner and outer margins. Fig. 722.

(a) 16171 *Callosobruchus chinensis* (L.)

LENGTH: 3-4 mm.

RANGE: cosmopolitan.

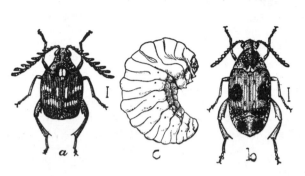

Figure 722

Grayish - black with white markings and two raised ivory spots. This weevil is commonly imported alive in stored products, but is not definitely known to be established in our country. (U.S.D.A.)

(b) 16172 *C. maculatus* (Fab.)
LENGTH: 3-4.5 mm.   RANGE: cosmopolitan.

Reddish-brown with thorax black and gray.   This "Cowpea Weevil" breeds continuously in beans and cowpeas, and has been known as the Southern Cowpea Weevil and the "Four-spotted Bean Weevil." Figure c shows its larvae.   (U.S.D.A.)

4b Hind femur with but one tooth and two small denticles.  Fig. 723.
16221 *Acanthoscelides obtectus* (Say)  Bean Weevil

LENGTH: 2.5-3.5 mm.  RANGE· cosmopolitan.

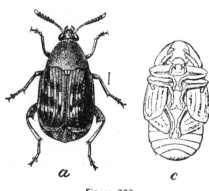

Figure 723

Robust, flattened above. Gray on brown, marked as shown; the legs reddish.   It attacks practically all varieties of beans and breeding continuously in stored seeds quickly reduces them to worthlessness. The pupa (c) is much the same as in all the members of this family. (U.S.D.A.)

# Suborder RHYNCHOPHORA

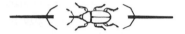

**1a** Beak absent or very short and broad; antennae short and always elbowed. Tibia usually with teeth..............................2

**1b** Tibia without teeth on outer edge; beak usually longer than broad. 3

**2a** First segment of front tarsi longer than the next three segments taken together. (Wide-headed Ambrosia Beetles) Fig. 724. Family 108, PLATYPODIDAE.                       18168 *Platypus wilsoni* Swaine

LENGTH: 5.5 mm. RANGE: British Columbia to California.

Shining, brown. Densely clothed with long yellowish hairs. It attacks many species of conifers.

*P. flavicornis* (Fab.) (18164), 5.2-5.7 mm. long, blackish with third interval of elytra raised and roughened at its base and less elevated in the male; ranges from New Jersey to Florida, Texas and Mexico.

The members of this family are slender cylindrical beetles which feed their larvae on ambrosia fungi within the burrows prepared for growing this food. Various species of trees are attacked, the deeply-cut "pinholes" doing much damage both to the living trees and to the lumber.

Figure 724

**2b** First segment of front tarsi shorter than the next three taken together. (Engraver Beetles) Fig. 725. Family 109, SCOLYTIDAE.
.....................................................page 348

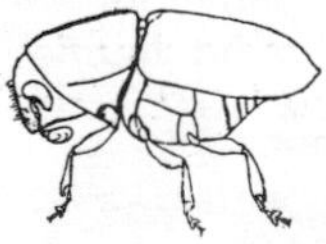

This family is usually poorly represented in beginners collections, likely because of the tiny size of many species and their habits of living in small burrows in wood.

Figure 725

307

**3a Antennae without a distinct club; not elbowed. Body long, slim and usually cylindrical. (Primitive Weevils) Fig. 726. Family 104, BRENTIDAE.**

**16256 *Arrhenodes minuta* Drury**

LENGTH: Male 7.2-17 mm.; Female 6.5-14 mm. RANGE: general.

Subcylindrical. Dark reddish-brown with yellowish, somewhat variable markings on elytra. The larvae bore through the heart wood of oak and other trees; the adults are found under the bark. Three varieties: a, *lecontei*; b, *sallei* and c, *pauperculus* have been named. (Courtesy N. Y. State Museum)

*Brentus anchorago* (L.) (16261), 10-52 mm., known from Florida and Lower California, is shining black or reddish black. The head is longer than broad in this genus.

Figure 726

In all, less than 10 species of this family have been named for our region. There are nearly 1000 species world-wide, most of them tropical.

**3b Antennae with distinct club, but either straight or elbowed.......4**

**4a Stout gray and black checkered beetle, 12-18 mm. long. Antennae not elbowed but with small oval club (a). Only one species known for North America. (New York Weevil) Fig. 727. Family 105, BELIDAE.**              **16234 *Ithycerus noveboracensis* (Forst.)**

LENGTH: 12-18 mm. RANGE: much of the United States and Canada.

Black, clothed with gray and brown prostrate hairs arranged in interrupted stripes on thorax and elytra. Beak with ridges, which are darkened; scutellum whitish.

Breeds in oak and is destructive to apple, peach, plum, pear and cherry trees. The larvae appear in early spring and eat both young buds and foliage. The family has only this one known species. They may be found hiding in the crevices in the bark of trees. It is one of our largest snout beetles.

Figure 727

**4b Not as in 4a.............................................5**

**5a Beak always short and broad; palpi flexible. Thorax with a transverse raised line. Antennae almost always not elbowed. (Fungus Weevils) Fig. 728. Family 106, PLATYSTOMIDAE.......page 309**

A few species are very common in bracket fungi and may be thus found rather easily. This family often appears in the literature as ANTHRIBIDAE.

Figure 728

**5b Snout often long and curved downward. Palpi rigid. Antennae almost always elbowed (a). (Typical Snout Beetles) Fig. 729. Family 107, CURCULIONIDAE................................page 312**

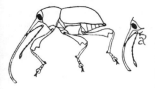

These beetles which range widely in size from tiny little fellows to large tropical species are variously colored. Members of the family are usually easily recognized by the definitely formed snout.

Figure 729

# Family 106 PLATYSTOMIDAE
## The Fungus Weevils

Less than 100 species of this family occur in our North American region. The beetles are gray, brown or blackish. The larvae feed in woody fungi and dead wood.

The beak is flat and usually very short. Two types of antennae prevail, long filiform structures or short antennae with a 3-segmented club. The tarsi are 4-segmented but since the triangular second segment obscures the third, there appears to be but three segments in all.

ANTHRIBIDAE is another family name which is sometimes used.

**1a Antennae arising from the sides of the beak.....................2**

**1b Antennae arising from the front of the head or from the base of the beak, eyes not notched. Fig. 730.**

16316 *Araecerus fasciculatus* (DeG.)

Figure 730

LENGTH: 2.5-4.5 mm. RANGE: cosmopolitan.

Dark brown or blackish with pubescence of yellow or brown. Antennae and legs in part reddish-brown. (U.S.D.A.)

This "coffee-bean weevil" has been scattered widely with coffee and cacao seeds. In our country it has found the seeds of cotton, pokeweed and other plant products to its liking.

**2a Thorax having the transverse ridge straight at middle and separated a short distance from the base; sides of beak spreading over the antennal cavities. Fig. 731.**

16279 *Eurymycter fasciatus* (Oliv.)

Figure 731

LENGTH: 6.5-10 mm. RANGE: Much of the United States and Southern Canada.

Dark brown or blackish; marked with patches of white pubescence on beak and elytra; thorax roughly sculptured and with broad impression in front of middle. On dead twigs and fungi.

*Ormiscus salator* Lec. (16263) is another widely scattered species. Its brownish-black surface is marked with numerous spots and bands of ash-gray pubescence. The antennal cavities are not covered by the sides of the beak as in the above species. It is a little fellow measuring only 1.2-1.6 mm.

Another related species known from Iowa eastward and from Canada south to Florida is *Eusphyrus walshii* Lec. (16275) 2.3-3 mm. in length. It is elongate-oval, brownish-black with a coat of ash-gray or brownish pubescence and with scattered patches of rather coarse yellowish-white hairs.

**2b Transverse ridge arising at the base of thorax, and its posterior side being perpendicular.............................................3**

**3a The sides of the beak parallel or nearly so. Fig. 732.**

**(a) 16293 *Anthribus cornutus* Say**

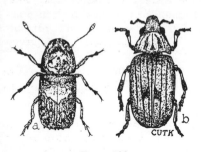

Figure 732

LENGTH: 3.5-6 mm. RANGE: Eastern half of United States and Canada.

Brown with conspicuous markings of darker hairs and large white spot on elytra, as pictured. Beak with feeble ridge above. (U.S.D.A.)

**(b) 16299 *Euparius marmoreus* (Oliv.)**

LENGTH: 4-9 mm. RANGE: Eastern half United States and Canada.

Dusky brown, marked with irregular pattern of pale brown and gray scales on upper surface; legs ringed with gray and black. Common in woody fungi and under bark.

*E. lugubris* (Oliv.) (16300) with a length of 4-7 mm., is reported from Florida, Texas, Arkansas, Indiana and District of Columbia. It is oblong, robust and velvety black with white markings on beak, front third of thorax and an irregular patch on each elytron. The apex of the elytra is white and the legs have alternating white and black rings.

**3b The sides of the beak narrowing from the eyes forward; thoracic ridge turning forward at hind angles. Fig. 733.**

**16305 *Brachytarsus tomentosus* (Say)**

Figure 733

LENGTH: 2-2.5 mm. RANGE: Eastern half United States.

Dark reddish-brown; tibiae and antennae lighter, upper surface with dense grayish yellow or brownish pubescence. Often found on common ragweed.

*Anthribulus rotundatus* Lec. (16315), with a length of 1.5-2.5 mm. and ranging widely, differs from the above genus in being more slender and in the thoracic ridge not turning forward. It is dark brown with bright gray and brown pubescence.

311

## Family 107   CURCULIONIDAE
### The Snout Beetles

This is one of the most important families of beetles, both in numbers and as economic pests. Over 40,000 species are known, ranging in size from near microscopic to large handsome fellows. The larvae (weevils) for the most part spend their life within plant fruits or stems although some are external plant feeders. They commonly "play 'possum" when disturbed.

1a Antennae straight, without a protecting groove on the beak. .................................... 2

1b Antennae with compact club, elbowed; beak with a protecting groove (a) to receive the scape. Fig. 734. ........................................ 8

Figure 734

2a Antennae definitely clubbed, the segments being closely united. Fig. 735................. 6

Figure 735

2b Antennal club absent or if present, with segments distinctly separated. Fig. 736...3

Figure 736

3a Prothorax with a definite acute margin: three dorsal abdominal segments exposed by shortened elytra. Fig. 737.

16370 *Pterocolus ovatus* (Fab.)

LENGTH: 2.5-3.5 mm.   RANGE: Eastern half United States and Canada.

Indigo blue; legs, antennae and snout darker. Elytra flattened, the striae with irregular punctures. Middle coxae small, rounded and widely separated. It has been taken on oak, peach, plum and grape.

Except for the snout this sole member of its subfamily somewhat resembles a hister beetle. The three abdominal segments exposed by the shortened and diagonally cut elytra are densely punctured.

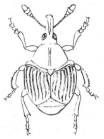

Figure 737

312

3b Thorax without a marginal ridge on its side, labrum absent; palpi
short and stiff.................................................4

4a Antennae not having a club, the last segment cylindrical and elongated, especially in the male; ant-shaped beetles. Fig. 738.
16371a Cylas formicarius elegantulus (Sum.)

LENGTH: 5-6 mm. RANGE: Florida to Texas.

Smooth and highly polished; salmon or reddish-
brown; elytra bluish-black; head and snout blackish. Elytra with weakly punctured fine striae. Last
segment of antennae oval in female; in male long
and slender.

This Sweet Potato Weevil came up from the
tropics and has long been a pest of yams and
sweetpotatoes in the Gulf States. Its distinct form
and coloring makes it readily recognized.

Figure 738

4b Antennae distinctly clubbed.................................5

5a Mandibles flattened with one or more teeth on both the inner and
outer sides (a). Claws two pointed or toothed (b). Fig. 739.
16348 Rhynchites bicolor Fab.

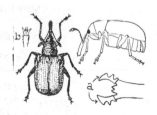

LENGTH: 5-7 mm. RANGE: much of
the United States.

Base of head and thorax and elytra
bright red; other parts black. This
"Rose Curculio" is often very common
within the flowers of wild roses and
occasionally becomes a pest of cultivated roses and some other members of the rose family.

Figure 739

Eugnamptus collaris Fab. (16343) measuring 3.5-5 mm. has its abdomen black and elytra blue-black, but its other parts variable in color
(a number of varieties have been named). It is common on several
species of trees and other plants. It ranges widely from Texas east to
the Atlantic.

313

**5b Mandibles heavy, without teeth on outer side; claws grown together at base; tibia with two sturdy hooks at tip. Fig. 740.**

(a) 16367 *Attelabus bipustulatus* Fab.

LENGTH: 3-4 mm. RANGE: Eastern half United States and Canada.

Black with bluish tinges. Each elytron with spot of red as pictured. Found on our nut trees.

(b) 16365 *A. analis* Ill.

LENGTH: 5-6 mm. RANGE: Texas, Florida, Canada.

Base of head and thorax, abdomen and elytra bright red; other parts bluish-black. Surface not at all pubescent. Found on hickory, oak and walnut.

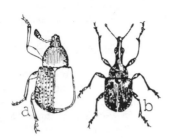

Figure 740

**6a Elytra short exposing pygidium; trochanters small.............7**

**6b Pygidium covered by elytra. Femora attached to the apex of the large trochanters. Small pear-shaped beetles. Fig. 741.**

(a) 16376 *Apion impunctistriatum* Sm.

LENGTH: 2 mm. RANGE: much of eastern half of United States.

Shining black; antennae piceous, very slender; front femora of male with large tubercule near tip.

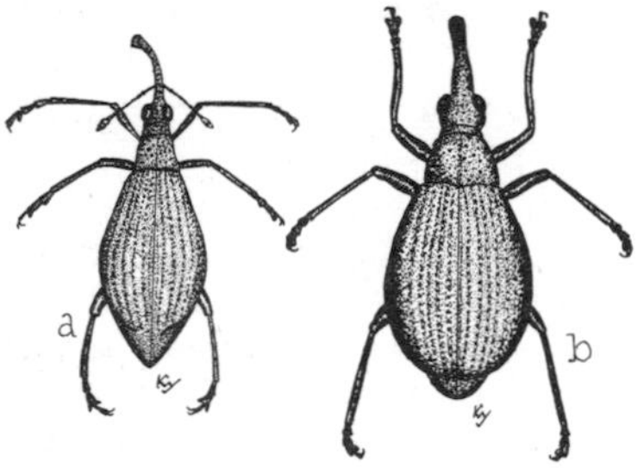

(b) 16439 *A. porcatum* Boh.

LENGTH: 2.4-2.7 mm.

RANGE: Eastern half United States.

Robust, shining, black. Front femur of male without tubercule and tibiae without teeth at tip.

Figure 741

Over 100 species of quite similar little beetles belong to this one genus.

7a First joint of antennae longer than second (a); hind femora broad (b).
Fig. 742.                                    16491 *Allocorhynus slossoni* Schffr.

LENGTH: 3.5-4.2 mm.  RANGE: Florida.

Reddish-yellow; elytra black, marked with red-dish yellow as pictured.  Beak punctured in male, smooth, shining and longer in female; head trans-verse, with scattered coarse punctures; thorax about twice as wide as long, broadly rounded in front. Both adults and larvae feed in the flowers of Flori-da arrow-root.  (After Blatchley and Leng)

Figure 742

7b First joint of antennae no longer than second joint; hind coxae wide-ly separated.  Fig. 743.                    16492 *Tachygonus lecontei* Gyll.

LENGTH: 2-2.5 mm.  RANGE: New Jersey to Texas.

Reddish-brown marked with black as pic-tured.  Surface with coarse white and black hairs and fine buff ones.  Lives on the leaves of young oak trees.  (Redrawn from Blatchley and Leng)

*T. gracilipes* Csy. (16494) 2.2-2.5 mm., and ranging in the eastern part of our region, is shining black with pale reddish-brown sutural stripe and median cross-bar on the elytra.

Figure 743

8a Abdomen of male with one more anal segment than female; club of antennae usually with rings, not shining; tarsi usually dilated with the third segment bilobed and brush-like beneath (a). Fig. 744. . . . . . . . . . . . . . . . . . . . . . . . . . . . . . . . . .9

Figure 744

8b Tarsi usually narrow and not brush-like beneath; anal segments the same number in both sexes; basal segment of club of antennae usu-ally either shining or enlarged or both. . . . . . . . . . . . . . . . . . . . . . . .61

315

9a Prosternum in front of the coxae, triangular; beak when at rest lying within the breast; tarsi not widened. Fig. 745.

18002 *Thecesternus humeralis* (Say)

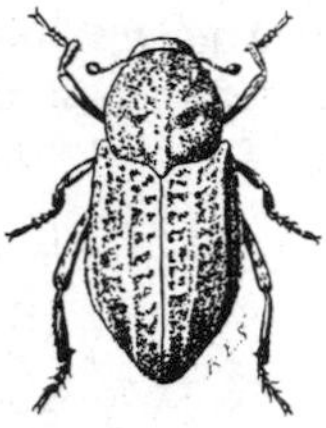

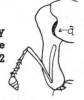

LENGTH: 6.5-9 mm. RANGE: Indiana to Colorado and south.

Robust; dull black, often densely covered with fine brownish-yellow scales. (After Snodgrass)

The small subfamily here represented has but the one genus and less than 10 species. They are sometimes known as the "Bison Snout Beetles."

Figure 745

9b Prosternum not triangular in front, sometimes with a groove to receive the beak.............................................10

10a Beak usually long and slender; but if short and slender then held within the breast when in repose, mandibles not marked with a scar. .....................................................19

10b Beak always short and rather thick; mandibles marked with a scar. (A round or oval depression on the face of the mandible; sometimes on a projection.)........................................11

11a Front of thorax with ocular lobes sometimes partially covering the eyes (a); eyes often elongate with the greater length longitudinal. Fig. 746............12

Figure 746

11b Without ocular lobes; eyes rounded or oval, if oval the greatest length transverse.............................................14

12a Mentum sufficiently large to cover the maxilla................13

316

12b Mentum small and retracted, antennal grooves deep, sometimes uniting beneath. Fig. 747.     16591 *Eudiagogus pulcher* Fahr.

LENGTH: 5-8 mm.  RANGE: Florida to Texas.

Black, heavily clothed with black and bright green or copper colored scales on suture and sides as pictured. Feeds on legumes.  (After Blatchley and Leng)

*Aracanthus pallidus* (Say) (16590), ranging widely through the eastern half of our country, is dusky brown with gray and reddish scales. It is around 3 mm. in length and is characterized by a very small scutellum.

Figure 747

13a Antennal grooves turning downward under beak or towards the eyes; beak rounded; eyes oval. Fig. 748.

(a) 16578 *Panscopus maculosus* Blatch.

LENGTH: 5.5-7.5 mm. RANGE: Indiana to New York.

Dark b r o w n with pattern of s i l v e r y a n d brown scales as pictured. (After Blatchley)

(b) 16547 *Aname-tis granulata* (Say)

Figure 748

LENGTH: 5-7 mm.  RANGE: Eastern half United States.

Dark brown, thickly clothed with grayish scales.  Antennae and tarsi reddish-brown.  Common on trees and shrubs.

13b Grooves short and visible from above; strongly curved. Fig. 749.

16499 *Phyxelis rigidus* (Say)

LENGTH: 3.5-4.5 mm.  RANGE: Eastern half of United States and Canada.

Dusky brown with coating of grayish scales and often a further waxy coat, yellowish or brownish.

*Eupagoderes geminatus* Horn (16513), lives in the desert areas of the Southwest. It measures 7-12 mm. and is wholly covered with white scales and is known as the White Bud Weevil.

Figure 749

**14a** Grooves linear and directed beneath the beak..................16

**14b** Grooves not both linear and directed beneath.................15

**15a** Claws united at the base; second joint of funicle equalling the
first. Fig. 750.                    16721 *Aphrastus taeniatus* Say

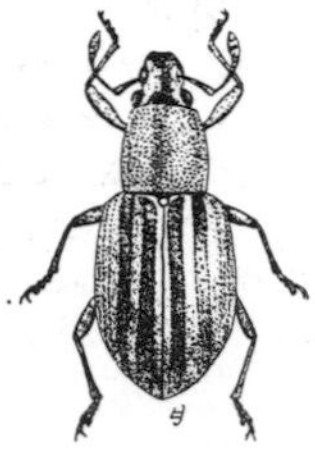

LENGTH: 5.5-6.5 mm.  RANGE: Eastern half of
United States.

Convex.  Densely clothed with tiny pale gray
scales, and marked on head and elytra as pictured
with brown scale. (Courtesy N. Y. State Museum)

*Thricolepis inornata* Horn (16702), black and
gray above and measuring 3-5 mm., ranges widely in the West and is fairly common.

*Paraptochus sellatus* (Boh.) (16698) is an abundant pest of apricots, peaches, apples, prunes, etc.
from British Columbia to California.  It is dark
brown and 3.5-5 mm. long.

Figure 750

**15b** Claws not fused, antennae long and slender; hind tibiae with two
short spurs. Fig. 751.

16679 *Brachyrhinus rugifrons* (Gyll.)

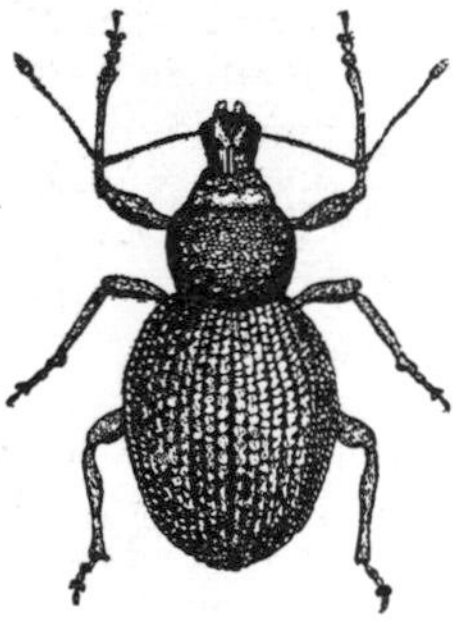

LENGTH: 7.5-8 mm.  RANGE: Eastern United
States and Canada.

Brownish-black, rather dull, the surface covered with rounded tubercules, each bearing
a hair.  Femora club-shaped. (After Pack)

*Sciopithes obscurus* Horn (16683) ranges
from California to British Columbia where it
is known as the Obscure Root Weevil.  It
is 5-7 mm. in length, and is brown with lines
of whitish.

Figure 751

**16a** Thorax with a fringe of short bristly hairs, or if without fringe,
then the front coxae separated by a narrow sternum.........18

**16b** Front coxae touching; thorax without fringe as in 16a.  Claws not
united. .....................................................17

**17a Mesoplural pieces very unequal, the episternum larger and reaching the margin of elytra; antennae slender. Fig. 752.**

16646 *Epicaerus imbricatus* Say

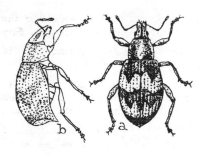

Figure 752

LENGTH: 7.5-11.5 mm. RANGE: much of the United States.

Upper surface densely clothed with small fuscous and grayish scales in the pattern pictured. This Imbricated Snout Beetle is a rather well known pest of economic plants (a, dorsal view; b, side view), such as apple, cherry, gooseberry, raspberry, melons, cabbage, cucumbers, sugar beet, etc. (U.S.D.A.)

**17b Mesopleural pieces diagonally and about equally divided; 10th elytral striae entire; segments of the flagellum elongated. Fig. 753.**

16659 *Pantomorus godmani* (Cr.)

Figure 753

LENGTH: 6.5-8.5 mm. RANGE: much of the United States.

Dark brown, rather lightly clothed with gray or pale brown scales; elytra marked with whitish as pictured. This "Fullers Rose Beetle" has been a pest in greenhouses. It feeds on many species of plants and in California is thought to spread citrus blast. Since the adults cannot fly, banding of trees and shrubs offers a means of control.

**18a Front coxae touching, or nearly so, thorax with fringe of ocular hairs. Fig. 754.**

16596 *Tanymecus confertus* (Gyll.)

Figure 754

LENGTH: 5-7 mm. RANGE: East of the Rockies.

Dusky brown with scattered grayish and cuperous scales; elytra with spots of brown as pictured.

*T. lacaena* (Hbst.) (16595), similar in color and shape, is considerably larger (8-9 mm.). It occurs from Florida to Texas.

319

18b Front coxae distant, front femora larger than others; front tibiae with tooth on inner edge. Fig. 755.

16605 *Pandeleteius hilaris* (Hbst.)

LENGTH: 4-5 mm.  RANGE: Florida to Texas and north to Canada.

Brown, densely clothed with fine fuscous and grayish scales in pattern as pictured.  A common species. (Courtesy N. Y. State Museum)

It breeds in oak, making small burrows.  The adults hibernate under logs and bark and may be taken by beating or sweeping New Jersey tea, smartweed and oak leaves.  It has been called the Gray-sided Oak Weevil.

Figure 755

19a Beak free, not received by the prosternum...................20

19b Beak when at rest lying within the prosternum; upper surface often much roughened...........................................53

20a Mesopleura protruding between the thorax and elytra and appearing from above as a wedge or as rounded knobs (a), and obliquely truncating the shoulder of the elytra.  Fig. 756a.............51

20b Not as in 20a...............................................21

21a Elytra extending so feebly over the abdomen that the angles of the first ventral abdominal segments are exposed to view (b).  Fig. 756b...49

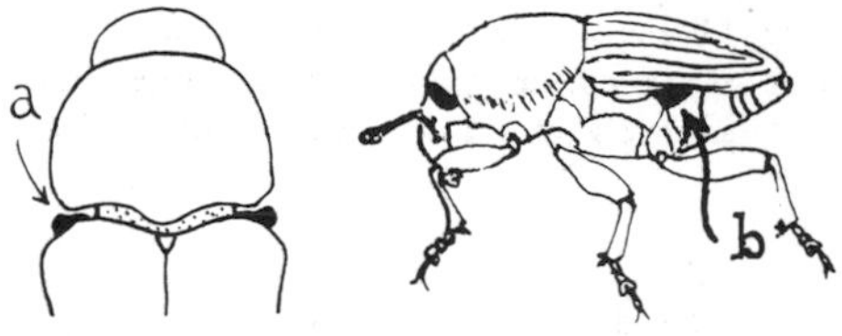

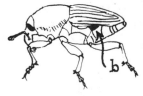

Figure 756

21b Angles of the first ventral abdominal segment covered by the elytra. .....................................................22

22a Beak usually at least as long as the prothorax; gular peduncle usually long. .............................................23

**22b Beak broad and short, claws simple, ventral abdominal segments about equal; guler peduncle short and broad; mentum large and quadrate. Fig. 757.** 16728 *Sitona hispidulus* (Fab.)

Figure 757

LENGTH: 3-5 mm. RANGE: Europe, Canada and United States.

Shining. Black with small oval scales, gray and cuperous forming the pattern pictured.

This is the "Clover Root Curculio."

*Sitona flavescens* Marsh. (16727) with a length of 4.5-5.5 mm. and ranging in Europe and much of the United States and Canada is black and densely clothed above with reddish-brown hair-like scales forming a pattern in fresh specimens. The under surface is covered with prostrate grayish hairs. Both the adults and the larvae are injurious to white and alsike clover.

**23a Ventral abdominal segments about equal in width; sometimes the first is wider; claws often with teeth..........................34**

**23b Third and fourth ventral abdominal segments narrow, their combined width scarcely or not exceeding the width of the second or the fifth. Fig. 758. .......................................24**

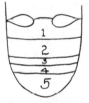

Figure 758

**24a Gular margin prominent, its peduncle and mentum retracted; beak rather heavy no longer than the prothorax; mandibles flat and punctured on the outer side. Fig. 759.**
16752 *Lepidophorus setiger* Ham.

Figure 759

LENGTH: 3-3.5 mm. RANGE: Eastern United States.

Black, antennae and legs reddish-brown; densely clothed above with small round brownish scales interspersed with scattered white ones to form three pale stripes on thorax and mottling on elytra. (After Blatchley and Leng)

**24b** Gular margin not prominent, its peduncle usually long; front coxae touching or almost so; claws simple..........................**25**

**25a** Mandibles usually with a notch at tip forming two teeth. Fig. 760a...............**26**

**25b** Mandibles with two notches and three teeth at tip. Fig. 760b......................**29**

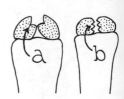

Figure 760

**26a** Third and fourth ventral segments narrow, the two together but equalling one of the others...................................**27**

**26b** Ventral abdominal segments not very unequal; space between eyes not more than their diameter...................................**28**

**27a** Second segment of funicle (a) much longer than the first; tibia sharp pointed at apex. Fig. 761.

(a) 16790 *Listronotus latiusculus* (Boh.)

LENGTH: 5-6 mm. RANGE: Eastern United States and Canada.

Black, usually covered with grayish, brownish, or reddish scales, forming a rather obscure pattern, as pictured; antennae and tarsi reddish-brown. Sometimes destructive to parsley. (U.S.D.A.)

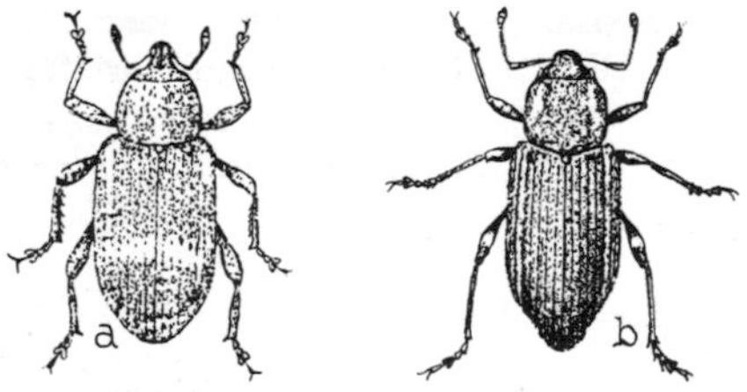

Figure 761

(b) 16788 *L. palustris* Blatch.

LENGTH: 6-8.5 mm. RANGE: Florida.

Black; upper surface with pattern as pictured set with brown and silver-gray scales; antennae, tibiae and tarsi dark reddish-brown; beak fairly heavy, as long as thorax. (After Blatchley)

**27b Second segment of funicle scarcely longer if at all and slimmer than the first. Fig. 762.** 16801 *Hyperodes solutus* (Boh.)

Figure 762

LENGTH: 3-5 mm. RANGE: Eastern United States and Canada, west to Montana.

Black to reddish-brown, the upper surface with rounded clay-yellow scales in pattern as pictured; antennae and legs reddish brown.

*H. hyperodes* (Dietz) (16805), measuring 4.5-6 mm., black with covering of dark brown and grayish-brown scales, has been reported as boring within the stems of tomatoes in California.

*Hyperodes* is a relatively large genus with about 40 species. *H. montanus* (Dietz) (16815) is known from Indiana and Iowa to the Dakotas. It measures 3.5 mm. and is blackish, with a covering of grayish-brown and white scales. The antennae and legs are reddish-brown. *H. sparsus* (Say) (16821) ranges widely. It measures 4-5 mm. and is reddish-brown or piceous with a covering of dull gray scales.

*H. humilis* (Gyll) (16835), measuring 4-5 mm., apparently ranges over much of our territory. It is dull black; the thorax has a stripe on each side, while the antennae, tibiae, tarsi and front of thorax are dark reddish-brown.

**28a Beak shorter than the prothorax; thorax much narrower than the well rounded elytra. Fig. 763.** 16754 *Hypera punctata* (Fab.)

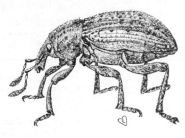

Figure 763

LENGTH: 5-8.5 mm. RANGE: introduced from Europe; now widely scattered through the United States.

Black, thickly clothed with scales of varying shades of gray, brown and blackish. Beak two-thirds as long as thorax.

This "Clover Leaf Beetle" may be found in almost any clover field; the green and pinkish larvae climb up the plants at night and feed on the leaves. External feeding by the larvae is rather unusual in this family.

**28b** Beak longer than the prothorax; thorax not more than one-third narrower than the elytra. Fig. 764.

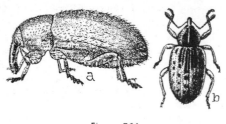

Figure 764

(a) 16765 *Hypera nigrirostris* (Fab.)

LENGTH: 3.5-4.5 mm.

RANGE: Europe and most of United States.

Reddish brown to black, appearing greenish or bluish-black or yellow from the heavy coat of scales and hairs; beak, head and legs black. It is often abundant in clover fields and is known as the "Lesser Clover Leaf Weevil." (After Webster)

(b) 16766 *H. postica* (Gyll.) **Alfalfa Weevil**

LENGTH: 3-5 mm. RANGE: introduced from Europe, especially abundant in the western United States.

Pale brownish to black with design of scales and hairs as pictured; antennae and legs paler. A serious pest of alfalfa and clover especially west of the Missouri river. (U.S.D.A.)

**29a** Tibia with corbels (an ovate area near apical end which is bounded by minute bristles) and with a long curved claw at apex, which is oblique, dilated and ciliate; length at least 4 mm. . . . . . . . . . . . . . . 33

**29b** Tibiae without corbels, truncate at tip; usually less than 4 mm. long, never over 7 mm. . . . . . . . . . . . . . . . . . . . . . . . . . . . . . . . . . . . . . . . . . . . . . . . 30

**30a** Body with usual coating of scales and hair; without a waterproof coat. . . . . . . . . . . . . . . . . . . . . . . . . . . . . . . . . . . . . . . . . . . . . . . . . . . . . . . : . . . 31

**30b** Body covered with a waterproof, varnish-like coat of scales; beak cylindrical and much longer than head; legs long and slender. Fig. 765. 17029 *Lissorhoptrus simplex* (Say)

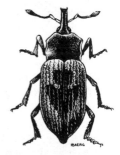

Figure 765

LENGTH: 2.8-3.2 mm. RANGE: Canada to the Gulf, west to Texas.

Black with coating of large olive-gray scales. Beak as long as thorax, heavy. Basal half of antennal club smooth and shining.

This "Rice-Water Weevil" feeds on various water plants and is often very destructive to rice. The larvae are known as the "rice-root maggot." The adults can live under water for a long period of time without drowning.

**31a Beak constricted at base, a transverse line separating it from the head; claws fused; club of antennae small.................32**

**31b Claws diverging; beak not constricted at base. Fig. 766.**

16893 *Dorytomus mucidus* (Say)

LENGTH: 5-6.5 mm. RANGE: Canada to Mississippi, New England to Kansas.

Dark reddish-brown, thinly clothed with prostrate yellowish hairs; antennae reddish-brown; femora toothed. Beak slender and curved only half as long as thorax. Breeds in the seed pods of cottonwood.

*Notaris puncticollis* (Lec.) (16922) is substantially the same in size and color but differs in having no teeth on the femora. It ranges from Newfoundland to Iowa.

Figure 766

**32a Eyes close together on underside of head (Fig. 767, a); tibiae with hooks or claws at apex. Fig. 768.**

**16947 *Smicronyx tesselatus* Dietz**

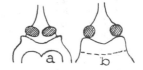

Figure 767

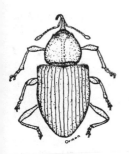

LENGTH: 2-2.4 mm. RANGE: Texas and eastward.

Very convex. Black to reddish-brown; with covering of brown and white scales, forming pattern as pictured. First segment of funicle thick.

*S. apionides* Csy. (16978), ranging widely from Texas to the East, may be readily told by its small size 1.7-2 mm. It is black with some white scales on sides of thorax and base of elytra.

Figure 768

*S. perpusillus* Csy. (16987) known from Florida, may be distinguished by its small size, 1.6 mm., and by the widely scattered large white scales on the elytra. The color is blackish with the legs reddish.

*S. quadrifer* Csy. (16966) seems to be distributed well across the southern part of the United States. It measures about 2.5 mm. and is black with a coat of large, pale brown or whitish scales. A large squarish, velvety-black spot near the middle of the elytral region makes it readily determined.

**32b** **Eyes more widely separated on underside of head (fig. 767, b). Hind tibiae ending in a sharp point. Fig. 769.**

16932 *Desmoris scapalis* Lec.

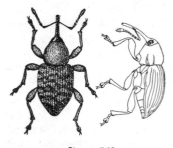

LENGTH: 4-5 mm. RANGE: Texas to New Hampshire.

Dark brown to black, with a dense coat of grayish-yellow scales. Legs dull red; male with first two segments of funicle about equal; female with the first segment considerably longer. (U.S.D.A.)

*D. sordidus* Lec. (16938), known from Illinois to Arizona, is colored much as the above but it is noticeably smaller. (2.5-3 mm.)

Figure 769

**33a** **Antennae attached wholly on the sides of the more slender cylindrical beak; their point of attachment not visible from above; front coxae not quite touching. Fig. 770.**

16845 *Pissodes strobi* (Peck)

LENGTH: 4.5-6 mm. RANGE: Wisconsin and eastward.

Light to dark brown, marked as pictured with yellowish. Elytra wider than thorax; striae punctured; third and fifth intervals somewhat higher than others. This "White Pine Weevil" infests several species of pines but is particularly destructive to the White Pine. (U.S.D.A.)

*P. costatus* Mann. (16856), measuring 5.5-7 mm. and light to dark brown, is known as the Ribbed Pine Weevil and ranges from Alaska to California. It is one of several species of the genus that attack pines, spruces and other conifers.

Figure 770

**33b** **Antennae attached toward the sides of the thicker and stronger beak, their point of attachment visible from above; front coxae touching. Fig. 771.**

16874 *Hylobius congener* Dalla T.

LENGTH: 6-7 mm. RANGE: Alaska, Canada and northeastern United States.

Oblong, robust. Dark reddish-brown with scant pattern of whitish hairs, as pictured. (After Brehm)

*Eudociminus mannerheimi* Boh. (16880), 10.5-15 mm. long, is another member of this tribe. It is black with side stripes on thorax and four small spots of brown scales on the fourth interval of the elytra. It ranges from New York to Louisiana and is known as the Cypress Weevil.

Figure 771

**34a Thorax narrowed at base into a neck-like stem. Fig. 772.**
**17121 *Myrmex chevrolati* (Horn)**

LENGTH: 3.5-4.5 mm. RANGE: New England to
Iowa and Texas south to the Gulf.

Convex. Highly shining, black. Densely covered with white hairs on sides but nearly hairless
on top. Elytra less than twice as long as wide;
disk with rows of closely-placed fine punctures.
Front of head as pictured (a). (After Snodgrass)

*M. floridanus* (Csy.) (17117) and *M. myrmex*
Hbst. (17118) are similar in size and color but
both have a large triangular tooth on the femora.
The first has rows of white hairs mingled with
black ones on the elytra while in *myrmex* the hairs
are wholly black.

Figure 772

**34b Thorax not as in 34a.................................35**

**35a Hind angles of thorax obtuse...............................36**

**35b Hind angles of thorax acute or produced; outline wedge-shaped
or broader behind. Fig. 773.**

**(a) 17144 *Magdalis aenescens* Lec.**

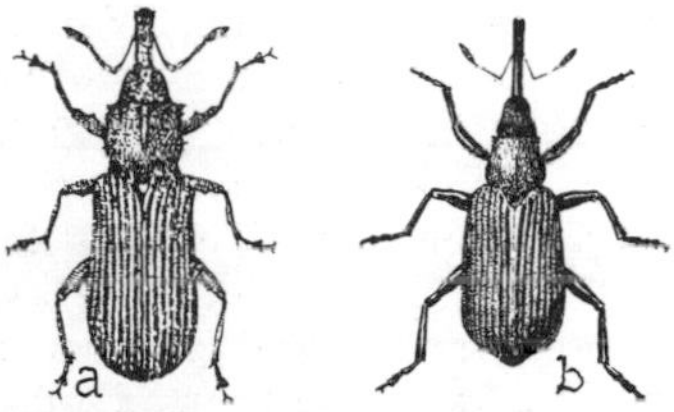

LENGTH: 4-6 mm. RANGE: Alaska
and California.

Black with bronzy-metallic sheen;
elytra distinctly striate. This "Bronze
Apple Tree Weevil" is a pest of
apple and some other fruit trees.
(U.S.D.A.)

**(b) 17150 *Magdalis barbita* Say**

Figure 773

LENGTH: 4-6 mm. RANGE: Canada
and New England to Texas.

Black, feebly shining; antennae and tarsi piceous. The larvae
live under the bark of oak, hickory and elm. (U.S.D.A.)

**36a The mandibles moving vertically; snout often very long and slen-
der, (nut and acorn weevils)................................37**

**36b Mandibles moving in a horizontal plane; claws divided, toothed or
with an appendage.......................................42**

**37a Beak never longer than the body (usually shorter), curved......41**

**37b Beak of female definitely longer than the body................38**

38a First joint of the funicle (in antennae) (d, fig. 775) usually much
longer than the second, never shorter.........................**39**

38b Second joint of funicle longer than the first. Feeds on chestnuts.
Fig. 774.                        **17155 *Curculio proboscideus* Fab.**

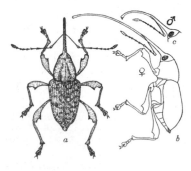

Figure 774

LENGTH: 8-11 mm. RANGE: Eastern
half United States.

Robust. Dark brown, clothed with
dense coat of yellowish or golden
hairs; thorax and elytra with fuscous
spots; fifth ventral segment square
cut, with a smooth area at apex and
a tuft of hairs on each side. It is
known as the Large Chestnut Weevil.
The female (b) has a much longer
snout than the male (c). (After Chittenden)

This fairly sizable genus is a most important one in the damage
caused by its larvae. The female drills a hole deep into developing
nuts or acorns. An egg is then placed at the bottom of the hole deep
within the fruit where the larvae spends most of its life, safely out of
reach of poisons.

39a Surface covered with hairs; femoral tooth rectangular; large; feeds
on hickories and pecan. Fig. 775.

                       **17156 *Curculio caryae* (Horn)**

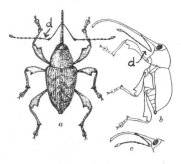

Figure 775

LENGTH: 7-9 mm. RANGE: Eastern
half United States.

Dull brownish with scattered yellowish hairs. Thorax wider than long,
densely and closely punctured. The
right angle of the femoral tooth is a
good identification character. It is
known as the Pecan Weevil. Side
views of the female (b) and male (c)
are shown. (U.S.D.A.)

39b Surface covered with scales...................................**40**

40a Beak of female (b) curved from end to end, pygidium of male with tuft of hair; feeds on chestnut. Fig. 776.

17177 *Curculio auriger* (Csy.)

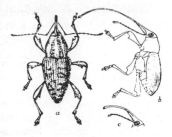

Figure 776

LENGTH: 4.5-7 mm. RANGE: Eastern half of United States.

This Chestnut Weevil has a coating of brownish hair-like scales over piceous. Thorax and elytra marked with yellow scales as pictured. Thorax longer than wide in female (a and b); length equal to width in male (c).

40b Beak of female straight nearly to its end, pygidium of male concave and fringed with hairs; feeds on oaks. Fig. 777.

17157 *Curculio rectus* (Say)

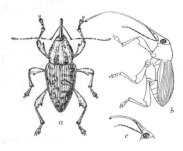

Figure 777

LENGTH: 8.5-9 mm. RANGE: Eastern half United States.

This pest of the acorns of the black oak group is brownish with a covering of pale brown hair-like scales. The beak of the male is somewhat shorter than the body while that of the female is nearly twice as long. The tooth on the femur is small.

41a Feeds on hazel-nuts. Outer edge of femoral tooth oblique; beak about equal in both sexes. Fig. 778.

17164 *Curculio obtusus* (Blanch.)

LENGTH: 6-8 mm. RANGE: Canada to Texas.

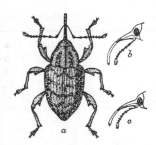

Figure 778

Blackish brown, clothed above with ash-gray to yellowish scale-like hairs; thorax and elytra marked with paler scales as pictured. Beak of female (b) only two-thirds as long as body; that of male (c) still shorter; pygidium of male with long yellow hairs. Appendices of claws broad, nearly or quite rectangular.

The eggs are laid in hazel-nuts where the larvae develop. The infested nuts fall early.

329

41b Breeds in acorns.   Outer edges of femoral tooth standing at a
right angle to the femur; beak of male slightly less than half the
length of the body, that of female three-fifths as long as the body.
Fig. 779.                                 17162 *Curculio baculi* Chitt.

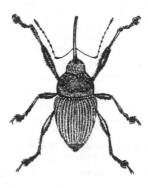

LENGTH: 5.5-7.5 mm.   RANGE: New York
to Alabama and Nebraska and Kansas.

Sooty to reddish brown, the body scant-
ily covered with short pale gray scales;
elytra with gray hairs which rub off to
leave bare areas.   First joint of funicle
longer than second; pygidium of male
with tuft of long yellowish hairs. (Courtesy Kans. St. Bd. of Agr.)

It seems to infest several species of
oaks of both the white oak and black
oak groups, but apparently prefers the
latter group which takes two years to mature its acorns.

Figure 779

42a Ventral sutures angling at sides.............................43

42b Ventral sutures straight and parallel........................44

43a Pygidium exposed; flagellum with but five segments.   Fig. 780.
                                       17359 *Gymnetron tetrum* (Fab.)

LENGTH: 2.5-4 mm.   RANGE: Europe and much of
North America.

Black with a clothing of yellowish-gray pubescence; thorax with many fine punctures; femora
toothed below. (After Kuhnt) This species is exceedingly common and can almost always be found
around its food plant, the common mullein, especially within the capsules.

*Miarus hispidulus* Lec. (17360) is a bit smaller.
It breeds in the seed capsules of some of the
lobelias.

Figure 780

**43b Pygidium covered; flagellum with 6-7 segments. Fig. 781.**

17352 *Odontopus calceatus* Say

LENGTH: 3-4 mm. RANGE: Eastern half United States.

Figure 781

Black, slightly shining; tarsi and antennae red-brown. Thorax heavily set with coarse punctures. Striae of elytra deep and coarsely punctured; intervals flat. Front femora with serrations for holding (a); ventral segments angulate at sides (b). Feeds on sassafras and tuliptree. (After Snodgrass)

*Piazorhinus scuttellaris* (Say) (17353), measuring 2-2.5 mm. and ranging through the eastern half of the United States, is closely related. It is black except for a white scutellum and yellow hairs on the thorax with white hairs on the elytra.

**44a Claws with a sharp tooth.....................................45**

**44b Claws with a short broad tooth at base; hind femora thickened for leaping. Fig. 782.**

17345 *Rhynchaenus pallicornis* (Say)

LENGTH: 2.5-3 mm. RANGE: Newfoundland to Oregon and Texas.

Figure 782

Shining, black, thinly clothed with grayish-yellow hairs; tarsi and antennae reddish-brown; beak short and heavy; elytral striae shallow, with coarse punctures, intervals flat. (After Forbes)

Its larvae mine in the leaves of several species of trees including apple and cherry.

*R. ephippiatus* (Say) (17337), similar in size and color, has a seven-jointed funicle instead of six as in the above. It is often abundant on willow and ranges widely.

**45a Hind tibiae ending in a sharp point (mucronate); scrobes long...46**

**45b Hind tibiae with hook at tip; pygidium covered; claws with a long tooth; beak long and slender. Fig. 783.**
17186 *Tachypterellus quadrigibbus* (Say)

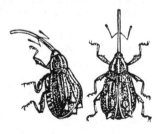

Figure 783

LENGTH: 3-4.5 mm. RANGE: general throughout the United States and Canada.

Dark red; beak, antennae and legs, paler; thin coat of grayish pubescence on elytra and thorax forming three lines on the thorax; elytra with two large tubercles on each, as pictured. (After Riley)

This Apple Curculio feeds not only on apples and pears but on other closely related plants also.

**46a Antennal grooves directed against the eye; antennal club elongated.** ................................................... **47**

**46b Antennal grooves directed below the eye; pygidium not elongated. Fig. 784.**
17299 *Pseudanthonomus crataegi* Walsh

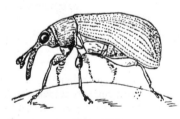

Figure 784

LENGTH: 2.5-2.8 mm. RANGE: Canada to Wisconsin and Florida.

Pale reddish-brown, thinly clothed with long yellowish pubescence in median streak on thorax and spots on elytra; thorax one-fourth wider than long. Elytra at base one-fourth wider than thorax. (U.S.D.A.)

It seems to have several food plants, various species of *Craetegus* and *Prunus* being frequently attacked.

**47a Fifth ventral abdominal segment of male not emarginate, or at the most but slightly so.** ...................................... **48**

**47b Fifth ventral of male short, with deep emargination behind. (a) Fig. 785.**
17189 *Anthonomus scutellaris* Lec.

Figure 785

LENGTH: 5-6 mm. RANGE: Massachusetts to Texas

This "Plum Gouger" got its start on wild plums but seems to like the cultivated ones even better and sometimes eats apples also. It is dark reddish-brown with a covering of long yellowish and gray hairs to form a mottled pattern on thorax and elytra. The striae on the elytra are narrow with fine punctures. (U.S.D.A.)

This genus is a large one with more than 100 named species, several of which are highly economic.

48a Front femora with two teeth, the forward one being smaller. Fig.
786.                                   17207 *Anthonomus grandis* Boh.  Boll Weevil

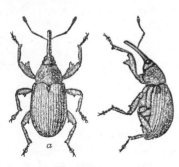

Figure 786

LENGTH: 4-7.5 mm.  RANGE: Mexico and much of our American Cotton belt.

This little pest literally removes the shirt from many backs. It came up from Mexico in the 1890's and has worried numerous cotton growers into an early grave. It is reddish-brown to blackish with a covering of pale yellow scales forming many small dots on the elytra. The eggs are laid within the cotton bolls and the larvae destroy the seeds and fiber.  (U.S.D.A.)

48b Front femora with but one tooth; elytra with darker mark back of
middle. Fig. 787.                     (a) 17219 *Anthonomus signatus* Say

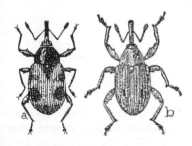

Figure 787

LENGTH: 2-3 mm.  RANGE: Canada to Florida and Texas.

Piceous with thinly placed whitish hairs; the dark red elytra are marked with two bare spots as pictured. The antennae are dull yellow with darker club. It occurs on various plants but has been named the Strawberry Weevil because of its damage to this plant.   (U.S.D.A.)

(b) 17296 *A. eugenii* Cano  Pepper Weevil
LENGTH: 2.5-3 mm.  RANGE: Mexico and our Southwest.

Reddish-brown or blackish with a brassy tinge. Pale yellowish brown scales make the design on thorax and elytra. It is highly destructive to peppers.  (U.S.D.A.)

*A. musculus* Say (17224) about 2 mm. long and known from Colorado to New England and Ontario to Florida is dark reddish-brown or piceous and covered with a thin white pubescence. The beak is slightly curved and is as long as the head and thorax taken together.

49a Elongate slender beetles with a slender curved beak..........50

333

**49b** Elongate but more robust beetles with thicker beak which becomes dilated near apex. Fig. 788.

17392 *Cleonus quadrilineatus* (Chev.)

LENGTH: 9-11 mm. RANGE: Southwestern United States.

Shining black, striped with yellowish pubescence as pictured. Feeds on the roots of some legumes. The Radish Weevil, *C. sparsus* Lec. (17390), another western species, is smaller (6.5 mm.). It has four bluish-gray stripes on each elytron.

A larger, more robust species, *C. carnicollis* Lec. (17385), known from Colorado and Florida, has four broad gray stripes on each elytron. It measures 12-14 mm.

Figure 788

**50a** Thorax broadly flattened with an impression extending most of its length. Fig. 789.        17418 *Lixus concavis* Say Rhubarb Curculio

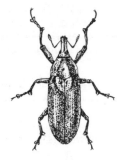

LENGTH: 10-13 mm. RANGE: much of the United States.

Black, sparingly clothed with fine ash-gray pubescence; often covered with rust-red pollen. Lives on curled dock and becomes a pest of rhubarb, puncturing the leaf stems. (U.S.D.A.)

This genus contains about 40 readily recognizable beetles.

Figure 789

**50b** Thorax with impression only near basal end; beak shorter than thorax. Fig. 790.        17426 *Lixus scrobicollis* Boh.

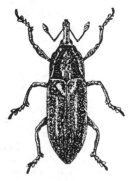

LENGTH: 6.5-9 mm. RANGE: Texas to Atlantic Coast.

Slender, black, with scanty gray pubescence forming pale stripes on thorax and elytra; frequently (freshly emerged specimens) coated with a rust-red dust. Breeds in ragweed. (U.S.D.A.)

*L. terminalis* Lec. (17439), known from Iowa to New England and Florida, measures 8-12 mm. is shining reddish-brown and has the second joint of the funicle longer than the third and fourth combined.

Figure 790

51a Claws united at base; parallel or nearly so..................52

51b Claws diverging, not united; club of antennae nearly round and polished at its base. Fig. 791.

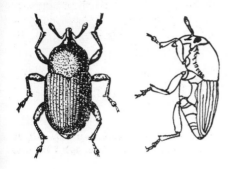

Figure 791

**17468 Baris interstitialis (Say)**

LENGTH: 3.5-5 mm. RANGE: New England to Florida, Texas and Colorado.

Black, antennae and legs reddish-brown; beak half as long as thorax, much curved. Thorax and elytra of equal width. (U.S.D.A.)

More than 50 species of *Baris* are known. A species introduced from Europe, *B. scolopacea* Germ. (17505), 3.5 mm., blackish, with white and pale brown scales, lives on ragweed and is becoming widely distributed.

*B. umbilicata* (Lec.) (17447) 3-5 mm. in length and ranging from Texas and Colorado to Wisconsin and Michigan is shining black with dark reddish-brown tarsi and antennae.

52a Front coxae widely separated; prosternum with a deep, wide excavation in front. Fig. 792.

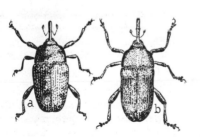

Figure 792

**(a) 17550 Ampeloglypter ater Lec.**

LENGTH: 2.5-3 mm. RANGE: New England to Indiana.

Shining, black; tarsi and antennae reddish-brown. First joint of the funicle as long as the next three combined.

**(b) 17552 A. sesostris (Lec.) Grape Cane Gall Maker**

LENGTH: 2.5-3 mm. RANGE: Eastern half United States. Shining, pale reddish-brown. Beak one-half longer than thorax, much curved at base. Elytral striae fine, without punctures. It feeds on grapes. (After Brooks)

335

**52b** Front coxae narrowly separated, beak short and robust; antennal club small. Fig. 793.        17566 *Trichobaris trinotata* (Say)

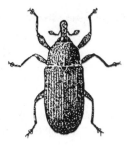

LENGTH: 3-4 mm.  RANGE: Canada to Colorado and Florida.

Black, thickly covered with white prostrate scale-like hairs; scutellum black; elytral striae very fine. This is the Potato Stalk Borer. It feeds on several species of the nightshade family as well as on the cocklebur and some other plants. (U.S.D.A.)

Figure 793

**53a** Elytra short, exposing pygidium; body broad.................54

**53b** Elytra covering pygidium; body oval........................56

**54a** Pectoral groove (in sternum) extending behind the front coxae into the mesosternum; thorax with four large tubercles. Fig. 794.
17729 *Craponius inaequalis* (Say)

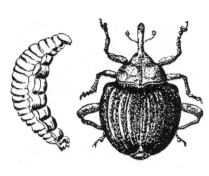

LENGTH: 2.5-3 mm.  RANGE: New England to Florida to Midwest.

Dark brown or piceous, with whitish and brown hairs forming spots and lines on elytra. Antennae and legs dark reddish-brown. A pest of grapes, known as the "Grape Curculio." (U.S.D.A.)

*Acanthoscelis acephalus* (Say) (17736), 3-4 mm., is blackish with gray-yellow scales. The front tibia has a toothed process on outer apical angle but has no teeth near the base; the tarsi is broad. It has no tubercules on the elytra.

Figure 794

**54b** Not as in 54a...............................................55

55a Beak short and heavy; no postocular lobes; funiculus with seven
segments. Fig. 795.          17841 *Rhinoncus pericarpius* (Fab.)

LENGTH: 3.5-4 mm. RANGE: Europe, Siberia and
much of North America.

Dark reddish-brown to blackish, with grayish-
yellow hairs, legs and antennae paler. Scutellar
spot conspicuous, triangular.

*Pelenomus sulcicollis* (Fahr.) (17828), measuring 2.5 mm., is black with brassy-brown scales.
The prosternum lacks the antecoxal ridges of the
above.

Figure 795

55b Beak slender and longer, eyes hidden at least in part by postocular lobes, hind femora toothed beneath. Fig. 796.
                              17764 *Ceutorhynchus rapae* Gyll.

LENGTH: 2.7-3.2 mm. RANGE: Europe and
America.

This "Cabbage Curculio" is black with
scales first yellowish but becoming white
above and larger white scales beneath; funicle 7-segmented, first and second segments
each about as long as third and fourth
measured together.

This genus has more than 50 species, small
but widely distributed.

*C. septentrionalis* Gyll. (17817), colored
much as above, is smaller (2-2.2 mm.) and
has but six segments in the funicle. Its
range is general and it too feeds on various
mustards.

Figure 796

56a Elytra with prominent humeri, abruptly wider than thorax; pectoral groove in prosternum only, open behind.................57

56b Elytra without prominent humeri; pectoral groove passing the front
coxae and entering the mesosternum........................60

57a Upper surface with scales, claws toothed or cleft.............58

337

**57b Upper surface without pattern of scales; claws simple; middle coxae but slightly separated. Fig. 797.**

(a) 17909 *Chalcodermus aeneus* Boh.

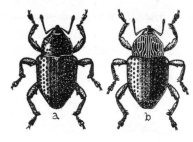

LENGTH: 4.9-5.5 mm. RANGE: Middlewest to Texas.

Black, often with bronze sheen. Beak longer than the thorax and nearly straight. Eyes close together; elytra with large punctures and intervals alutaceous. This is the Cowpea Curculio.

Figure 797

(b) 17911 *C. collaris* Horn

LENGTH: 4.7-5.5 mm. RANGE: Massachusetts, Iowa, Florida and Texas.

Much like *aeneus* except that the thorax is deeply marked with wavy lines. Elytra brown marked with a lighter reddish-brown; scutellum, smooth and bronzed. (U.S.D.A.)

*Rhyssematus* is a closely akin genus, distinguished from the above by claws that are toothed or cleft. *R. lineaticollis* Say (17899) about 6 mm. long and widely distributed, breeds in the seed pods of milkweeds. The elytra are black with brownish spots and the antennae and tarsi reddish-brown.

**58a Thorax with a broad shallow groove, with two low crests in front; elytra marked as pictured. Fig. 798.**

17890 *Conotrachelus anaglypticus* (Say)

LENGTH: 3.5-4.7 mm. RANGE: Iowa to New England.

Dark reddish-brown to black with scant covering of yellowish and whitish hairs, forming the pictured pattern on thorax and elytra. (Courtesy N. Y. State Museum)

*C. erinaceous* Lec. (17895), about 3 mm. in length, dark reddish-brown with pattern of grayish-yellow and white scales, has cleft claws.

About fifty American species of this genus have been described.

Figure 798

**58b Thorax without groove as in 58a.............................59**

**59a Femora with two teeth; elytra with an interrupted longitudinal ridge. Fig. 799.** (a) 17851 *Conotrachelus nenuphar* (Hbst.)

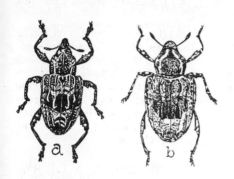

LENGTH: 4.5-6.5 mm. RANGE: general east of the Rockies.

Dark brown and black with markings as pictured of yellow and white. This "Plum Curculio" is a pest also of peach, cherry and apple. (U.S.D.A.)

**(b) 17852 *C. juglandis* Lec.**

LENGTH: 5-7 mm. RANGE: Eastern half United States and Canada.

Figure 799

This "Butternut Curculio" breeds in walnuts, butternuts and hickory nuts, causing the nuts to fall when about half grown. It is dark brown with grayish-yellow markings on legs, thorax and elytra. (Courtesy N. Y. State Museum)

**59b Femora with but one tooth; elytral humeri with small blunt tooth on outer side. Fig. 800.**

17866 *Conotrachelus crataegi* Walsh   Quince Curculio

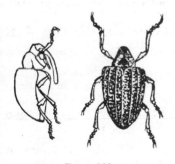

LENGTH: 4-6 mm. RANGE: Iowa to New England and southward.

Brownish-black with clay-yellow and ash-gray scales. Each elytron with four prominent carinae. It lives on *Crataegus* and related plants. (After Riley)

*C. posticatus* Boh. (17877), similar in size, color, habits and range to the above, has its beak heavy, short and curved instead of long and slender as in *crataegi*.

Figure 800

A closely related genus, *Phyrdenus*, differs from *Conotrachelus* in having the head sulcate and with a prominent tubercle on each side; the tibiae are but feebly spined at tip. *P. divergens* (Germ.) (17848) 4.5-4.8 mm. and known from New Jersey to Florida and westward to Missouri and Texas is blackish with a pale brown coat of mixed bristles and scales. It feeds on *Solanum nigrum*.

**60a Funicle of antennae with but six segments; femora without teeth; elytra glabrous. Fig. 801.**     17924 *Tyloderma fragariae* (Riley)

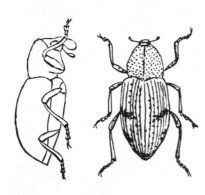

Figure 801

LENGTH: 3.5-4.2 mm. RANGE: Eastern half United States.

Piceous, elytra and legs reddish-brown, the wingcovers marked with blackish and yellowish as pictured; beak longer than head. This "Strawberry Crown Borer" is a destructive pest. (After Riley)

*T. aerea* Say (17928), smaller (2.2-2.8 mm.) and with similar range, but with sides of elytra parallel instead of oval, is a bronzy-black species which seems to live around damp places.

**60b Funicle with seven segments, tibiae with strong hook at tip; ventral abdominal segments two to four, practically equal. Fig. 802.**
17972 *Cryptorhynchus pumilus* Boh.

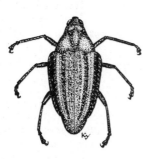

Figure 802

LENGTH: 4-5 mm. RANGE: Eastern half United States.

Black, marked with brown and white scales as pictured. Elytra at base less than one-third wider than thorax.

*C. obtentus* (Hbst.) (17980), measuring 5-7 mm. and sooty-black, has a large yellowish spot crossing its suture, and a Y-shaped mark on thorax. The scutellum is white or yellow. The elytra are but slightly wider at their base than the thorax.

**61a Pygidium covered by elytra; number of segments in funicle often reduced; mentum shortened in the peduncle**..................**62**

**61b Pygidium exposed; funicle with six segments, peduncle of mentum elongated.** ................................................**64**

**62a Front coxae but narrowly separated; beak no longer than the head; funicle with segments 2-7 transverse, elytral striae deep and with coarse serrated punctures. Fig. 803.**

18062 *Rhyncolus oregonensis* Horn

LENGTH: 2.8-3.5 mm. RANGE: much of the United States.

Shining black; legs and antennae dark reddish-brown, club paler; beak as wide as long. Under surface with rather dense coarse punctures.

*Phloeophagus apionides* Horn (18047), similar in color and size to the above, has a much longer beak which attains its greatest width where the antennae are attached. It ranges from Canada and New England to Ohio and Michigan.

Figure 803

*Stenocelis brevis* (Boh.) (18073) with a length of 2.8-3.2 mm. differs from the above species in having a beak much shorter than the head. It is black, nearly dull, with the elytra and legs brownish and the antennae and tarsi paler; the thorax is nearly one-half wider than long. The cylindrical elytra have their sides parallel and have broad, coarsely punctured serrations. It apparently may be found in much of the eastern part of the United States and Canada and is often common in the dead wood of many species of trees.

**62b Front coxae separated by more than half their width; beak usually longer than the head......................................63**

**63a Body depressed; beak dilated at tip; antennae attached near tip of beak. Fig. 804.**

18020 *Cossonus platalea* Say

LENGTH: 5.5-6.5 mm. RANGE: Iowa to Virginia and Canada.

Shining black; tarsi and antennae reddish-brown. Disk of thorax flattened with scattered coarse punctures at middle, finer and more numerous at edges. (Courtesy N. Y. State Museum)

*Himatinum errans* Lec. (18016), measuring 2 mm., is reddish-brown and is covered with a coarse yellowish pubescence. It ranges from Nova Scotia to Ohio and Florida.

Figure 804

**63b Body not flattened; beak not dilated at tip; antennal club large (a). Fig. 805.**      **18042 *Caulophilus latinasus* (Say)**

Figure 805

LENGTH: 3 mm. RANGE: Southeastern United States.

Reddish-brown. Thorax as broad as long, with fine even punctures on top. Elytra deep with coarse punctures. It is sometimes a pest of dried cereals and is known as the "Broadnosed Grain Weevil." (U.S.D.A.)

A much more slender, tiny little fellow (measuring but 1.5 mm. and linear), *Stenomimus pallidus* Boh. (18042) is known to range in several of the Central and Middle States, and is found in association with walnut and hickory. It is shining pale reddish-yellow. The thorax is oblong and in width equal to the elytra at their base. The elytral striae are fine with rather coarse, close-set punctures.

**64a Large beetles, 20 mm. or longer; side pieces of metathorax very wide. Fig. 806.**      **18077 *Rhynchophorus cruentatus* (Fab.)**

Figure 806

LENGTH: 20-31 mm. RANGE: South Carolina and Florida to Louisiana.

Shining black; thorax often red with black markings; elytra with red spots on black, as pictured; elytral striae deep and punctured; legs with fringe of long yellow hairs on inner side. Some specimens are wholly black and have been given variety significance *zimmermanni*. Fahr.

The larvae feed within the dying trunks of the cabbage palmetto and other palms. The other species are tropical.

**64b Smaller, not over 18 mm.; side pieces of metathorax not unusually wide.** ...................................................65

342

**65α Antennal club oval; small slender beetles about 4 mm. or less. Fig. 807.**

**(a) 18157 *Sitophilus granarius* (L.)**

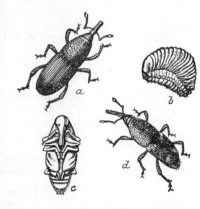

Figure 807

LENGTH: 3-4 mm. RANGE: cosmopolitan.

This, the "Granary Weevil," is shining chestnut brown to blackish. Thorax with scattered punctures; elytra with punctured deep striae, the intervals smooth. It is flightless but lives in stored grain and travels with its food. The larva (b) and the pupa (c) of this and the following species are highly similar.

**(d) 18159 *Sitophilus oryza* (L.)**

LENGTH: 2.1-2.8 mm. RANGE: cosmopolitan.

Its common name is "Rice Weevil"; its habits are much like those of the above. It is dull reddish-brown to blackish; the elytra often have four reddish spots as pictured. The elytral striae are coarsely punctured, with each puncture bearing a short yellowish hair. (U.S.D.A.)

**65b Antennal club wedge-shaped, larger, 5 mm. or over..........66**

**66α Third tarsal segment broad and spongy beneath; red marked with black as pictured. Fig. 808.**

**18087 *Rhodobaenus tredecimpunctatus* (Ill.)**

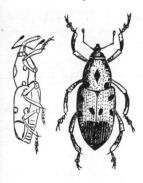

Figure 808

LENGTH: 7-10 mm. RANGE: general.

This is the "Cockle-bur Billbug" but it seems to feed on many species of plants. It is black beneath and red with somewhat variable black markings above, resulting in variety names. The beak is black. It hibernates as an adult.

The "Yucca Weevil" *Scyphophorus yuccae* Horn (18081), 15-17 mm. long and black, feeds on yucca in California.

343

66b Third tarsal segment smooth at middle though sometimes spongy or hairy at the sides......................................67

67a Third segment of hind tarsi but little if at all dilated...........68

67b Third segment of all tarsi much dilated, but glabrous at the middle. Fig. 809.                    18102 *Calendra aequalis* (Gyll.)

Figure 809

LENGTH: 11-17 mm. RANGE: New York to South Dakota.

Black with a shiny coating varying in color, light bluish-gray, pale yellowish to reddish-brown, with three darkened elevated streaks on thorax and frequently dark stripes on the elytra. This "Clay-colored Billbug" normally feeds on reeds and bulrushes, but when low places, where these plants grow, are plowed the billbugs frequently attack the young corn plants. (U.S.D.A.)

The "Tule Billbug" *Calendra discolor* (Mann.) (18104) feeding on tules and cat-tails, but attacking grain crops in California is similar in size. It is white beneath and usually black with white streaks above.

In contrast to *aequalis*, pictured and described above, *C. inaequalis* Say (18101) is short with wedge-shaped form and has the outer apical angles of the front tibiae prolonged; middle and hind tarsi truncate and the tarsi slender. It ranges from New York to Florida and Texas and measures 6 mm. Further description follows.

Black, often covered with a brownish superficial coat. Beak two-thirds as long as thorax, feebly compressed; base somewhat swollen and finely grooved above. Thorax as long as wide and coarsely punctate; usually with a large elevated smooth space at middle and two smaller ones on either side. Elytra at base as wide as thorax but rapidly narrowing toward apex; striae with coarse, widely spaced punctures.

68a Third joint of first and second tarsi not at all dilated, wholly glabrous or nearly so............................................71

68b Third joint of first and second tarsi feebly dilated, with spongy pubescence at the sides......................................69

69a Thorax with three flattened, elevated, smooth longitudinal lines...70

**69b** Thorax with only the mid-elevated line distinct and it not extending the entire distance. Fig. 810.

18117 *Calendra maidis* (Chitt.)

LENGTH: 10-15 mm.  RANGE: South Carolina to Texas.

Blackish or dark reddish, without much clay-colored coating; beak three-fifths the length of the thorax, with fine punctures. Vitta (mid-thoracic stripe) but slightly elevated. This "Maize Billbug" often does serious damage to corn. (U.S.D.A.)

C. *soltaui* (Chitt.) (18119), 7.5 mm., a rather dull-black species differs from *maidis* in having a fusiform body. It ranges rather widely.

Figure 810

C. *cariosa* Oliv. (18120) with a length of 8-11 mm., differs markedly from the above in the much elevated third elytral interval extending thus from the base to the middle of the elytra. It is black with the raised places and the under-parts shining. The disk of the thorax has three longitudinal stripes, the outer ones irregular and entire and the middle one widening to a rhomboid figure midway of the thorax then ending abruptly or sometimes continuing as a fine line. It apparently ranges rather generally east of the Mississippi river.

**70a** Beak somewhat compressed; all of the elytral intervals about evenly convex, of the same color and about equal in width. Fig. 811.

18113 *Calendra robustus* (Horn)

LENGTH: 11-14 mm.  RANGE: Central and Western States.

Shining black or reddish-black, quite robust. Thorax as wide as long, outer elevated lines widening to the base, the median one widest at its midpoint.

C. *peninsularis* (Chitt.) (18112) averaging a bit larger, is black but has a clay covering. It has been reported from Florida.

Figure 811

**70b** Beak nearly cylindrical, a bit narrow at its base; alternating elytral intervals elevated, irregular and sometimes interrupted. Fig. 812.

18108 *Calendra pertinax* Oliv.

Figure 812

LENGTH: 11-15 mm. RANGE: much of United States.

Shining black, often with reddish tinge, the interspaces on elytra and thorax covered with a whitish coating.

It breeds in cat-tail and calamus.

*C. setiger* (Chitt.) (18110) is similar to *pertinax* but has a somewhat compressed beak. It is black with a grayish coating and measures 10-13 mm. It ranges the New England States to Dakota and Texas.

**71a** Thorax without longitudinal vittae (smooth elevated ridges), surface punctured throughout. Fig. 813.

(a) 18122 *Calendra parvulus* (Gyll.)

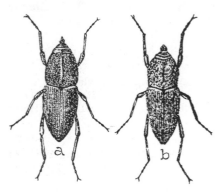

Figure 813

LENGTH: 5-6.5 mm. RANGE: New England to Florida and Texas.

Black with clayey coating of ash-gray; tarsi and antennae reddish-brown. Beak three-fourths as long as thorax. Thorax sometimes with narrow median line. This "Blue-grass Billbug" attacks the roots of timothy and blue-grass.

(b) 18123 *Calendra minimus* (Hart)

LENGTH: 5-6 mm. RANGE: New York to Florida and Texas.

Black, usually covered with clay-yellow or ash gray coating.

Beak two-thirds the length of thorax. Thoracic punctures coarse and irregularly placed; elytra widest in front. (U.S.D.A.)

**71b** Thorax with one or more vittae..............................72

**72a Middle thoracic vitta forked in front. Fig. 814.**

18141 *Calendra venatus* Say

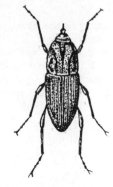

Figure 814

LENGTH: 6-10 mm. RANGE: Maine to Iowa to Florida.

Blackish or reddish; beak three-fourths as long as thorax. Vittae as pictured. Elytra narrowing from base to apex, striae fine with coarse punctures. (After Forbes)

C. *reticulaticollis* Boh. (18146) 7.5-10 mm., seems to range across our whole country. It differs from *venatus* in having the ridges on the thorax but poorly developed instead of prominent as in *venatus*.

**72b Median vittae not forked. Fig. 815.**

(a) 18132 *Calendra zeae* (Walsh)

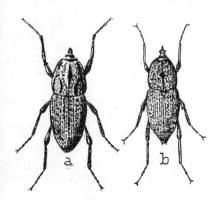

Figure 815

LENGTH: 7.5-9 mm. RANGE: New England to Florida and Kansas.

This "Timothy Billbug" sometimes attacks corn as well as feeding on timothy. It is shining black or reddish-brown, and lacks the artificial coating of many members of this genus. The thoracic vittae, as pictured, are characteristic.

(b) 18136 *Calendra melanocephalus* Fab.

LENGTH: 7-10.5 mm. RANGE: New England to Kansas and Georgia.

Black or piceous but covered above with a dense brownish coating. Median vitta ending at half the length of the thorax in a dilated part as pictured. (After Forbes)

* * * * *

It might seem from the four pages devoted to this one genus that some partiality were being shown. The fact that not many genera of beetles have as many highly destructive species as this one, seems to justify the amount of attention given it.

# Family 109 SCOLYTIDAE
## The Barkbeetles

This last family of Coleoptera, while only a fairly large family, is a very important one. More than 2000 species are known. They are plant feeders and attack all parts of plants but so many species live within the cambium of trees that the group is known as "barkbeetles," or as "engraver beetles," because of the designs they cut in tree trunks. They are especially destructive to conifers. The larger species measure only a few millimeters in length, while the majority are very small.

1a Front tibiae with long curved hook on the outer apical angle; elytra nearly glabrous, but with many rows of punctures. Fig. 816.

  18171 *Scolytus rugulosus* (Ratz.) Shot-hole Borer

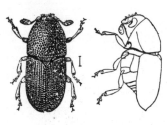

Figure 816

LENGTH: 2-2.5 mm.

RANGE: Europe and much of United States.

This introduced beetle is dull blackish with the apex of the elytra reddish-brown. The head of the male is broader and more flattened than that of the female. Several species of fruit trees belonging to the rose family frequently suffer from their attacks on the less healthy trunks and limbs. The side view and pupa are also shown.

S. *quadrispinosus* Say (18169) Hickory Bark Beetle measuring 4-5 mm. and ranging widely; feeds under the bark of several species of hickories. The abdomen of the male is armed with several spines.

1b Front tibia not as in 1a........................................2

2a The head covered from above by the thorax; the pronotum usually more roughened at its front........................................7

2b The head visible from above; rounded........................3

3a Antennal club of but one elongated segment which is attached by
its side to the five segmented funiculus. Fig. 817.

18202 *Chramesus hicoriae* Lec.

LENGTH: 1.5 mm. RANGE: Eastern United
States and Canada.

Dull black; clothed above with stiff ash-
gray hairs and erect bristles on the elytra. Thorax broader than long; elytra
about twice as long as thorax; antennae
yellow. Lives on hickory. (After Swaine)

Figure 817

*Polygraphus rufipennis* (Kby.) (18193),
2-2.5 mm, black with dull-red elytra and
rufus legs and antennae, has its front
coxae touching instead of separated as in *C. hicoriae*.

It is abundant in Canada and ranges widely in the United States.

3b Antennae not as in 3a. . . . . . . . . . . . . . . . . . . . . . . . . . . . . . . . . . . .4

4a The segments of the antennal club loosely joined and lamellated.
Fig. 818.          (a) 18207 *Phthorophloeus frontalis* (Oliv.)

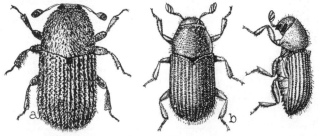

Figure 818

LENGTH: 1.5-2 mm. RANGE: Eastern half of United States.

Brown. Clothed with short stiff hairs; antennae and legs reddish.
Thorax with fine granular punctations. Mulberry and Hackberry
seems to be its preferred food plants.

(b) 18206 *P. liminaris* (Harr.)

LENGTH: 2-2.2 mm. RANGE: Canada to North Carolina and Michigan and Ohio.

Light brown to nearly black. Thorax more finely punctate than
in the above, and with much longer lamelate joints in the club of the
antennae. It is the Peach Tree Barkbeetle.

4b The segments compacted and not at all lammelate. . . . . . . . . . . . . .5

349

5a Funicle of antennae with seven segments; club with four segments; front coxae widely separated. Fig. 819.

18255 *Hylastinus obscurus* (Marsh.) Clover Root Borer

Figure 819

LENGTH: 2-2.5 mm. RANGE: Europe and much of the United States.

Dark brown; elytra with deeply punctured striae; a single row of bristles on each interval. Feeds on red clover and related plants, spending the winter in the roots. (U.S.D.A.)

*Hylurgops rugipennis* (Mann.) (18268) 4 mm. is a western species. It differs from the above in having the first and fifth ventral segments longer than the others.

*Hylurgopinus rufipes* (Eich.) (18257), known rather commonly from Iowa to Virginia and Canada, measures 2-2.5 mm. and is dull brownish-black and thinly covered with short, yellowish hairs. The beak is short, the funicle has 7 segments and the club is about twice as long as wide.

5b Funicle of antennae with but five segments; front coxae very narrowly separated. ............................................. 6

6a Pronotum somewhat elongate, not much narrower in front; thorax as broad as elytra. Fig. 820.

(a) 18215 *Dendroctonus frontalis* Zimm.  Southern Pine Beetle

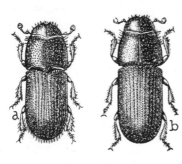

Figure 820

LENGTH: 2.5-4 mm. RANGE: Eastern half of United States.

Light to reddish-brown or blackish. Sides and apical ends of elytra with long hairs. An enemy of pines and spruce. (U.S.D.A.)

(b) 18213 *D. barberi* Hopk. Southwestern Pine Beetle

LENGTH: 4.5 mm. RANGE: Western States.

Dark brown or black, without long hairs on sides of elytra. It attacks yellow pine and Douglas fir and is highly destructive.

HOW TO KNOW THE BEETLES

6b Pronotum definitely narrowing in front; dorsal face of elytra with long hairs on basal half. Fig. 821.

(a) 18221 *Dendroctonus simplex* Lec.

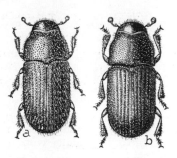

Figure 821

LENGTH: 3.5-5 mm. RANGE: Maine and West Virginia to Alaska.

Reddish to reddish-brown, in part nearly black.

Thoracic punctures large and small mixed. Lives on the tamarack and is known as the Eastern Larch Beetle. (U.S.D.A.)

(b) 18218 *D. monticolae* Hopk.

LENGTH: 4-6 mm. RANGE: Montana, Wyoming, Idaho, Nevada and California.

Pure brown to black; anterior part of pronotum transversely impressed. It is known as the Mountain Pine Beetle. (U.S.D.A.)

7a Eyes divided; no distinct sutures on the antennal club...........8

7b Eyes not divided; antennal club with at least some visible sutures..9

8a The horny basal segments of the antennal club angulate in front. Fig. 822.     18309 *Trypodendron bivittatum* (Kby.)

Figure 822

LENGTH: 3-3.4 mm. RANGE: United States and Canada, also Alaska and Europe.

This Spruce Timber Beetle is known to infest several species of conifers. The galleries of the larvae are rather wider apart and are parallel to the wood fibers, the walls being blackened. The adults are brownish or black and sculptured as pictured.

*T. retusum* (Lec.) (18306), 4.5 mm., is shining blackish-brown; the elytra have well defined striae.

351

**8b The horny basal segments of the antennal club rounded in front.**
**Fig. 823.**                                        18304 *Xyloterinus politus* (Say)

LENGTH: 2.8-3 mm.    RANGE: Eastern United States and Canada.

This species, while usually infesting a number of broad-leaf trees, including beech, oaks, maples, elms, ash and hickory, is also known to occur in spruce and hemlocks. The galleries often extend deep into the wood and are blackened. The adults vary from light brown to nearly black.

Figure 823

Two fairly large but not too well-known genera, *Hypothenemus* and *Stephanoderes,* each with more than 20 widely scattered species would fall in this proximity. Several of these species are but a fraction of a millimeter in length, and only a few measures as much as 2 mm.

**9a Funicle of antennae of more than three segments..............11**

**9b Funicle of less than three segments.........................10**

**10a Funicle with two segments, the second, small and closely joined to the club; front tibiae with transverse ridges on its face. Fig. 824.**
                                        (a) 18298 *Monarthrum fasciatum* (Say)

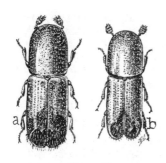

LENGTH: 2.5-3 mm.   RANGE: Canada to Florida.

Piceous; antennae and legs rusty-yellow, front of elytra yellowish; shining and smooth; elytra at tips clothed with yellow hairs. Infests both broad-leaves and conifers of several species.

**(b) 18299 *Monarthrum mali* (Fitch)**

LENGTH: 2-2.2 mm.   RANGE: Canada to Florida.

Figure 824

Differs mostly from the above in its smaller size and in two small teeth at the apex of the elytra as pictured. It too, has a wide range of recorded host trees. It is known as the Apple Wood-stainer.

352

10b Funicle with but one segment; front tibiae without ridges as above.
Fig. 825.                    18301 *Corthylus punctatissimus* (Zimm.)

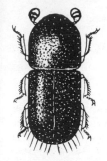

LENGTH: 3.7-4 mm.  RANGE: Much of the United States.

Dark brown to black, with reddish legs and antennae. Thorax smooth and shining behind; elytra with prominent scattered punctures. It has been called the Sugar Maple Timber Beetle but is known also to infest huckleberry, the American hornbeam and the eastern hophornbeam. Like several other species in this family the larvae are fed by the adults on a fungus food, *ambrosia*.

Figure 825

11a Club of antennae with pubescence and rings on both sides.  Fig. 826.                    18400 *Gnathotrichus materiarius* (Fitch)

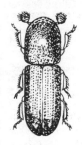

LENGTH: 3 mm.  RANGE: Eastern half United States and Canada.

Shining, brown; elytra paler at base; undersurface and head black; feet and antennae yellow; elytra thinly clothed with short yellow hairs. It feeds on pine.

*Ips. calligraphus* (Germ.) (18462), a widely scattered species feeding on pine—is considerably larger (4.5-6.5 mm.) than most members of the family. It is piceous or brownish with yellow antennae.

Figure 826

11b Club of antennae with pubescence and rings at most on but one side.  Fig. 827.                    18512 *Xyleborus celsus* Elch.
LENGTH: 2.7 mm.  RANGE: New Jersey and South Carolina to Indiana.
Shining, brownish-black.  Elytral striae feeble, the fourth interval broader than the others.  It seems to feed only on hickory.
*X. xylographus* (Say) (18507), widely scattered throughout much of North America and Europe, is shining, reddish-brown, with thin covering of short hairs.  The elytrae are striate with deep punctures.  It lives on a rather wide range of broadleaf and coniferous trees, and measures 2.5 mm. or a little more.

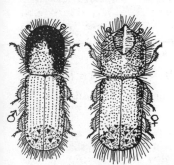

Figure 827

# INDEX AND PICTURED-GLOSSARY

## A

Abacidus
  permudus 35
  sculptus 35
ABDOMEN: the third or posterior part of the insect
  body, composed of several
  segments. 3, 8 Fig. 828

Figure 828

Abstrulia
  tesselata 223
Abundance of beetles 1
Acanthocinus
  fasciatus 267
  spectabilis 267
  triangulifera 267
Acanthoscelis
  acephalus 336
ACCESSORY: an added or
  extra part.
Acholerops
  zimmermanni 88
Acilius
  mediatus 62
  semisulcatus 62
Acmaeodera
  pulchella 170
  tubulus 170
Acmaeops
  bivittatus 256
  pratensis 256
Acratrichis
  moerens 90
Acritus
  exiguus 123
Acropteroxys
  gracilis 188
  lecontei 188
ACUMINATE: tapering to a
  long slender point.
ACUTE: pointed; sharper
  than a right angle.
Acylomus
  ergoti 196
  piceus 196
Acylophorus
  flavicollis 98
  pronus 98
Adalia
  annectans 207
  bipunctata 202
  frigida 207
Adelocera
  discoidea 161
  impressicolis 160
  marmorata 160
Adephaga 12
ADEPHAGOUS: belonging to
  the group Adephaga.
Aderocharis
  corticinus 95

Adoxus
  obscurus 280
ADULT: the sexually mature
  stage.
Aegoschema
  modesta 267
Aeolus
  amabilis 164
  melillus 164
AERIAL: flying insects; living in the air.
AESTIVATE: to become dor-
  mant in order to pass
  through unfavorable per-
  iods during warm months.
Agabus
  disintergratus 59
  lugens 59
  nigroaeneus 59
Agathidium
  oniscoides 86
  politum 86
Agonoderus
  comma 52
  indistinctus 53
  pallipes 52
  partiarius 53
  pauperculus 53
  testaceus 53
Agonum
  caudatum 42
  cincticollis 43
  decorum 42
  extensicollis 42
  hypolithos 42
  octopunctatus 43
  pallipes 43
  picipennis 44
  punctiformis 43
  sinuatum 43
Agrabia
  cyanoptera 207
Agrilus
  angelicus 170
  anxius 171
  bilineatus 171
  ruficollis 170
  vittaticollis 170
Agriotes
  insanus 167
  mancus 167
  oblongicollis 167
  pubescens 167
Alaudes
  singularis 218
Alaus
  lusciosus 161
  melanops 161
  myops 161
  oculatus 161
Alder Borer 269
Alder Flea Beetle 293
Aleochara
  lata 107
Aleodorus
  bilobatus 106
Alfalfa Weevil 324
Alleculidae 208
Allocorhynus
  slossoni 315
Alobates
  barbata 219
  pennsylvanica 219
Alphitophagus
  bifasciatus 215

Amara
  cupreolata 37
  impuncticollis 37
Amarochara
  fenyesi 107
Amblycheila
  cylindriformis 16
  baroni 16
Amblyderus
  pallens 158
AMBROSIA: a fungus food
  raised by some beetles.
AMBULATORY: fitted for
  walking.
Ampedus
  linteus 165
  nigricollis 165
  obliquus 165
  sanguinipennis 165
  sayi 165
Ampeloglypter
  ater 335
  sesostris 335
Amphasia
  interstitialis 51
Amphicerus
  hamatus 229
ANAL: relating to the last
  segment of the abdomen.
ANAL ANGLE: the posterior
  angle of a wing when the
  wing is extended. Fig. 829

Figure 829

ANAL APPENDAGES: a n y
  appendages attached to
  the posterior part of the
  abdomen; the external reproductive parts.
Anametis
  granulata 317
Anaspis
  rufa 144
ANASTOMOSING: joining
  with each other.
Anatis
  ocellata 201
  quindecimpunctata 201
  rathvoni 207
Ancaeus
  exiguus 103
Anchicera
  ephippiata 190
  ochracea 190
Andranes
  lecontei 66
Androchirus
  erythropus 208
  femoralis 208
Anisocalvia
  duodecim-maculata 207
  quatuordecimguttata 207
Anisostricta
  strigata 205

# INDEX

# INDEX

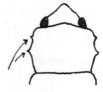

Figure 833

# INDEX

Figure 834

Figure 835

# INDEX

# INDEX

Deloyala
 clavata 303
Deltometops
 amoenicornis 169
Dendroctonus
 barberi 350
 frontalis 350
 monticolae 351
 simplex 351
Dendroides
 canadensis 154
 concolor 154
DENTATE: toothed.
 Fig. 837

Figure 837

Dermestes
 caninus 181
 lardarius 181
 marmoratus 181
 talpinus 181
Dermestidae 180
Derocrepis
 erythropus 296
Desert Corn Flea Beetle 299
Desert June Beetle 242
Desmocerus
 auripennis 258
 californicus 258
 cribripennis 258
 palliatus 258
 piperi 258
Desmopachria
 convexa 58
Desmoris
 scapalis 326
 sordidus 326
Diabrotica
 duodecimpunctata 289
 longicornis 289
 soror 289
 trivittata 289
 vittata 289
Dianchomena
 bivittata 47
Dianous
 nitidulus 92
Diaperis
 maculata 215
 rufipes 215
Dibolocelus
 ovatus 80
Dicaelus
 dilatatus 40
 elongatus 39
 furvus 39
 ovalis 40
 purpuratus 39
 sculptilis 39
 splendidus 39
Dicerca
 divaricata 173
 punctulata 173

Dichelonyx
 elongata 242
 fulgida 242
Dilandius
 myrmecops 158
DILATED: widened or ex-
 panded.
DIMORPHIC: having two distinctly marked forms.
Dinapate
 wrighti 229
Dineutes
 assimilis 63
 carolinus 63
 ciliatus 63
 discolor 63
DIOECIOUS: with distinct
 sexes.
Diplotaxis
 harperi 240
 tenebrosa 240
Dircaea
 quadrimaculata 222
Discodemus
 reticulatus 210
Disonycha
 glabrata 292
 pennsylvanica 292
 quinquevittata 292
 triangularis 292
 xanthomelaena 292
DIURNAL: active only by
 day.
Diving Beetles 57
Dogwood Twig Borer 272
Donacia
 emarginata 272
 piscatrix 272
 pubicollis 272
Doraschema
 nigrum 266
 wildii 266
Dorcatoma
 dresdensis 227
Dorcus
 parallelus 249
DORSAL: relating to the upper surface.
DORSUM: the upper surface,
 or sometimes confined to
 the meso- and the meta-
 thorax.
Dorytomus
 mucidus 325
Drapetes
 geminatus 76
Drug-store Beetles 225
Dryland Wireworm 167
Dryobius
 sexfasciatus 263
Dryopidae 67
Dynastes
 hercules 233, 243
 tityus 243
Dysidius
 mutus 36
 purpuratus 36
Dytiscidae 57
Dytiscus
 fasciventris 61
 harrisi 61
 marginicollis 61

# E

Eastern Larch Beetle 351
Eburia
 quadrigeminata 264

Elaphidion
 mucronatum 264
Elaphrus
 ruscarius 27
Elateridae 159
ELBOWED: as applied to antennae, sharply bent; a
 slight curvature of the
 basal joint is not considered an elbow. Fig. 838

Figure 838

Eledona
 agaricola 214
Eleodes
 gigantea 221
 granosa 221
 opaca 221
 suturalis 221
 tricostata 221
Eleusis
 pallida 102
Elm Borer 270
Elm Calligrapha 284
Elm Leaf Beetle 288
Elmidae 67
ELYTRA: the first wings
 (hardened wing covers) of
 beetles. 3. Fig. 839

Figure 839

EMARGINATE: with a notch
 in the margin.
Embaphion
 muricatum 220
Endomychidae 194
Endomychus
 biguttatus 195
Engraver Beetles 348
Enicmus
 minutus 194
Ennearthron
 thoracicorne 231
Enochrus
 ochraceus 81

Figure 840

Figure 841

# F

Figure 842

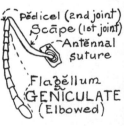

pedicel (2nd joint)
Scape (1st joint)
Antennal
suture

Flagellum
GENICULATE
(Elbowed)

Figure 843

# INDEX

Flat Bark Beetles 186
Flat Grain Beetle 188
Flatheaded Apple Tree
  Borer 172
Flea Beetle 293, 294
Flour Beetle 217
Flower Beetles 130, 143, 155,
  195, 245.
FOOT: the tarsus of the leg.
Four-spotted Bean
  Weevil 306
FRASS: the excrement of
  insects.
Fringe-winged Fungus
  Beetles 90
FRONT: the part of the head
  lying between the base of
  the antennae and the com-
  pound eyes.
Fullers Rose Beetle 319
Fungus Beetles 90, 117,
  188, 190, 191, 194.
Fungus Weevils 309
FURCATE: forked into two
  parts.
FUSIFORM: tapering at both
  ends; spindle-shaped.
Fustiger
  fuchsi 66

# G

GALEA: the outer lobe of
  the maxilla. 7 Fig. 844

Figure 844

Galerita
  bicolor 40
  janus 40
Galerucella
  cavicollis 288
  decora 288
  notata 288
  nymphaeae 288
  xanthomelaena 288
GALL: a swollen abnormal
  plant growth produced by
  insects.
Gastrellarius
  honestus 34
Gastrophysa
  cyanea 284
  polygoni 284
Gaurotes
  cyanipennis 255
GENA -AE: the part of the
  head below the eyes; the
  cheek.
GENITALIA: external parts
  of the reproductive or-
  gans. 8

GENUS: the first word of a
  scientific name. (always
  capitalized)
Geopinus
  incrassatus 49
Geotrupes
  blackburni 237
  opacus 237
  splendidus 237
Gibbium
  psylloides 224
Giraffe Stag Beetle 248
GLABROUS: smooth, without
  hairs or other covering.
Glipa
  hilaris 146
Glischrochilus
  fasciatus 183
  sanguinolentus 183
GLOBOSE: the shape of a
  globe or sphere.
Glowworms 126, 128
Glycobius
  speciosus 262
Glyptina
  brunnea 295
  cerina 295
Glytocelis
  albida 280
  liebecki 280
Gnathocerus
  cornutus 217
  maxillosus 217
Gnathoncus
  communis 124
Gnathotrichus
  materiarius 353
Goes
  debilis 266
  pulchra 266
Gold Bug 303
Goldenrod Beetle 287
Grain Beetle 186, 188, 191
Granary Weevil 343
GRANULATED: appearing as
  covered with small grains.
GRANULOSE: same as
  granulated.
Grape Cane Gall Maker 335
Grape Curculio 336
Grape Rootworm 279
Grape-vine Hoplia 240
Graphoderes
  cinereus 62
Graphops
  curtipennis 279
  pubescens 279
Gray Blister Beetle 152
Gray Leaf Beetle 280
Gray-sided Oak Weevil 320
Great Basin Wireworm 167
Green Blister Beetle 150
Green June Beetle 244
Green Peach Beetle 244
Ground Beetles 24
GROUP: an indefinite divi-
  sion of classification.
GRUB: the larva of beetles.
GULA: a sclerite forming
  the throat. Fig. 845a
GULAR SUTURE: a line
  bounding the gula.
  Fig. 845b

Figure 845

Gymnetron
  tetrum 330
Gyrinidae 63
Gyrinus
  affinis 64
  analis 64
  minutus 64
  ventralis 64
Gyrohypnus
  obsidianus 99
Gyrophaena
  dissimilis 104
  fasciata 104

# H

HABITAT: the region or
  place an insect inhabits.
Habrocerus
  magnus 97
  schwarzi 97
Hairy Fungus Beetles 191
Hairy Spider Beetle 224
Haliplidae 55
Haliplus
  borealis 55
  ruficollis 55
  triopsis 55
Hallomenus
  scapularis 224
Haltica
  bimarginata 293
  chalybea 293
  foliacea 293
  ignita 293
  torquata 293
Ham Beetles 136
Handsome Fungus
  Beetles 194
Harpalus
  caliginosus 50
  herbivagus 50
  pennsylvanicus 50
Harpilinae 24
Head 3, 6
Helichus
  striatus 67
Helluomorpha
  bicolor 44
  texana 44
Helodes
  pulchella 180
Helodidae 179
Helophorus
  lacustris 79
  lineatus 79

Figure 846

Figure 847

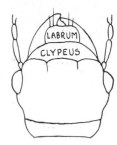

MALA: a grinding surface; ridged.
Malthodes
  concavus 129
MANDIBLE: the principal jaws of the beetles. 6, 7
MANDIBULAR SCROBE: a deep groove on the outer edge of the mandible in some beetles.
MANUBRIUM: a part of the mesoternum which articulates with the prothorax in the Elateridae.
Margined Blister Beetle 152
Matus
  bicarinatus 60
MAXILLA: the second jaws of the beetles. 7
  Fig. 850

Figure 850

MAXILLARY PALPI: jointed, antennae-like sense organs borne on the maxillae. 7  Fig. 850a
May Beetles 241
Mecas
  inornata 271
  pergráta 271
Mecynotarsus
  candidus 156
Megacephala
  carolina 18
  virginica 18
Megacyllene
  antennata 261
  caryae 262
  decora 263
  robiniae 262
Megalodachne
  fasciata 189
  heros 189
Megalopsidia
  caelatus 111
Megarthrus
  americanus 108
  excisus 108
  sinatocollis 108
Megasattus
  costatus 210
  erosus 210
Melanactes
  consors 166
  densus 166
  niceus 166
Melandryid Beetles 222
Melandryidae 222
Melandrya
  striata 222
MELANISM: being unusually dark colored; the opposite to albinism.
Melanophila
  fulvoguttata 171
Melanophthalma
  distinguenda 194

Melanotus
  castanipes 162
  fissilis 162
Melasid Beetles 168
Melasidae 168
Melasis
  pectinicornis 168
  rufipennis 168
Melba
  parvula 116
Meloe
  americanus 148
  angusticollis 148
  impressus 148
Meloidae 148
Melyridae 130
MENTUM: one of the basal sutures of the labium. 7
Meracantha
  contracta 213
Merinus
  laevis 219
Meronera
  venustula 106
MESO: a prefix meaning middle.
Meso-leg 5
MESOTHORAX: the second or middle segment of the thorax. 4
META: a prefix meaning posterior.
Metachroma
  marginalis 278
  parallelum 278
Metallic Woodborers 169
Metapoloba
  pruinosa 212
Metaponium
  bicolor 213
METATHORAX: the third or last segment of the thorax. 4
Metriona
  bicolor 303
  bivittata 303
Mexican Bean Beetle 201
Mexican Bean Weevil 304
Mexican Grain Beetle 191
Mezium
  americanum 225
Miarus
  hispidulus 330
Micromaseus
  femoralis 34
Micropeplus
  cribratus 92
Microphotus
  angustus 128
Microrhagus
  triangularis 169
Microweisea
  misella 199
  suturalis 199
Minute Brown Scavenger Beetles 193
Minute Tree-fungus Beetles 230
MM.: millimeter; about one twentyfifth of an inch.
MOLA; MOLAR; the ridged grinding surface of a mandible.
Molamba
  ornata 90

Molorchus
  bimaculatus 259
Monarthrum
  fasciatum 352
  mali 352
MONILIFORM: shaped like a string of beads.
  Fig. 851

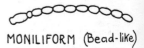

## MONILIFORM (Bead-like)

Figure 851

Monochamus
  titillator 265
MONOCHROMATIC: having only one color.
Monophylla
  terminata 132
Monotoma
  picipes 91
Monotomidae 91
Monoxia
  consputa 287
  punticollis 287
Mordella
  discoidea 146
  marginata 146
  octopunctata 146
  serval 146
Mordellidae 143
Mordellistena
  aspera 145
  comata 145
  lutea 145
  marginalis 144
  pubescence 144
  scapularis 145
  sexnotata 144
  splendens 145
  vapida 145
MOULT: shedding the larval skin to permit further growth.
Mountain Pine Beetle 351
Mud-Loving Beetles 178
Mycetaeid Beetles 175
Mycetaeidae 175
Mycetina
  perpulchra 195
Mycetochara
  binotata 209
  foveata 209
Mycetophagidae 191
Mycetophagus
  flexuosus 192
  punctatus 192
Mycetoporus
  americanus 109
  splendidus 109
Mycterus
  scaber 222
Mylabridae 305
Myllaena
  dubia 104
  minuta 104
  vulpina 104
Myochrous
  denticollis 280
  longulus 280

Figure 852

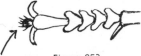
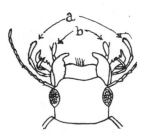

# INDEX

Pilopius
  lacustris 115
Pinching bugs 248
Pink Glowworm 128
Pinodytes
  cryptophagoides 87
Pinophilus
  latipes 93
Pinotus
  carolinus 235
Pisenus
  humeralis 223
Pissodes
  costatus 326
  strobi 326
PLANE: a level, flat
  surface.
Plant Beetles 179
Plateros
  modestus 126
  sollicitus 126
Platyceroides
  agassii 249
  latus 249
Platycerus
  virescens 249
Platydema
  ellipticum 216
  erythrocerum 216
  excavatum 216
  ruficorne 216
  subcostatum 216
Platypodidae 307
Platypus
  flavicornis 307
  wilsoni 307
Platysoma
  basale 122
  coarctatum 122
  depressum 122
Platystomidae 309
Pleasing Fungus Beetles 188
Plectrodera
  scalator 265
Pleocoma
  fimbriata 239
PLEURA: the sclerites along
  the side. Fig. 855

Figure 855

Plum Curculio 339
Plum Gouger 332
Podabrus
  modestus 129
  rugulosus 129
  tomentosus 129
Poecilus
  chalcites 36
  lucublandus 36
Pogonocherus
  mixtus 269
  penicellatus 269
POLY-: a prefix meaning
  many.
Polycaon
  confertus 228
  stouti 228

Polygraphus
  rufipennis 349
Polyphaga 64
Polyphylla
  crinata 241
Pomphopoea
  aenea 149
  sayi 149
Popilius
  disjunctus 233
Popillia
  japonica 238
Poplar Borer 270
POSTERIOR: hind or hinder-
  most; opposite to anterior.
POSTERIOR ANGLES: the
  angles at the back of the
  pronotum in beetles.
  Fig. 856

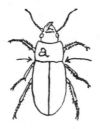

Figure 856

Potato Bug 151
Potato Flea Beetle 297
Potato Stalk Borer 336
Powder-post Beetles 227,
  229
Prasocuris
  phellandrii 282
  vittata 282
PRE-: meaning before.
PREDACEOUS: said of in-
  sects which attack and
  consume other organisms.
Predaceous Diving
  Beetles 57
Primitive Weevils 308
Priocera
  castanea 133
Prionus
  californicus 251
  imbricornis 251
  laticollis 251
PROCUMBENT: lying flat.
Prometopia
  sexmaculata 184
PRONOTUM: the upper or
  dorsal surface of the pro-
  thorax. 3
  (See "a" Fig. 856)
Propygidium 8
PROSTERNUM: a sclerite between the front coxae.
Proteinus
  automarius 108
  brachypterus 108
  limbatus 108
PRO-THORAX: the anterior
  or first segment of the
  thorax. 3
Prothyma
  leptalis 19
Psammodius
  interruptus 236

Psapharochrus
  quadrigibbus 267
Pselaphidae 113
Psenocerus
  supernotatus 265
Psephenidae 67
Psephenus
  lecontei 67
Pseudamphasia
  sericea 51
Pseudanthonomus
  crataegi 332
Pseudargutor
  erythropus 34
Pseudebaeus
  oblitus 131
Pseudo Click Beetles 76
Pseudoanophthalmus
  tenuis 29
Pseudolucanus
  capreolus 248
  mazama 248
  placidus 248
Pseudopsis
  obliterata 108
  sulcata 108
Psoa
  maculata 228
Psylliodes
  convexior 296
  punctulata 296
Psyllobora
  viginta-maculata 205
Pterocolus
  ovatus 312
Pterostichus
  adoxus 33
Ptilidae 90
Ptilinus
  pruinosus 226
  ruficornis 226
Ptilodactyla
  augustata 179
  serricollis 179
Ptinidae 224
Ptinus
  fur 224
  hirtellus 225
  villiger 224
PUBESCENT: covered with
  fine soft erect hairs.
PULVILLUS -I: soft pad-like
  structure between the tarsal claws.
PUNCTATE: with impres-
  sions or punctures.
PUNCTURE: a sharp depres-
  sion as if made with a
  needle.
PUPA: the resting stage in
  which the beetle trans-
  forms from the larva to
  the adult. Fig. 857

Figure 857

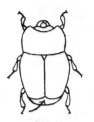
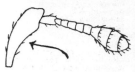
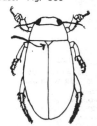

# INDEX

Scymnus
  amabilis 205
  caudalis 198
  collaris 205
  myrmidon 205
  nanus 199
  ornatus 205
  tenebrosus 199
  terminatus 198
Scyphophorus
  yuccae 343
SEGMENT: a ring of the insect body; a part of an
  appendage as of a leg or
  antenna.
Semanotus
  lignea 252
Serica
  anthracina 241
  evidens 241
  sericae 241
Serropalpidae 222
SETA -AE: stiff pointed
  bristles or hairs.
Shining Flower Beetles 195
Shining Fungus Beetles 117
Short Circuit Beetle 228
Shot-hole Borer 348
Siagonium
  americanum 102
Silis
  latilobus 130
  percomis 130
Silken Fungus Beetles 190
Silpha 82
  americana 85
  bituberosa 86
  inaequalis 85
  lapponica 85
  novebroracensus 85
  opaca 86
  ramosa 86
  surinamensis 84
Silphidae 82
Simsonia
  bivittata 67
Sinodendron
  rugosum 249
SINUOUS: curving in and
  out.
Sitodrepa
  panicea 226
Sitona
  flavescens 321
  hispidulus 321
Sitophilus
  granarius 343
  oryza 343
Size of beetles 1
Skin Beetles 180, 246
Skipjacks 159
SLUG: a larva with a
  slimy appearance.
Smicronyx
  apionides 325
  perpusillus 325
  quadrifer 325
  tesselatus 325
Snapping Beetles 159
SNOUT: a prolonged part
  of the head as in the
  Rhynchophora.
  Fig. 861

Figure 861

Snout Beetles 312
Soft-bodied Plant
  Beetles 179
Soft-winged Flower
  Beetles 130
Soldier Beetle 149
Somatium 103
Sonoma
  tolulae 115
Southern Corn Root-
  worm 289
Southern Corn-leaf
  Beetle 280
Southern Cowpea
  Weevil 306
Southern Lyctus Beetle 230
Southern Pine Beetle 350
Southern Pine Sawyer 265
Southwestern Pine
  Beetle 350
SPARSE: widely scattered.
SPECIES: the second word
  in a scientific name. (al-
  ways begins with a lower
  case letter)
Spermophagus
  hoffmanseggi 304
  vitis 304
Sphaericus
  gibboides 225
Sphaeridium
  scarabaeoides 81
Sphaeroderus
  nitidicollis 25
Spider Beetles 224
Spinach Flea Beetle 292
SPIRACLE: a breathing
  pore. 8
Spondylidae 250
Spotted Appletree Borer 271
Spotted Asparagus
  Beetle 274
Spotted Blister Beetle 152
Spotted Cucumber
  Beetle 289
Spotted Lady Beetle 203
Spotted Limb Borer 228
Spruce Timber Beetle 351
SPUR: a short stiff, often
  blunt process as at the
  end of the tibia.
SPURIOUS: false.
Square-necked Grain
  Beetle 186
Squash Beetle 201
Stag Beetles 247
Staphylinidae 92
Staphylinus
  cinnamopterus 100
  maculosus 100
  violaceus 100
Stelidota
  geminata 184

Stenispa
  collaris 300
  metallica 300
Stenocelis
  brevis 341
Stenocellus
  rupestris 51
  tantillus 51
Stenolophus
  carbonarius 52
  conjunctus 52
  ochropezus 52
  plebejus 52
Stenomimus
  pallidus 342
Stenus
  flavicornia 92
Stephanoderes 352
Stereopalpus
  mellyi 155
STERNUM: the mid part of
  the under surface of the
  thorax.
Stethorus
  punctatum 199
Stictocranius
  puncticeps 93
STIGMA: an opening on the
  side for breathing; spiracle.
Stilbus
  apicalis 196
  nitidus 196
Stilicus
  angularis 97
  dentatus 97
STIPES: segments of the
  maxilla.
Stone Beetles 88
Storehouse Beetle 224
Strangalia
  soror 257
  subhamata 257
Strategus
  antaeus 243
Strawberry Crown Borer 340
Strawberry Flea Beetle 293
Strawberry Weevil 333
STRIA -AE: (a) a depressed
  line extending lengthwise
  of the elytra; often with
  punctures, (b). Fig. 862

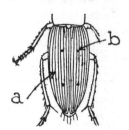

Figure 862

STRIATED: marked with
  striae.
Striped Blister Beetle 151
Striped Collops 131
Striped Cucumber Beetle 289
Striped Flea Beetle 294
Stromatium
  pubescens 263

369

## T

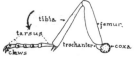

Figure 863

TAWNY: brownish yellow.
TAXONOMICAL: dealing
  with classification.

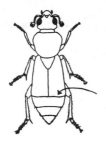

# INDEX